Unfolding Consciousness

Exploring the Living Universe and Intelligent Powers in Nature and Humans

Volume IV

Index, References and Resources, Further Reading

EDI BILIMORIA, DPhil, FIMechE, FEI, FRSA

SHEPHEARD WALWYN PUBLISHERS

First published in 2022 by Shepherd-Walwyn (Publishers) Ltd
107 Parkway House, Sheen Lane, London SW14 8LS
www.shepheardwalwyn.com
www.ethicaleconomics.org.uk

British Library Cataloguing in Publication Data
A catalogue record of this book is available from the British Library

ISBN: 978-08-5683-544-5

Copyedit by Elizabeth Medler
Typeset by Ian Wileman

Printed and bound through
s|s|media limited, Rickmansworth, Hertfordshire

Outline Contents for the Four Volumes

VOLUME I

Proem: The Purpose and Justification for this Work xxxvii
Introductory: The Plan of the Contents and Route Map lvii

1 Who, or What Am I? 1
2 The Mind–Brain–Thought Problem: Even Nobel Scientists Disagree 7
3 The Paradigm of Science – its Ideology, Assumptions, and Beliefs 22
4 Limitations in the Modern Scientific Picture 65
5 Straining Our Eyes to See Beyond – 'Uncomfortable Science' 132
6 A New Continent of Thought 160
7 The Mystery Teachings of All Ages – A General Overview 178
8 What Occult Science Affirms – its Contrast with Natural Science 228
9 The Mystery Teachings About Man – Who, or What Am I? 260

Recapitulation: Unifying Consciousness Through Science and the Mystery Teachings 316
Appendix I-A: Timeline of the Progression of the Physical Sciences – Physics and Cosmology 331
Appendix I-B: Timeline of the Progression of the Life Sciences – Biology and Evolution 345
Endnotes to Volume I 359

VOLUME II

Prefatory: 'Man, Know Thyself'– but Who, or What is Man? xv

1 What Occult Science says about the Composition of Man – Clearing the Decks 1
2 The Occult Constitution of Man – How Man is 'Builded Up' 16
3 The Occult Nature of Man – How Man Functions 34
4 The Three Selves – Man's Three Primary Vehicles of Consciousness 51
5 Death is Transition – Time at the Door of Eternity 63
6 Clarifying Some Common Misconceptions 105
7 Is the Brain a 'Wet Computer' – Are Humans 'Lumbering Robots'? The Closing of the Scientific Mind 112
8 Diverse Classifications of the Composition of Man – Harmony with Different World Teachings 146

Coda: How to Construct and Energize a Human Being – a Temple of the Divine 195

Appendix II-A: Light, Ether, and the Theory of Relativity – An extended example of 'Knowledge Filtration' in Science 207
Appendix II-B: Antaḥkaraṇa – its Purpose and Function 215

APPENDIX II-C: The Traditionalist Stance and Mindset – Truth from just One Authority? 218
ENDNOTES TO VOLUME II 227

VOLUME III

PREAMBLE: MAN, A MINIATURE UNIVERSE – A MIRROR OF COSMOS xvii

1 SYMBOLISM – THE LANGUAGE OF THE MYSTERY TEACHINGS 1
2 SYMBOLIC REPRESENTATIONS OF THE UNITY OF COSMOS, NATURE, AND MAN 22
3 MAN IS THE MEASURE OF ALL THINGS – THE HUMAN BODY IN SYMBOLISM 33
4 SYMBOLIC REPRESENTATIONS OF THE PRINCIPLES OF MAN 55
5 THE HERMETIC AXIOM AND THE LAW OF ANALOGY 70
6 COSMOGENESIS: THE UNFOLDING OF CONSCIOUSNESS – KOSMIC PLANES TO TERRESTRIAL PLANES 82
7 ANTHROPOGENESIS: THE UNFOLDING OF CONSCIOUSNESS – DIVINE SELF TO HUMAN BODY 101
8 FROM EXTERNAL SENSATION TO INTERNAL EXPERIENCE – THE SUBJECTIVE PERCEPTION OF AN OBJECTIVE UNIVERSE 134
9 DIVINE FORCES IN THE HUMAN BEING – THE AWAKENING OF LATENT FACULTIES AND POWERS OF CONSCIOUSNESS 171
10 MAN'S LIMITLESS EVOLUTION – OUR UNFINISHED JOURNEY 216
11 SUMMARY OF THE THEME – CONSCIOUSNESS IS AN ELEMENT 261

EPILOGUE: TOWARDS IMMORTALITY 302
A MATHEMATICAL CODICIL: Mathematics Alludes to the World as Mind, the Matrix of all Matter 349
ENDNOTES TO VOLUME III 375

VOLUME IV

INDEX, REFERENCES AND RESOURCES, FURTHER READING

Detailed Contents for Volume IV

Foreword   vii

Timeline   1
Profiles   5
Definitions   13
Editorial Notes   19
Glossary   21
Further Reading   39
General Index   69

Confucius counselled:

> By three methods we may learn wisdom: First, by reflection, which is noblest; second, by imitation, which is easiest; and third
> by experience, which is the bitterest.
>
> From the online publishing platform *medium.com/mind-cafe*

Isaac Newton reflected:

> And ... does it not appear from Phaenomena that there is a Being incorporeal, living, intelligent, omnipresent, who in infinite Space, as it were in his Sensory, sees the things themselves intimately ... Of which things the Images only carried through the Organs of Sense into our little Sensoriums,[i] are seen and beheld by that which in us perceives and thinks.
>
> Query 28 from *Opticks* (1717)

Albert Einstein advised a schoolgirl:

> Every one who is seriously engaged in the pursuit of science becomes convinced that the laws of nature manifest the existence of a spirit vastly superior to that of men, and one in the face of which we with our modest powers must feel humble. In this way the pursuit of science leads to a religious feeling of a special sort, which is indeed quite different from the religiosity of someone more naïve.
>
> Letter to Phyllis Wright, 24 January 1936, trans. from the original German in Max Jammer, *Einstein and Religion: Physics and Theology,* Princeton: Princeton University Press, 1999, pp. 92–3

Aldous Huxley similarly realized:

> Technological advance is rapid. But without progress in charity, technological advance is useless. Indeed, it is worse than useless. Technological progress has merely provided us with more efficient means for going backwards.
>
> *Ends and Means (an Enquiry Into the Nature of Ideals and Into the Methods Employed for Their Realization),* London: Chatto & Windus, 1937, p.14

Erwin Schrödinger declared in his Tarner Lectures at Trinity College, Cambridge, 1956:

> The recognition ATHMAN [*sic*] = BRAHMAN (the personal self equals the omnipresent, all-comprehending eternal self) was in Indian thought considered, far from being blasphemous, to represent the quintessence of deepest insight into the happenings of the world.
>
> 'Mind and Matter: On Determinism and Free Will' in *What is Life?* with *Mind and Matter* and *Autobiographical Sketches,* foreword by Roger Penrose (Cambridge: Cambridge University Press, 1993), p. 87

---

i 'Sensorium' means the seat of sensation involving the whole sensory apparatus and nervous system.

Foreword

This Volume serves as a practical guide enabling the reader to navigate the three foregoing Volumes. The material throughout is presented in a systematic and intelligible manner. Volume IV serves to highlight this and focuses on matters of syntax and terminology. It begins with a helpful *Timeline and flowchart* which set the scene, so to speak, tracing the golden thread of the *philosophia perennis* through the world's wisdom traditions, both prehistoric and historic. This is followed by a series of four *Profiles*—towering figures whose contributions to spiritual philosophy and science are embedded in this work. The section on *Definitions* will assist the reader in terms of understanding the meaning of terms and the distinct manner in which they are employed by the writer. This is immediately followed by an *Annex* outlining the genesis of the term 'science' and its evolution through both Western and Eastern streams. *Editorial Notes* sets out the writer's sevenfold approach to practical matters such as the use of diacriticals, nouns, capitalization, and italics. As one might expect in a work of this magnitude, the *Glossary* is extensive and constitutes an interesting and rewarding section in its own right. Thence follows *Further Reading*, an wide-ranging selection of books, papers and electronic resources which will help the reader to deepen his understanding and explore the subjects which are propounded throughout these Volumes. Finally, there follows the *General Index* prefaced by a brief protocol.

Although Volume IV is the last Volume, in another sense, it could be seen as the first as it provides the reader with an overview of the way in which the entire work has been woven, from a practical point of view. For this reason, when reading Volumes I, II, and III, it is recommended that the reader makes of this Volume his constant companion as it will elucidate many points which, at first, may not be self evident. It is hoped that Volume IV will not only make the entire work coherent and transparent, but contribute greatly to an understanding of the work as a whole. In the spirit of the work, the writer freely admits that his work is not exhaustive, but constitutes insights, or ways of looking at the material unfolded. This is said in the spirit of humility encapsulated by the mature reflections of Sir Isaac Newton: *I do not know what I may appear to the world, but to myself I seem to have been only like a boy playing on the seashore, and diverting myself in now and then finding a smoother pebble or a prettier shell than ordinary, whilst the great ocean of truth lay all undiscovered before me.*

Timeline

It is hoped that readers might find a timeline helpful in terms of indicating the outpouring of *theosophia*, the *philosophia perennis*, through the various traditions, both prehistoric and historic. The illustration overleaf, reproduced under the heading *One Source: Many Tributaries*, has been adapted from William Doss McDavid, *An Introduction To Esoteric Principles* (Wheaton, Illinois: The Theosophical Society in America, 1983), page 3. The adjacent flowchart is a reproduction of the writer's Figure I-8 on page 185 of Volume I. It can readily be seen that so many streams of the same wisdom must have a common Source.

There has been no time in pre-history or history, down to modern times, when this venerable and ever *living* tradition, emanating from One Source, has not been embodied by august men and women and been a potent force for good in all progressive movements. In truth, it forms the bedrock of all civilizations.

One Source: Many Tributaries

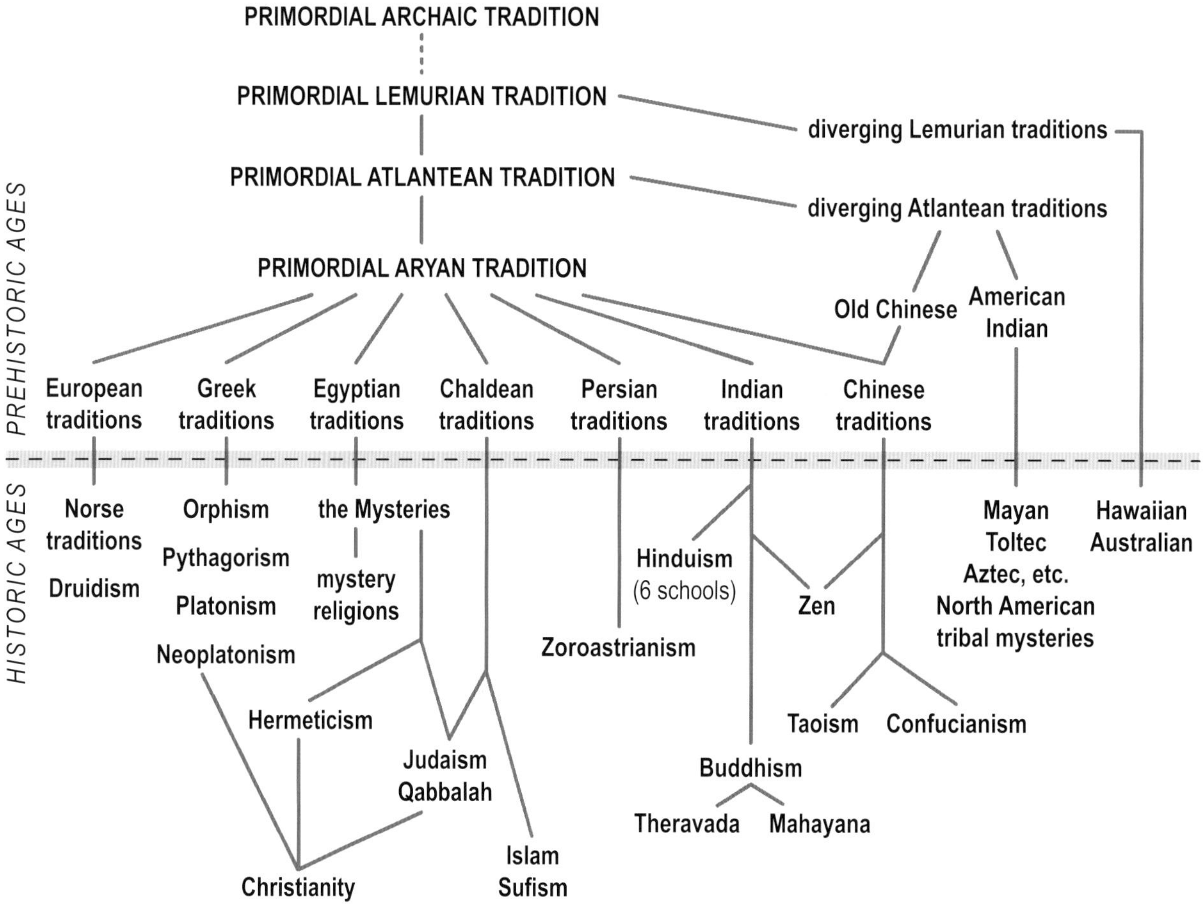

The Outpouring of *theosophia*, the *phlosophia perennis*

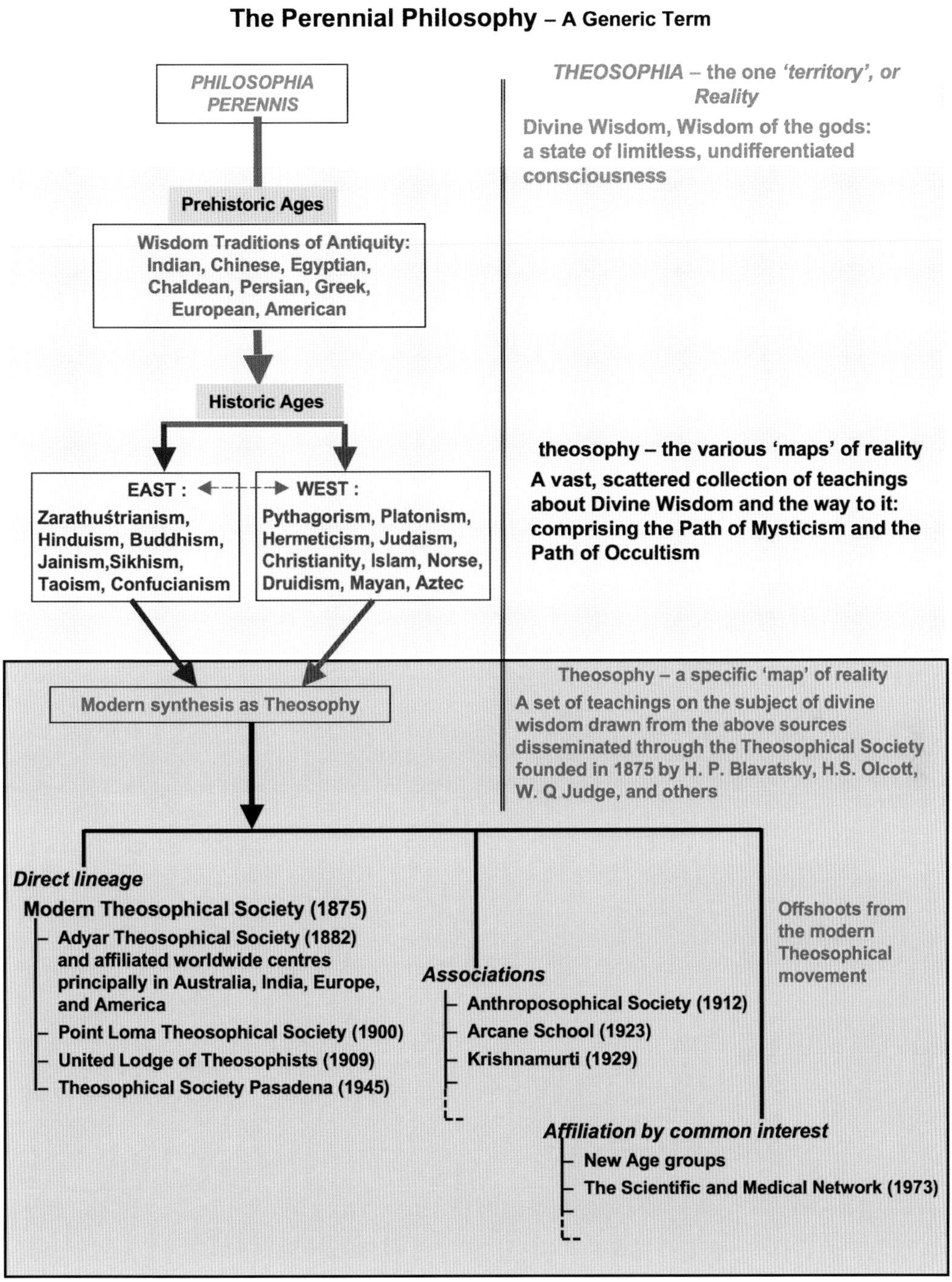
The Perennial Philosophy – A Generic Term
PHILOSOPHIA PERENNIS
Prehistoric Ages
Wisdom Traditions of Antiquity: Indian, Chinese, Egyptian, Chaldean, Persian, Greek, European, American
Historic Ages
EAST :
Zarathuštrianism, Hinduism, Buddhism, Jainism,Sikhism, Taoism, Confucianism
WEST :
Pythagorism, Platonism, Hermeticism, Judaism, Christianity, Islam, Norse, Druidism, Mayan, Aztec
THEOSOPHIA – the one 'territory', or Reality
Divine Wisdom, Wisdom of the gods: a state of limitless, undifferentiated consciousness
theosophy – the various 'maps' of reality
A vast, scattered collection of teachings about Divine Wisdom and the way to it: comprising the Path of Mysticism and the Path of Occultism
Modern synthesis as Theosophy
Theosophy – a specific 'map' of reality
A set of teachings on the subject of divine wisdom drawn from the above sources disseminated through the Theosophical Society founded in 1875 by H. P. Blavatsky, H.S. Olcott, W. Q Judge, and others
Direct lineage
Modern Theosophical Society (1875)
Adyar Theosophical Society (1882) and affiliated worldwide centres principally in Australia, India, Europe, and America
Point Loma Theosophical Society (1900)
United Lodge of Theosophists (1909)
Theosophical Society Pasadena (1945)
Associations
Anthroposophical Society (1912)
Arcane School (1923)
Krishnamurti (1929)
Offshoots from the modern Theosophical movement
Affiliation by common interest
New Age groups
The Scientific and Medical Network (1973)

Profiles

Profiles concerns the contributions of four leading figures whose ideas have figured strongly in this work: Helena Blavatsky, Paul Brunton, Manly P. Hall, and Rupert Sheldrake. The objective is not to present biographies, which can be found in quality publications, but to highlight their unique contributions, which the writer regards as instrumental in the sequential and progressive dissemination of the *philosophia perennis* through occultism, spiritual philosophy, and modern, enlightened science.

Helena Petrovna Blavatsky

Photo Credit: Theosophical Publishing House, Adyar, Chennai, India

Helena Blavatsky can be likened to a powerful spiritual floodlight. She sought to dispel the huge darkness of spiritually impoverished humanity and in so doing, throw up in sharp relief the creatures of malevolence who choose to inhabit a world of shadows and so become attracted to the light in order to destroy that which seeks out their gloom.

It seems to be virtually axiomatic that the amount of calumny and abuse heaped by the ignorant upon a person stand in direct proportion to their nobility and desire to elevate the common human lot. Ironically, a noble and spiritual life in no way automatically implies that circumstances will be free from powerful vicissitudes—in fact, invariably quite the reverse, as such light bearers are tested by dark forces attracted to the former as moths to the light. Such was the case with those redeemers of mankind whose unswerving mission, born out of their selfless love of humanity, was to lead men out of the mire of limited existence towards eternal peace and brotherhood; the likes of Zarathuśtra, Jesus the Christ, Muhammad, and Giordano Bruno (see Volume I, Chapter 7 on pages 218–19, for further examples). Alas! This most certainly applied to the Russian born Helena Petrovna Blavatsky (1831–1891) and those who followed her.

But who was this Russian noblewoman Helena Petrovna Blavatsky fondly referred to as just 'HPB' by Theosophists? Sages, prophets and messengers of Light, the world over, from every religion and culture all came to heal and to bless. Not a single one of them ever wasted his time and life-energy preaching a material Utopia by developing new technologies or inventing new socio-economic schemes and commercial ventures to improve the world's, suffering, poverty, and conflict. Each one of them realized that it is unregenerate man who is the ubiquitous spawner of the ugliness around him and so it is, through man himself, that the way must be found to peace and truth. Such was also the case with HPB who devoted every ounce of her energy to promoting the brotherhood of humanity by way of making generally available those portions of the perennial wisdom that could

legitimately, and safely, be revealed to the public at large. For this magnanimous self-sacrifice she had to drink her cup of slander and ingratitude to the dregs.

Witness her achievements! Besides being an illimitable occultist, philosopher, and scientist (in the true sense of the term), she was also an explorer, prolific writer, linguist, poet, and concert pianist.[1]

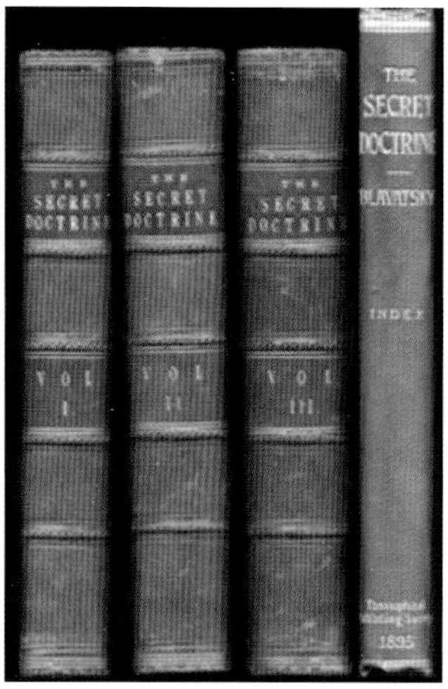

Image Credit: Theosophical Publishing House, Adyar, Chennai, India

Her unique contribution was to reveal the common origin of the accumulated wisdom of the ages, by virtue of a synthesis of science, religion, and philosophy through the unifying medium of occult science. In this way she forcefully demonstrated that nature, like man, is not a fortuitous concurrence of material atoms, but a living, organic being. In the consideration of this writer, Blavatsky's work is unequalled in terms of making these facts known in the wider public domain. In his autobiography, the founder of the London Buddhist Society and celebrated Old Bailey judge Christmas Humphreys (1901–1983), who produced an abridged version of HPB's celebrated work *The Secret Doctrine*, states that in his estimation, this volume is unique, there being 'no other which sets forth the vast process of cosmogenesis and anthropogenesis, not as a pastiche of doctrine found in one form or another in the religions of the world, *but as their common source* [emphasis added]. Not all their scriptures combined describe with the clarity and totality of *The Secret Doctrine* the Wisdom of which each is a partial and generally mangled expression.'[2]

Blavatsky did provide a plan, a purpose and a way—but for the most advanced and dedicated student undaunted by all the difficulties along the way. There is practically nothing in her writings that caters for the earnest, struggling neophyte desperately needing a route map: simple instructions and directions so as not to lose his way, and his mind, in a minefield of highly abstruse, vast, and complex doctrines, and seemingly confusing paths. What practical guidance she provided is contained in small books like *Practical Occultism* and one of the priceless gems of mystical literature—*The Voice of the Silence* (being chosen fragments from the 'Book of Golden Precepts'). The latter is a little guidebook for the daily use of lanoos (disciples) and all those dedicated to achieving enlightenment through altruistic service to humanity through the Bodhisattva[i] ideal of finding the SELF by forgetting the self in service to other Selves. It is 'Dedicated to the Few', which, exactly as is implied, is written at such a high level that it would be quite unsuitable for the ordinary student in practical terms. Simple instructions were left to Blavatsky's personal students, chiefly Annie Besant, and other senior members in the Theosophical succession, like Professor I. K. Taimni. These attempts at simplification have not been without a measure of success. However, the explanations, interpretations, and practical guidance are now in need of updating and refreshing. This is one of the unique contributions of Paul Brunton.

---

i In Buddhism, a Bodhisattva is one who needs just another incarnation, or a few more, to attain the Enlightenment of Buddhahood, but who renounces Nirvana (the state of absolute consciousness as well as absolute existence) for the benefit of all sentient beings so that they too may attain Enlightenment.

Paul Brunton

Photo Credit: Paul Brunton Philosophic Society

Paul Brunton (1898–1981), the pen name of the British born Raphael Hurst, was a researcher and explorer widely recognized as the philosopher-sage who contributed substantially to the spiritual renaissance of modern culture in the Orient and, especially, the dissemination of Eastern philosophy and mysticism in the Occident. Although versed in the Theosophical doctrines as well as attending meetings of the Theosophical Society, he did not follow in the direct line of the occult teachings as promulgated by its Founders. Instead he placed the emphasis on spirituality rather than occultism, a fine distinction, but highly significant. Dedicating his entire life both to the spiritual quest and disseminating his knowledge and experiences, he relinquished a productive journalistic career to explore spiritual traditions and live among yogis, mystics, and holy men, first in India (Ramana Maharshi being the prime influence), then in Egypt. He later met with other teachers and traditions around the world.

His unique contribution was to express the wisdom-teaching at its highest level in the form of graduated teachings in plain, but supremely eloquent English tailored to the personal circumstances and grade of the student, leading him by stages towards truth and enlightenment. Thus, all students, spanning the range from elementary, through intermediate to advanced, had a 'spiritual toolkit' and working instructions to use in daily life in order to progress from the 'what I have to do' to the 'how I do it' on their spiritual journey. Especially noteworthy in this regard are the *Notebooks* comprising the major body of posthumously published works. Twenty eight categories of practical philosophic material spanning the whole range of philosophic enquiry, its trials and tribulations, and its fruits, are arranged in sixteen volumes and seventeen titles as shown in the accompanying picture. Volume 1: *Perspectives* is a representative selection of notes from all twenty eight categories.

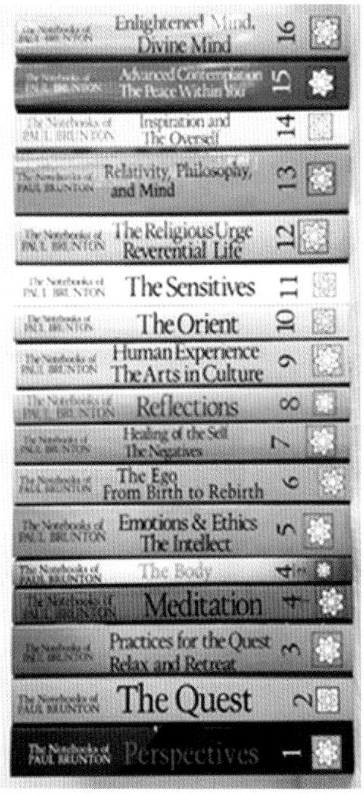

Image Credit: Paul Brunton Philosophic Society

The *Notebooks* are not written in the conventional narrative style of his earlier books but as short essays or pithy commentaries (invariably just one or two sentences) dealing with a specific topic. They are in the nature of seed thoughts for the reader to plant in the soil of his mind to flower into his own awakened insights and intuitions in his own good time. In all issues dealing with the life-problems faced by the aspirant, he first identifies the nature of the problem itself, how it can affect one at different levels in daily life, and how to deal with it. This is especially relevant to matters such as karma, the potential dangers of mysticism and wrongful meditation, negative influences, death, loss and suffering, all of which are addressed from the higher standpoint of consciousness and spiritual progress, not from the limited perspective of the personal self.

The extracts on self-development span all levels from physical disciplines, yoga, emotional refinement, and mental culture, along with the practices pertaining to the religious quest, mystical experience, and philosophic enquiry. Probably his finest gift to seekers is the art and adventure of meditation and here he deals with consciousness at the highest and deepest levels. Aligning the personal self to the Overself, and to the higher purpose of universal Mind, is of paramount importance.

The observations on science and intellect bear close scrutiny because they are powerfully illuminated by a higher metaphysic and spiritual philosophy. Here he exposes the blessings to mankind that accrue from the wise use of science and the calamities in the wake of its misuse or exploitation. Needless to say, he regards the worst legacy of modern science to be the materialistic paradigm dogmatized as the sole explanatory framework for the existence of the universe, all life, the human mind and consciousness.

Like Blavatsky, Brunton demonstrated and taught that truth is what it was, is, and shall be – universal and eternal; that the truth cannot be made sectarian by being Hinduized or Christianized, nor made geographical according to the East or the West, nor dogmatized as either science or mysticism.[3] Nonetheless, regarding its expression and understanding in the Occident, he counselled that the Western peoples would never be converted wholesale to Hinduism or Buddhism as religions, nor, he believed, would their intelligentsia take wholesale to Vedānta or Theosophy as philosophies, because these forms are too alien and too exotic to affect the general mass. Historically, they have only succeeded in affecting scattered individuals. Therefore, the West's spiritual revival must come primarily out of its own creative and native mind.[4]

Such a reawakening must necessarily occur through a renaissance of both spiritual philosophy and science. Regarding the former, Manly Hall is probably the finest example of one who kindled a modern renaissance, particularly in America. Regarding the latter, major breakthroughs have occurred, especially at the turn of the twenty-first century by a few contemporary researchers and writers working with sincerity and dedication at the interface of science and spirituality,[ii] amongst whom Rupert Sheldrake is one of the best examples.

Manly Palmer Hall

Photo credit: Theosophy Wiki/Theosophical Society in America Archives

Widely regarded as a sage and teacher steeped in the wisdom of antiquity, Canadian born Manly Hall (1901–1990) was one of the leading esoteric scholars and writers of the twentieth century, having produced over 200 printed volumes, given 8000 lectures, and instituted a hand-picked library, which is one of the finest in the field. He was the founder of The Philosophical Research Society, a non-profit organization founded in 1934, which continues in his spirit of universal exploration and learning for the purpose of assisting thoughtful persons to live more graciously and constructively in a confused and troubled world.

ii This is in complete contradistinction to many writers nowadays who choose to make a name for themselves by jumping onto the fashionable 'science and spirituality bandwagon'.

Hall published a massive codex to the mystical and esoteric philosophies of antiquity, emphasizing the Western mysteries and occult tradition. His books explore subjects which range from Native American mythology to Pythagorean mathematics to Ancient Egypt, the lost keys of Masonry, and the occult anatomy of man. However, his *magnum opus* is undoubtedly *The Secret Teachings of All Ages: An Encyclopedic Outline of Masonic, Hermetic, Qabbalistic and Rosicrucian Symbolical Philosophy – Being an Interpretation of the Secret Teachings concealed within the Rituals, Allegories and Mysteries of all Ages.* Apollo Astronaut Edgar Mitchell (1930–2016) said of this timeless book: 'Manly Hall's great work is a classic in the world's literature. It will guide historians, philosophers, and lay seekers of esoteric wisdom for centuries.'[5]

Writer's own photograph

Each of the forty-six chapters is so comprehensive and far-reaching as to constitute virtually the equivalent of an entire short book on the subject in question. These include Qabbala, Alchemy, Tarot, Ritual and Ceremonial Magic, Neoplatonic Philosophy, Mystery Religions, Rosicrucianism, Freemasonry, the Bacon-Shakespeare controversy, Islam, and American Indian symbolism. Having no *-ism* of his own to promulgate, the original writings have not been twisted to substantiate preconceived notions. His unique contribution is that the whole body of the Western wisdom-teaching deriving from sages and adept-philosophers—secrets of the Mysteries that are obviously metaphysical, philosophical, and esoteric—is encapsulated in glowing language of rare eloquence and clarity. The enormous range of subjects covered is divided into digestible chapters that speak directly to the earnest beginner as to the advanced student. Symbolism and ritual are explained with immense lucidity. Another matchless feature amongst esoteric writers is the profusion of diagrams, pictures, and rare colour plates. These include portraits of initiates like Pythagoras, Comte De St-Germain, Paracelsus, Francis Bacon, and Hypatia; the macrocosm-microcosm relationship; the key to Dante's Divine Comedy; the symbolism of Astrology and the Tarot cards; the human body in symbolism; and Hermetic and alchemical figures. These illustrations in themselves speak volumes. They are worthy of deep and prolonged contemplation.

Hall's fleeting contact with high finance during a brief career on Wall Street in the late 1920s convinced him that materialism was in complete control of the economic structure, the ultimate objective of which was to mould the individual to become a cog within an economic system providing economic security at the expense of the human body, mind, and soul. Thus, his abiding message to humanity was that living in the world purely as a socio-economic entity without becoming aware of the inner meaning of the world would be like wandering aimlessly in a magnificent library without touching, let alone reading the books on the shelves. He declared that symbolism (to which the writer would add mythology) should be restored to the structure of world education. Few would argue with him that in these days of smartphone texting, along with Twitter, Facebook, and other forms of social media, the young are hardly ever encouraged to seek the truths, dynamic and eternal, hidden within the outward form and behaviour of living beings. The force of Hall's influence is a perpetual undercurrent in the spiritual revival of the West, and espe-

cially in America, and deserves more recognition. In 2010 it was reported that President Ronald Reagan adopted some ideas and phrasing from Hall's book *The Secret Destiny of America* (1944), using them in speeches and essays.[6]

Rupert Sheldrake

Photo credit: Rupert Sheldrake

It is widely known that the British born Rupert Sheldrake (*b.*1942) studied natural science and biochemistry at Cambridge University, was appointed a Fellow of Clare College and then, as a Rosenheim Research Fellow of the Royal Society, carried out research on the development of plants and the ageing of cells. What is probably less well-known, but of major importance to the theme of this work, is that he also studied philosophy and the history of science at Harvard University where he was a Frank Knox Fellow. According to the writer, this added dimension was instrumental in shaping his thoughts and scientific perspective towards a much wider and universal outlook beyond, but not excluding, the mechanistic paradigm.

Sheldrake's first work, *A New Science of Life*, now in its third edition in the UK (published as *Morphic Resonance: The Nature of Formative Causation* in the USA), is his most popular and widely circulated book, not least because it attracted intemperate criticism from establishment dogmatism, as summarized in Part II, Chapter 7.

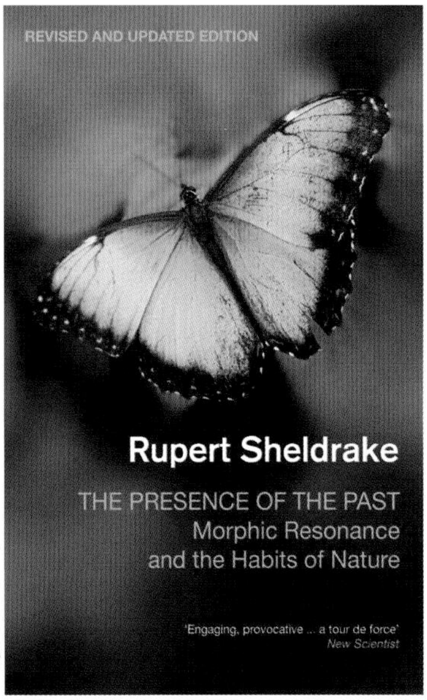

Image credit: Rupert Sheldrake

However, his second book *The Presence of the Past*, in the revised and expanded edition as seen in the accompanying picture, is the more significant from the standpoint of this work since it alludes, in numerous ways, to the perennial philosophy. His overall hypothesis, backed by considerable evidence, is that memory is inherent in all of nature and, in the case of humans, not the product of material traces stored within the 'memory banks' of the brain. The universal and inherent nature of this memory implies the notion of extended mind and the habits of nature. This effectively undercuts the mechanistic paradigm as the sole explanatory framework of individual species growth, or formative causation. These ideas make a scientific connection to the esoteric dictates about *ākāśa*, or æther (primordial spatial substance) and *mahat* (Universal Mind, the producer of *manas*, the thinking principle). His especial contribution has been to undermine, through evidence from Western science itself, the materialistic paradigm of establishment biology, thus pointing out that the cosmos now appears more like a living and evolving being instead of a machine—a fundamental tenet of esotericism, which maintains that there is no such thing as dead matter anywhere in the

universe: everything from the tiniest speck of matter, to the smallest infusoria, to man, and to giant galaxies, is imbued with life and consciousness at its own level.

Sheldrake's other books advance the cause of science, spirituality, and esotericism in different ways. *The Science Delusion* is an eminent exposition on 'freeing the spirit of enquiry' as per the subtitle. His books on animal behaviours, telepathy, and extended mind (for example, *Dogs That Know When Their Owners Are Coming Home, The Sense of Being Stared At,* and *The Evolutionary Mind*) show that there are unexplored and unexplained laws, or rather habits of nature,[iii] the effects of which (if not the understanding of the laws themselves) are receiving robust scientific validation (refer to Part I, Chapter 4). Again, this furthers one of the key objectives of the esoteric researcher: as stated in terms of the Third Object of the Theosophical Society, 'To investigate unexplained laws of Nature and the powers latent in man'. His latest books *Science and Spiritual Practices* and *Ways to Go Beyond And Why They Work* persuasively argue that spirituality is being authenticated by science in that the benefits of age-old spiritual practices, such as prayer and meditation, music and pilgrimage, are now being confirmed by scientific studies.

NOTES

1 Edi Bilimoria, 'H. P. Blavatsky – A Spiritual Floodlight', *The Blavatsky Trust* <http://www.blavatskytrust.org.uk/html/articles/hpb%20spiritual%20floodlight.htm> accessed 26 April 2020.

2 Christmas Humphreys, *Both Sides of the Circle: The autobiography of Christmas Humphreys* (London: George Allen & Unwin, 1978), 42–3.

3 *NPB-10, The Orient: Its Legacy to the West,* 'Universality of truth', ¶ 314, 54.

4 *NPB-10, The Orient: Its Legacy to the West,* 'Western assimilation of Eastern thought', ¶ 140, 25.

5 Manly P. Hall, The Secret Teachings of All Ages (Reader's Edition, Jeremy P. Tarcher / Penguin, 2003) quote on front cover.

6 Mitch Horowitz, 'Reagan and the Occult', *The Washington Post,* 30th April 2010. See also Mitch Horowitz, *Occult America: The Secret History of how Mysticism Shaped Our Nation* (New York: Bantam), 2009.

iii 'Habits' is a term preferred by Sheldrake to convey the sense of laws of nature that need not be immutable but subject to change according to past experience.

Definitions

As the axis around which the entire work revolves is the Unfolding of Consciousness expressed in relation to the universe, nature, and man, it is important to define as clearly as possible terms that are in common usage but have a definite meaning in the context of this work.

As a general rule, terms:

- ❖ written in capitals refer to the universal, ultimate or noumenal nature of elements or principles pertaining to beings, things, and conditions (e.g. SPIRIT, MAN);
- ❖ beginning with an upper case letter refer to their use as a principle (e.g. Consciousness) or the specific application of a principle (e.g. 'Spirit'); also to the immortal aspect of man's constitution (e.g. 'Spiritual Soul');
- ❖ beginning with a lower case letter refer to their generic or common usage (e.g. 'spirit'); also to the mortal aspect of man's constitution ('Animal soul').

REALITY
The Ultimate Reality, the Unmanifest, the Absolute, Parabrahman, Divine Consciousness, are all parallel terms from different cultures.

Reality
REALITY in the manifest.

God
The ABSOLUTE, or Divine Consciousness, having nothing whatsoever to do with the crude anthropomorphic concept of a 'Creator God' in orthodox religions.

Other than in quotations, this term has been used as sparingly as possible, due to its common overuse and associated wide range of connotations in the popular milieu.

gods
Always in the plural, this term refers to the various orders of conscious powers and forces in intelligent Nature. They are known as the *devās* and *devatās* in Hindu philosophy; in Christianity as the angelic members of the hierarchy of beings. From the highest perspective, the gods are the revelation of God and cannot be separated from Him, much as rays of the Sun cannot be divorced from the solar disk.

Kosmos
The term 'Kosmos' written with an upper case *K* refers to the numberless, infinite Universes, the innumerable Solar systems of the infinite Cosmos, unmanifest and manifest, subjective and objective.

kosmos
The term 'kosmos' written with a lower case *k* refers to the objective aspect of Kosmos. The term 'multiverse' in scientific cosmology approximates to kosmos.

Cosmos
Etymology: from the Latinized form of the Greek *kósmos* 'order', 'orderly arrangement'. Originally, the word appears to have been applied by Pythagoras and his School in reference to the orderliness of creation.

The term 'Cosmos' written with an upper case *C* refers to our solar system, unmanifest and manifest, subjective and objective, to emphasize its ordered and harmonious characteristic.

cosmos
The term 'cosmos' written with an lower case *c* refers to the objective aspect of Cosmos, that is, the manifest, objective aspect of our solar system.

Universe
Etymology: from the Latin *universum*, neuter of *universus* 'turned or combined into one', 'whole'; from *uni-* 'one' and *versus* 'turned' (past participle of *vertere*).

The term 'Universe' written withn an upper case *U* is practically equivalent to Kosmos, emphasizing its holistic and organic nature.

universe
The term 'universe' written with a lower case *u* is practically equivalent to kosmos.

world
Etymology: from the Old English *weorold (-uld)*, worold *(-uld, -eld)*, a compound from Proto-Germanic *wer 'man' and *ald 'age'; hence, the ancient root of 'world' meant 'age or life of man'.

The term refers to our planet, Earth in a general sense especially during the period of the human race, mankind.

Nature
The term 'Nature' written with an upper case *N* refers to the Universal aspect: the invisible and visible, that is, the subjective and objective, the synthesis of laws or conditions governing the evolution of Conscious Being.

nature
The term 'nature' written with an lower case *n* refers to the objective aspect of Nature. That which is ever becoming and ever evolving.

MAN

Etymology: derived from the Proto-Indo-European **men-* 'mind', 'to think'. Cognate with Sanskrit *manas,* 'mind' and *Manu,* 'Human being' in the sense of progenitor of the human race;[i] 'a thinking entity', that which sets him apart from all other species being his mind principle.

The term MAN written in capitals refers to the Idea of Man in Divine Mind.

Man

The term 'Man' written with an upper case *M* refers to the reflection of MAN; that is to say, Heavenly Man, or Paradigmatic Man—known in the West as Adam Kadmon in the Qabbalah and Puruṣa (Purusha) in the Sāṁkhya (Samkhya) philosophy of India—as a prototype encompassing the totality of Mankind, the Human Kingdom; hence, the archetype, or paradigm of man, the human being. Man stands at the midway point of the evolutionary ladder of life evolving towards the superhuman kingdoms of nature—an entity, so to speak, as the expression of a central consciousness-centre through one or another particular phase of the evolutionary unfoldment, over aeons, of its inherent faculties and powers.

man, human

The term 'man' written with a lower case *m*, refers to the reflection of Man on the physical plane. Hence, terrestrial physical man, the embodiment of spirit (a spark of the Divine), is a triform entity comprising spirit, soul, and body. This human composition is therefore tripartite: an organism of graded consciousness and substance which the human constitution contains, or rather, is. Essentially, man is a replica, in miniature, of the graded consciousness and substance of the universe in its various planes of being, inner and outer, the former being by far the more important, because it is causal. Hence, as a microcosm of the macrocosm, man embodies all the principles of the cosmos in both their subjective and objective aspects.

The term 'man' is cognate with 'human'. Etymologically, 'human' comes from Latin *hūmānus*. Like *homō* 'person', it is related to the Latin *humus* 'earth', and was used originally for 'people' in the sense of 'earthly beings' in contrast with the immortal gods.[ii]

Note that the esoteric philosophy thus distinguishes sharply between *Man* and *man,* the former being an evolving divine entity that projects an aspect of itself into the lower world—the terrestrial plane—as a *(hu)man* being embodied. Thus, there is a clear distinction between the human body and the human being. The spiritual Man remains ever *in situ,* while the projected fragment becomes the lesser 'spark' of intelligence embodied within the nature of the objective human individual on Earth.

Note also that 'man' and 'Man' apply to all ages, historic, and prehistoric. The terms have absolutely nothing whatsoever to do with physical age (such as child contrasted with man) or gender (such as male or female or transgender).

---

i Michiel de Vann, *Etymological Dictionary of Latin and the Other Italic Languages* (Leiden Indo-European Etymological Dictionary Series), Volume 7 (Leiden, Netherlands: Brill, 2008).

ii John Ayto, *Dictionary of Word Origins* (London: Bloomsbury, 1991).

individual

Etymology: from the Latin *individuum* 'an indivisible thing', neuter of *individuus* 'indivisible', 'undivided'; from the prefix in- and *dividuus* 'divisible', derived from *divido* 'divide'.

Hence, essential nature or unique actions of a single human being as distinct from a group. The distinct character of a human being.

person

Etymology: from the Latin *persōna* 'mask used by actor', 'role', 'part', 'character'.

Hence, to refer to the external characteristics or role adopted by the human being. Thus concerning the outward characteristics, or personality; a human being considered as someone with their own particular character.

SPIRIT

For all intents and purposes, the term 'SPIRIT' written in capitals is practically synonymous with the spark of Divine, or Universal Consciousness in man, i.e., *Ātma,* the Divine Self.

Spirit

The term 'Spirit' written with an upper case *S* refers to a universal and active principle, or potency on any plane of manifestation.

spirit

The term 'spirit' written with a lower case *s* is used in the generic sense to refer to an active principle, or potency.

MATTER

The term 'MATTER' written in capitals is the correlate of SPIRIT.

Matter

The term 'Matter' written with an upper case *M* is the correlate of Spirit on any plane of manifestation.

matter

The term 'spirit' written with a lower case *m* is used in the generic sense for the correlate of spirit.

Annex: Science – Its genesis, evolution, and Western and Eastern streams

The philosophy, assumptions, and beliefs that frame the scientific world-view are described in Chapter 3 of Volume I, particularly regarding the metaphysical basis and rationale for materialism, or physicalism, to use the term in vogue. Chapter 8 went on to contrast the paradigm and ensuing methodology of science with occult science (see especially Table I-2 on page 255). Since the term 'science' has now become such common currency with a wide range of meanings in the popular milieu, and also in academe, it is hoped that the following outline of the genesis of natural science might provide a clear focus on the essential meaning of this term by first explaining its forerunner in natural philosophy, and then the contrast between Western science and Eastern science in their respective philosophies and approaches to investigating nature.

What we now refer to by the collective term 'science' is generally regarded as originating in Greek philosophy in antiquity. From the ancient world, starting with Aristotle, to the nineteenth century, *natural philosophy* was the common term for the practice of studying nature. It was in the nineteenth century that the concept of 'science' received its modern connotation with new titles emerging such as 'biology' and 'biologist', 'physics' and 'physicist', among other technical fields and titles. Institutions and communities were founded, and unprecedented applications to, and interactions with, other aspects of society and culture occurred. Isaac Newton's book *Philosophiae Naturalis Principia Mathematica* (1687), whose title translates to 'Mathematical Principles of Natural Philosophy', reflects the then-current use of the term 'natural philosophy', akin to 'systematic study of nature'. Even in the nineteenth century, a treatise by the British mathematical physicist and engineer William Thomson, Lord Kelvin PRS, FRSE (1824–1907) and the Scottish mathematical physicist Peter Guthrie Tait FRSE (1831–1901), which helped define much of classical physics, was entitled *Treatise on Natural Philosophy* (1867).[iii] Thereafter, the term 'natural science', or its contraction to 'science', gradually succeeded over the classical term natural philosophy.

'Hard science', and 'soft science' are colloquial terms used to compare scientific fields on the basis of perceived methodological rigor, exactitude, and objectivity. Roughly speaking, the natural sciences are considered 'hard', or exact sciences, whereas the social sciences (e.g. psychology, sociology, political science) are usually regarded as 'soft'. As empirical sciences, natural sciences use tools from the formal sciences, such as mathematics and logic, converting information about nature into measurements which can be explained as clear statements of the 'laws of nature'. Mechanisms such as peer review and the replication of findings are generally employed in order to ensure the validity of scientific advances. In essence, then, natural science is that branch of science concerned with the identification, description, classification, prediction, and understanding of the natural phenomena of the physical world, based on empirical evidence from observation and experimentation. In addition to the physical sciences such as physics, chemistry, astronomy, and geology, natural science also includes the life sciences such as biology,

iii William Thomson (Baron Kelvin) and Peter Guthrie Tait, *Treatise on Natural Philosophy*, 2 Volumes, Cambridge Library Collection – Mathematics (Oxford: Oxford University Press,1867; Cambridge: Cambridge University Press, 2009).

marine science, and zoology. Environmental science and ecology are also branches of natural science—having obviously gained increasing importance as our planet swings from one ecological crisis to the next.

What is generally regarded as 'modern science' is post twentieth century—spearheaded by the foundational discoveries of relativity theory and quantum mechanics (physics) that undermined the strictly deterministic concepts of classical physics.

Given the preoccupation, especially in the West, with the objective attribute of science and the consequent emphasis it places on the systematizing and categorizing of knowledge, as well as the discovery and exploration of the laws governing each domain, the term 'Western science' is frequently used as a virtual synonym for 'natural science'. The distinction, albeit a fine one, underscores the contrast between Western science and Eastern science in their respective philosophies and approaches to investigating nature.

Western science and Eastern science (along with indigenous knowledge) represent two different, but complementary, ways of looking at the world around us. In essence, the distinction is this. The former constitutes a clear path of knowing the material universe, understanding the natural world by systematizing and categorizing knowledge, finding the laws governing each domain when discovered and explored, and studying individual parts. The latter seeks to understand the world in a more holistic way by observing the connections between all of the parts and integrating such knowledge gained into a general perspective. Because of these differences, Eastern science has the potential to complement and counterbalance the system of Western science. (See again Chapter 8, Volume I.) Notwithstanding promising signs from individuals and special interest groups, the union of the two has not yet been achieved in actuality in mainstream science, but when it is it might be called Integral Science.

Editorial Notes

1. Where pertinent, Sanskrit words have their transliteration in brackets adjacent to them.

2. Diacriticals are applied to original Sanskrit words—not their Anglicization in grammar; thus Ātma, but Atmic (not Ātmic).

3. Throughout the work, quotations containing words in a foreign language are presented exactly as they appear in their sources.

4. A word written:
   - in capitals denotes its highest, noumenal sense;
   - as a proper noun is employed to distinguish its use in a transcendental sense rather than in its conventional, everyday use;
   - as a common noun is to be understood in the ordinary, restricted meaning.

   Keywords are explained in the previous section on Definitions.

5. In each chapter, the first mention of a foreign word will appear in italics; all subsequent and frequent use will be in non-italics, unless the word occurs infrequently many pages further on.

   Note, however, that H. P. Blavatsky's *The Secret Doctrine* is always written in upper case italics. This is in order to distinguish it from the universal secret doctrine, invariably known as the Secret Doctrine—that ageless wisdom denominated by a variety of names such as, *philosophia perennis*, theosophy, occultism, *prisca sapientia* (see the flowchart on page 3). There is no doubt that Blavatsky's work faithfully encapsulates this ageless wisdom, suitably adapted to the exigencies of the time and the current epoch of humanity.

6. Owing to the wide range of sources quoted, brief biographical information, such as professional qualifications and roles, years of birth and death, is provided on the occasion of first mention so that readers can appreciate the quoted or cited contents in their historical and cultural context. Details are accurate at the time of writing but naturally may change.

7. In explaining the finer points of the perennial philosophy, some sentences may appear, at first, to be verbose for reason that it is not always viable to split up long sentences into shorter ones, since a sentence should be *a unit of thought*, not an arbitrary unit of length. In such cases, the fashionable saying 'less is more' does not apply as there are no superfluous words and each complete thought is well considered

Glossary

A = Avestan G = Greek H = Hebrew P = Pali S = Sanskrit T = Tibetan

ābhāsa caitanya (abhasa chaitanya) (S)
Sons of God (the Holy Ghost in Christianity); puruṣa *q.v.* in Sāṁkhya *q.v.* philosophy—the absolute Consciousness (God) as spiritual rays reflected in man. (*See also* puruṣa.)

adhyātma (adhyatma) (S)
God manifested as the soul of all beings.

ādi (adi) (S)
The First and the highest, the primeval.

agami (S)
The returning karma *q.v.* from this and other lifetimes.

agni (S)
'Fire', especially 'sacrificial fire', related to the Latin *ignis* and the English 'ignite'.

ahaṁkāra (ahamkara) (S)
Literally, 'I-making', hence, Self-consciousness, Self-identity, the sense of 'I', the source of egotism rooted in the illusion of the separate 'I am I'.

ain (H)
The negatively existent, Deity in repose and absolutely passive—what occultists refer to as THE ABSOLUTE.

ain soph (H)
Deity emanating and extending as the Boundless, or Limitless.

ain soph aur (H)
The Boundless, or limitless, Light.

ājñā (ajna) (S)
The brow cākra *q.v.*

ākāśa (akasha) (S)
Literally, 'shining', or 'luminous'; hence, the primordial, supersensuous spiritual essence which pervades all space and constitutes Space itself. It is the fifth cosmic Element, the fifth essence, or 'quintessence', called Æther by the ancient Stoics; but it is not the ether of science which is one of its lower elements. As the first and most fundamental of the five Elements—the others being marút *q.v.*, tejas *q.v.*, āp *q.v.*, and kṣíti *q.v.*—ākāśa is the primordial substance that is the foundation of the cosmos and embraces the properties of all five Elements. Thus it is the womb from which everything we perceive has emerged and into which everything will ultimately be reabsorbed. For this reason, ākāśa constitutes the 'tablet of memory', also known as

the 'Akashic Record', or 'Akashic Chronicle', the enduring record of all that happens, and has ever happened, in the whole of the universe.

anāhata (anahata) (S)
The heart cākra *q.v.*

ānanda (ananda) (S)
Bliss, delight, felicity, used to designate a form of consciousness in the compound term satchitānanda *q.v.*

ānandamaya-kośa (anandamaya-kosha) (S)
The 'Sheath of Bliss' (lit. 'bliss-made-sheath'), the Vedantic name for the highest kośa *q.v.* identical in Theosophical terminology with buddhi *q.v.*, the Spiritual Soul.

anandatwa (S)
Manas *q.v.*, the Mind Principle, which becomes dual when manifesting in the human nature: as Higher Manas and Lower manas.

angra-mainyush (akem-mainyu) (A)
The Zarathuśtrian (Zoroastrian) name for Ahriman, the 'hostile', or 'evil' spirit, the counteracting and opposing force.

aṇimā (anima) (S)
To become very small.

annamaya-kośa (annamaya-kosha) (S)
The 'sheath built of food' (lit. food-made-sheath), the Vedantic term for the lowest kośa *q.v.* identical in Theosophical terminology with sthūla-śarīra *q.v.*, the physical or biological body.

anoia (S)
'Want of understanding', 'folly', the irrational Animal soul, *psyche q.v.*; the name given by Plato and others to the Lower manas when too closely allied with kāma *q.v.*

antaḥkaraṇa/antaskaraṇa (antahkarana/antaskarana) (S)
Literally, the 'internal instrument', the intermediate instrument functioning as bridge, or medium of communication, between the Lower manas and Higher Manas. In this sense, therefore, a vehicle of consciousness.

antarātma sādhanā (antaratma sadhana) (S)
The innermost quest.

aṇu (anu) (S)
'Primordial atom', or 'particles of creation', the concealed, or unmanifest, deity.

anupādaka (anupadaka) (S)
'Parentless', or 'self-existing', in the sense of born without any parents or progenitors; thus pertaining to the self-created gods, the originants, or roots, from which the Hierarchies of Buddhas (Dhyāni Buddhas) of various grades emanate.

āp (ap) (S)
Liquids as a cosmic Element.

arhats (S)
Literally, 'deserving divine honours', the name first given to the Jain, and subsequently to the Buddhist holy men initiated into the esoteric mysteries.

arūpā (arupa) (S)
'Formless', or 'bodiless', as opposed to rūpa *q.v.*, 'form', or 'body'.

āsana (asana) (S)
One of the prescribed postures of Haṭha-Yoga.

asīah (assiah) (H)
The Physical, or Material World.

aṣṭāṅga (ashtanga) (S)
Eight-limbed.

ātma (atma) (S)
The Divine Self, 'Pure Consciousness', the correspondence in Man of Ātman, the Divine Principle; hence, the highest part of man. (cf. ātman.)

ātman (atman) (S)
The Universal Divine Principle. (cf. ātma.)

atzīlūth (atziluth) (H)
The Archetypal, or Prototypal World.

aum (S)
Also written *Om*, the sacred triple-lettered unit of the trinity-in-one. A syllable, or mantra *q.v.* of invocation, benediction, and affirmation.

avatāra (avatara) (S)
Divine incarnation, literally, 'descent' of a divine or exalted being who has progressed beyond the necessity of rebirths, into a pure mortal body. For example, Kṛṣṇa (Krishna) is an Avatar of Viṣṇu (Vishnu); the Dalai Lama is regarded as an avatar of Avalokiteśvara, 'The down-looking Lord'.

avidyā (avidya) (S)
Ignorance, or lack of knowledge of Reality, as opposed to vidyā *q.v.* knowledge, which proceeds from, and is produced by, illusion, or māyā *q.v.*

avītchi (avitchi) (S)
Literally, 'waveless', referring to a state of the greatest isolation and stagnation attained after physical death as the result of a life of utter evil. Also a generalized term for places of evil realization (but not of 'punishment' in the orthodox Christian sense) where the will for evil and unsatiated evil desires find their chance for expansion—before final extinction of the entities.

avyaktam (S)
The unmanifest, the unrevealed cause, unable to be realized by the mind and senses.

berīāh (beriah) (H)
The Intellectual, or Creative World.

Bhagavad Gītā (Bhagavad Gita) (S)
Literally, 'the Lord's Song', an episode of the Mahābhārata *q.v.*, the great epic poem of India. It contains a dialogue between the Lord Kṛṣṇa—the 'Charioteer'—and Arjuna, his Chelā (disciple) upon the highest spiritual philosophy. The work is pre-eminently esoteric and occult.

bhaktī (S)
Devotion, affectionate attachment.

bhūta (bhuta) (S)
Literally, 'has beens'. In one sense it refers to the five basic Elements (earth, water, etc.) as stimulators of the senses, being the leftovers of the corresponding Mahabhūta *q.v.*, or Gross Element–Principles. In another sense of leftover, it is the post-mortem 'shell', or 'spook' from which the real entity—all that is spiritual and intellectual—has fled, leaving behind a decaying astral corpse.

bīnāh (binah) (H)
Understanding.

Brahmā (Brahma) (S)
The spiritual energy–consciousness, or so-called Creator who breathes forth (*see* bṛh) our solar universe (solar system) at the dawn of creation and withdraws it at the end of his Day. Hence, the Reality underlying the Universe. Identified as the first Person of the Hindu Trimūrti *q.v.* (Trinity). (cf. brahman.)

brahma caitanya (brahma chaitanya) (S)
Reality in its subjective aspect (See kutastha caitanya.)

brahmacarya (brahmacharya) (S)
Celibacy, literally, 'The path that leads to brahman'.

brahman (S)
The impersonal and uncognizable principle of the universe—its supreme and ultimate Reality. This must be sharply distinguished from the masculine Brahmā *q.v.*

brāhmaṇas (brahmanas) (S)
Hindu sacred books. Works composed by, and for, Brahmins. In anther sense, a member of the first of the four Vedic classes comprising commentaries on those portions of the Vedic literature containing rules, explanations in detail, and guidance for ritualistic use.

bṛh (brh) (S)
Literally, 'to expand', 'to breathe forth'.

buddhi (S)
Literally, 'to awaken', 'to enlighten'; hence 'intuition', 'insight' (mistranslated as 'reason' or, even worse, 'intellect', which are aspects of the mind *per se*). Hence, the Spiritual Soul in Man, the vehicle of Ātma *q.v.*

cākra (chakra) (S)
Literally, a spinning 'wheel', or 'disk' generally. In man, cākra refers to the psycho-energetic vortices of force spanning the levels from the mental to the astral to the

etheric, finally manifesting as the major ductless glands of the physical body. Note: although their physical correspondences are found in the glands, cākras themselves are not visible physically.

chhāyā/chāyā) (chhaya) (S)
Literally, a 'shadow', 'copy', or simulacrum. In esoteric philosophy it refers to the astral image of a person.

chidākāśa (chidakasha) (S)
Mental space(s).

chit (S)
Literally, 'pure thought' as abstract consciousness, pure consciousness used to designate a form of consciousness in the compound term satchitānanda *q.v.*

chitta (S)
Mind, or intelligence, used in some yoga systems to mean 'mind substance' which can be modified by perception, or other factors, from which arises understanding.

da'at (daath) (H)
Doorway, also 'The Abyss'.

daena (A)
Essentially the same as Antaḥkaraṇa *q.v.*: the intermediate instrument functioning as bridge, or medium of communication, between Lower manas and Higher Manas. In this sense, therefore, a vehicle of consciousness.

daivīprakṛti (daiviprakriti) (S)
Primordial Light, or Primordial Nature. (See fohat.)

dangma (T)
A purified soul, a seer and an initiate; one who has attained full wisdom; hence, free from the necessity of rebirth. It is equivalent to jīvanmukti *q.v.*, the Hindu term for the adept, master, or mahātma as in theosophy.

deśā (desa) (S)
Space.

devachan (S)
Literally, the 'dwelling of the gods', being a state intermediate between two Earth-lives into which the human monad enters and there rests in repose and bliss before the subsequent urge to reincarnate. It is not identical with the Heaven of orthodox Christianity conceived of as a permanent state.

devās (devas) (S), (P)
Celestial beings, of which there are various classes, good, bad or neutral (*See* devatās.)

devatās (devatas) (S), (P)
Conscious Principles—gods in Hindu philosophy. (*See* devās.)

dhāraṇā (dharana) (S)
Mental concentration in the sense of firmness, or steadiness, or resolution in holding the mind set or concentrated on an object, or a topic of thought.

dhyāna (dhyana) (S)
Abstract contemplation or meditation when freed from exterior distraction.

dhyāni-chohans/dhyān-chohans (dhyani-chohans/dhyan-chohans) (S)
The collective hosts of spiritual beings equivalent to the Elōhīm of Life—the Angelic Hosts of Christianity—'divine intelligences', i.e., celestial beings charged with the supervision of the Kosmos by way of administering and enacting Divine Laws; and 'celestial' in the sense of being in a stage on the Ladder of Life superior to the Human Kingdom, because of having evolved through the human stage in far past aeons.

dṛṣṭi (drsti) (S)
Spiritual vision, focus, gaze, unwavering concentration. It relates to the fifth limb of yoga, pratyāhāra *q.v.* concerning sense withdrawal, as well as the sixth limb dhāranā *q.v.* relating to concentration.

elōhīm (elohim) (H)
The minor created gods by whose power and ministration the lower world is organized.

fohat (T)
An extremely mystical term of Turanian origin. Used in Tibetan occultism for what in Sanskrit is called Daivīprakṛti *q.v.*, Primordial Light, representing Cosmic Prāṇa—the universal propelling vital force, or primeval vitality in the cosmos. It is the active (masculine) potency of the female reproductive power (śakti *q.v.*) in nature; the essence of cosmic electricity (understanding that the essence of electricity is consciousness). It is that which links spirit and matter in the first stages of manifestation; the means through which Ideas in the Universal Mind are impressed upon matter. In the manifested stages of the universe, the Force that causes differentiation from the One to the many—the original homogeneous Substance–Principle to become atomic.

garimā (garima) (S)
To become very heavy.

geburah (H)
Power.

guṇas (gunas) (S)
The qualities, attributes, and characteristics of differentiated matter based on motion, prakṛti *q.v.*, but not to be identified with the properties of physical matter. The three guṇas (triguṇas) are sattva *q.v.*, rajas *q.v.*, and tamas *q.v.*

gupta-vidyā (gupta-vidya) (S)
Divine Knowledge, or Wisdom.

haṃsā/haṅsa) (hamsa/hansa) (S)
Literally, 'swan' or 'goose', a mystical bird in Eastern
Occultism analogous to the Rosicrucian Pelican. (*See also* kalahaṃsā.)

ḥesed (chesed) (H)
Mercy.

hiraṇayagarbha (hiranyagarbha) (S)
Radiant Essence of the Divine Self, or Monadic Essence.

hod (H)
Splendour.

ḥokhmāh (chokhmah) (H)
Wisdom.

iddhis (P)
Psychic faculties, the phenomenal powers in man.

indriyas (S)
The generic term for the five senses and their controlling faculty.

īśatva (ishatva) (S)
To create anything.

iśvara (ishvara) (S)
The presiding Deity of a manifested solar system.

jīv (jiv) (S)
Live, be alive.

jīva (jiva) (S)
Life-entity, or principle of life, the equivalent of the Theosophical term Monad (ātma-buddhi).

jīvanmukta (jivanmukta) (S)
A liberated being who has reached the ultimate state of holiness, such as an adept, yogi, or mahātmā.

jīv-ātma/jīvena ātmanā (jiv-atma/jivena atmana) (S)
Living essence.

jñāna (jnana) (S)
True knowledge, in the sense of knowledge of Reality.

jñānendriyas (jnanendriyas) (S)
The five sense powers (organs) by which we know and perceive the material world, i.e., the cognitive functions of consciousness as hearing, seeing, touching, seeing, tasting, and smelling.

kāla (kala) (S)
Time, a measure of time, and in another sense, fate.

kalahaṃsā (kalahamsa) (S)
The sacred, mystic name haṃsā, when preceded by that of kāla *q.v.*, infinite time; i.e. the 'Bird out of Space and Time', signifying the idea that the unknowable Absolute, endless and infinite, is said to descend into the universe, for the purposes of manifestation, using Humanity as a vehicle.

kāma (kama) (S)
Literally, 'longing for', 'desire', 'wish'; hence, volition, the cleaving to existence—the driving and impelling force in the human constitution. In its divine aspect, creating

happiness and love for all beings; in its infernal aspect, lust, sensuality, greed, and self-gratification. (*See also* kāma-manas, kāma-loka, kāma-rūpa.)

kāma-loka (kama-loka) (S)
The semi-material plane, subjective and invisible to human beings as a rule, which surrounds and encloses our physical globe. Commonly called the astral world, or 'desire-world', it is the habitat, or dwelling place, where the kāma-rūpa *q.v.*, i.e., the astral forms, or shades of the departed, remain for a certain length of time. It is the the land of Silent Shadows, Hades of the Greeks, Amenti of the Egyptians.

kāma-manas (kama-manas) (S)
The Lower mind: the thinking principle gravitating towards desire, similar to anoia *q.v.* of the Greeks.

kāma-rūpa (kama-rupa) (S)
The 'desire-body', or 'shade', being the subjective form created by means of the thoughts and desires of a person during life, which is projected into the astral world after the death of the physical body as a form and vehicle of the higher principles of the man that was.

kāraṇopādhi (karanopadhi) (S)
The 'causal instrument' in which reside the causal aspects of man's terrestrial existence on Earth.

karma (S)
Physically, action: metaphysically, the Law of Retribution, the Law of Cause and Effect, or Ethical Causation. Nemesis, only in one sense, that of bad karma. But it is wrong to associate karma with so-called punishment. Karma is neither punishment nor reward *per se*, but becomes either depending on the cause that generated the logical effects. There is the karma of merit and the karma of demerit.

karmendriyas (S)
The five powers (organs) used for action in order to interact with the material world, i.e., the conative functions of consciousness viz. speaking, grasping, walking, ejaculating, and evacuating.

kether (kether) (H)
The Crown.

kośa (kosha) (S)
Sheaths, used in Vedānta philosophy for describing the five sheaths of Ātma *q.v.*

kriyā (kriya) (S)
Action (of thought).

kriyamāṇa (kriyamana) (S)
The immediate karma *q.v.* from present actions.

kriyāśakti (kriyashakti) (S)
The power of action. A latent power of thought in man that enables him to produce a visible form from his thoughts, i.e., external, perceptible phenomenal results, by means of its own inherent energy.

kṣíti (kshiti) (S)
Solids as a cosmic Element.

kumāras (kumaras) (S)
Great Beings of original spiritual purity untouched by gross elements of matter, forming the highest in the spiritual hierarchy, who help the evolution of humanity.

kuṇḍalinī-śakti (kundalini-shakti) (S)
'Serpent fire', the spiral-like energy as one of the Forces of Nature. A recondite power in the human body.

Kūrma (Kurma) (S)
Tortoise.

kutastha caitanya (kutastha chaitanya) (S)
Analogous to the Holy Ghost in Christianity.

laghimā (laghima) (S)
To become very light.

liṅga (linga) (S)
Model, or pattern.

liṅga-śarīra (linga-sharira) (S)
The Model body, or Etheric double.

lokas (S)
A region or circumscribed place, that is, a world, sphere, or plane, as states of consciousness rather than geographical localities.

Mahābhārata (Mahabharata) (S)
The celebrated epic poem of India. The *Bhagavad Gītā* is an episode in the great epic.

mahābhūtas (mahabhutas) (S)
The Gross Element–Principles of matter, as the resultants of the developed, or evolved, tanmātras *q.v.*; equivalent to prakṛti *q.v.*, when the latter word is used in the plural form to signify the primary essences which evolve the whole visible world.

mahākala (mahakala) (S)
'Great Time', the ultimate and subtlest time.

mahākāśa (mahakasha) (S)
'Great Space', the ultimate and subtlest space.

MAHĀMĀYĀ (MAHAMAYA) (S)
The GREAT ILLUSION of manifestation (this universe and all in it in their mutual relation).

mahat (S)
Cosmic Ideation, or Universal Mind, the producer of manas *q.v.*, the thinking principle.

mahātmā (mahatma) (S)
'Great Soul', or 'Great Self', exalted beings who are in possession of knowledge and

power commensurate with the stage they have reached in spiritual evolution. They are perfected men (not spirits), relatively speaking, also known by names such as Elder Brothers, Masters, Adepts, Sages, Seers, Rishis, and Arhats.

maheśa (mahesha) (S)
The Great Lord, the (First) Logos; an aspect of Śiva *q.v.* as the Regenerator. (*See also* rudra.)

mahimā (mahima) (S)
To become very big.

malkuth (H)
The Kingdom.

manas (S)
Mind as a principle; the mental faculty which makes of man an intelligent and moral being, and distinguishes him from the animal.

maṇipūra (manipura) (S)
The solar plexus cākra *q.v.*

manomaya-kośa (manomaya-kosha) (S)
The 'sheath of manas' (lit. 'manas-made-sheath'), the Vedantic name for the kośa identical in Theosophical terminology with the Lower mind, or Kāma-manas *q.v.*, the desire-driven mind.

mantra (S)
A sacred word or phrase having spiritual power or special significance either spoken aloud or repeated soundlessly in the mind.

manvantara (S)
A period of manifestation applied to various cycles. When applied to a planet it represents the period of activity throughout the life-cycle of that planet, in contradistinction to a pralaya *q.v.*, which represents a period of repose.

marút (marut) (S)
Gaseous substances as a cosmic Element.

Matsya (S)
The avatar of Viṣṇu, the second person of the Hindu Trimūrti (Trinity), in the form of a fish.

māyā (maya) (S)
The popular meaning of illusion, or delusion, is misleading. It does not mean that the exterior world is non-existent; if it were, it obviously could not be illusory. It exists, but as an appearance, conditioned and limited by our own senses. Māyā is illusion in the sense that it is a cosmic power which renders phenomenal existence and its perceptions thereof possible. That alone which is changeless and eternal is the Real; all that is subject to change through differentiation and decay is transitory—hence, regarded as illusion. Existence *is*, but not as it appears to be; things *are* but not as they appear. Eloquently stated by the late José Saramago, Portuguese writer and recipient of the 1998 Nobel Prize in Literature, 'Not everything is as it seems, and not everything that seems is.'

māyāvi (mayavi) (S)
An adjectival form of the term māyā; hence with the connotation of 'illusion', 'an appearance'.

māyāvi-rūpa (mayavi-rupa) (S)
The 'illusive form', 'illusory body', 'illusion body', 'dream body', 'thought body', all such terms indicative of a higher astral-mental form. Similar terms in German and French are *doppelgänger* and *perispirit*, respectively. It is important to note that the māyāvi-rūpa pertains to the living person. It is dual in its function, being the vehicle both of thought and of the animal passions and desires. The higher part of this body, containing the spiritual elements gathered during life, merges after death entirely into the vijñānamaya-kośa *q.v.*, or Causal Body; while the lower part, containing the animal elements, forms the Kāma-rūpa *q.v.*

monad (G)
The Unity, the One—eternal, life-centres, consciousness-centres. Technically, in Occultism, it refers to the unified triad, ātma–buddhi–manas, or the duad, ātma–buddhi, that immortal part of man which reincarnates in the lower kingdoms, and gradually progresses through them to Man and then to the final goal. Monads are spiritual–substance entities, or seeds, wherein the sum-total of powers appertaining to their divine origin are latent, i.e. unmanifested; and evolution consists in the development and growth of these seeds, whereby the universal Life expresses itself in innumerable forms and beings.

mūladhāra (muladhara) (S)
The base of spine cākra *q.v.*

Myalba (T)
The Northern Buddhist name for our Earth, which they consider a 'hell', strictly in the sense of a place of punishment for those whose karma it is to reincarnate on it for the purgation of suffering and to learn from experience.

Narasiṃha (Narasimha) (S)
Man-lion.

netzah (H)
Victory.

nirmānakāya (nirmanakaya) (S)
One who has so purified his whole system that he is above even the divine illusion of Devachan.

nirvāṇa (nirvana) (S)
Popular connotations of escape or annihilation are misleading, as is the orthodox idea of heaven. Nirvāṇa literally means 'blown out'; but what is 'blown out' refers only to man's lower principles. Nirvāṇa is thus a state of absolute existence and absolute consciousness. Thus, a state of utter bliss where the personal–individual is completely absorbed in pure kosmic Being—the wondrous destiny of those who have attained superhuman knowledge and spiritual illumination through the personal–individual absorption into, and identification with, the SELF.

niyāma (niyama) (S)
Religious observances such as fasting, praying, penance.

nous (S)
The Higher Mind, or Spiritual Soul; the name given by Plato, and others, to the Higher Manas when allied with buddhi. The distinction between nous and anoia *q.v.*, or the irrational Animal soul, is very sharp, and the two must not be confused.

ōlām (olam) (H)
Manifest 'World Systems'.

pañca tattwa (pancha tattwa) (S)
The five Root-Causes.

parabrahma(n) (S)
The Absolute, literally, 'Para-brahman', 'Beyond brahman'. Hence, the impersonal and nameless universal Principle.

paramārtha-satya (paramartha-satya) (S)
Supreme, or absolute Truth—direct knowledge of Reality.

paramātman (paramatman) (S)
The 'Self Beyond', the permanent SELF, the Supreme Soul of the Universe, virtually identical with Brahman.

Paraśurāma (Parasurama) (S)
Rama with an axe.

parinirvāṇa (parinirvana)(S)
Absolute Non-Being, which is equivalent to absolute Being or Be-ness, the stage reached by the human monad at the end of the a Great Cycle.

prākāmya (prakamya) (S)
To attain all desire.

prakṛti (prakriti) (S)
Nature, or Matter in general as the harmonized and integrated condition of properties. The great Producer of entities or things; hence, the productive veil, or sheath, of puruṣa *q.v.*, its correlate.

pralaya (S)
A period of dissolution, or repose applied to various cycles. When applied to a planet it represents the period of rest, in contradistinction to a manvantara *q.v.*, which represents a period of activity throughout the life-cycle of a planet.

prāṇa (prana) (S)
The Life principle, the breath of Life; hence, the vital force which flows in the subtler counterpart, Liṅga-śarīra *q.v.*, of the physical.

prāṇamaya-kośa (pranamaya-kosha) (S)
The 'sheath of life' (lit. 'prāṇa-made-sheath'), the Vedantic name for the kośa *q.v.* identical in Theosophical terminology with the Etheric double.

prāṇava (pranava) (S)
The sacred Word, equivalent to Aum *q.v.*, the Cosmic Vibration.

prāṇāyāma (pranayama) (S)
Various methods of regulating and circulating the breath.

prāpti (prapti) (S)
To reach anywhere.

prārabdha (prarabdha) (S)
The karma *q.v.* for a particular birth, or incarnation.

pratibha bhava (S)
Non-instrumental perception; pertaining to the spiritual planes and corresponding, in the astral body, to the jñānendriyas *q.v.* as instruments of the cognitive functions of consciousness.

pratyāhāra (pratyahara) (S)
Signifying, 'withdrawal', but technically and esoterically in the sense of withdrawal of consciousness from sensuous or sensual concerns, or from external objects.

psuche (S)
The vital force which animates the body and shows itself in breathing; akin to prāṇa *q.v.*

psyche (S)
The Animal soul in Theosophy; soul, in a collective and general sense in Greek philosophy.

Purāṇas (Puranas) (S)
A collection of symbolical and allegorical writings supposed to have been composed by Vyāsa, the author of the Indian epic, Mahābhārata *q.v.*

puruṣa (purusha) (S)
The monad *q.v.*; eternal Spiritual Soul in man; the Ideal Man, or Heavenly Man; Son of God. (*See also* ābhāsa caitanya.)

purushottma (S)
Analogous to the Holy Ghost in Christianity—see kutastha caitanya *q.v.*

rājas (rajas) (S)
The quality of differentiation and activity. One of the three guṇas *q.v.* representing form and change.

rākṣasas (rakshasas) (S)
Demonic beings in the epic Rāmāyaṇa *q.v.*

Rāma (Rama) (S)
The seventh avatar, or incarnation of Viṣṇu *q.v.*, and the hero of the Rāmāyaṇa. His full name is Rāma-Chandra.

Rāmāyaṇa (Ramayana) (S)
The celebrated epic poem collated with the Mahābhārata *q.v.*, either the original of the Iliad or vice versa.

Rāvana (Ravana) (S)
The King-Demon of the Rākṣasas *q.v.*, the Sovereign of Lankā (Ceylon), who abducted Sīta, wife of the Lord Rāma, which precipitated the great war described in the Rāmāyaṇa *q.v.*

ṛta (rta) (S)
The natural rule and order of things.

rudra (S)
The Great Lord, the (First) Logos; an aspect of Śiva *q.v.* as the Destroyer. (*See also* maheśa.)

rūpa (rupa) (S)
'Form', or 'body' (as opposed to arūpā, 'formless', or bodiless').

śabda-brahma/brahman (shabda-brahma/brahman (S)
Reality as 'Sound', that is, its vibrational, or wave aspect, the root of the objective phenomenal universe. (*See also* māyā.)

sahasrāra (sahasrara) (S)
The head cākra *q.v.*

śakti (shakti) (S)
Matter, power.

samādhi (samadhi) (S)
Complete absorption of the consciousness and its faculties into oneness or union with the monadic essence, ātma *q.v.*

Śambhala (Shamballa) (S)
A Sanskrit place-name of highly mystical significance.

Sāṁkhya/Sāṅkhya (Samkhya/Sankhya) (S)
The system of philosophy and analytical metaphysics founded by the Rishi Kapila, being one of the six Darshanas, or systems of Indian philosophical thought.

samyama (S)
A yogic technique for awakening, and quickening into activity, powers hitherto latent in man.

sañcita (sanchita) (S)
The totality of karma *q.v.* from all lifetimes.

saptaparṇa (saptaparna) (S)
The 'sevenfold': physically, a plant which gave its name to a famous cave with seven chambers in Râjâgriha, near Buddha Gaya (Bodh Gaya), where the Lord Buddha used to meditate and teach his Arhats *q.v.*; esoterically, the symbol of the 'seven-leafed Man-Plant'.

śarīra (sharira) (S)
'Form', 'body', which is impermanent and transitory, and therefore 'wastes away'.

sat (S)
Used to designate a form of consciousness in the compound term satchitānanda *q.v.*

satchitānanda (satchitananda) (S)
The three aspects of consciousness.

sattva/sattwa (S)
The quality of truth, goodness, quiescence. One of the three guṇas *q.v.* representing harmony.

sephīrāh (sephirah) (H)
An emanation and attribute of Deity.

sephīrōth (sephiroth) (H)
The ten emanations and attributes of Deity.

shekhīnah (shekhinah) (H)
The middle Pillar of the Sephirothic Tree—the veil of ain soph *q.v.*

siddhis (S)
Phenomenal powers acquired through various techniques of yoga, and other means, ranging from the lowest psychic powers to the highest spiritual powers.

Sīta (Sita) (S)
Wife of the Lord Rāma.

Śiva (Shiva) (S)
The Great Lord, the (First) Logos. As pure, undifferentiated Divine Consciousness, the correlate of śakti *q.v.* Identified as the third Person of the Hindu Trimūrti *q.v.* (Trinity). Popularly known as 'the Destroyer', Rudra *q.v.*, destroys only to regenerate as Maheśa *q.v.* on a higher plane.

skandha (S)
Literally, 'bundles', or groups of attributes, which unite at the birth of man and constitute his personality. (*See also* karma.)

śloka (shloka) (S)
The Sanskrit epic metre formed of thirty-two syllables: verses in four half-lines of eight, or in two lines of sixteen syllables each.

spento-mainyush (A)
The 'good twin', or 'good spirit', namely, good thoughts, expansive thoughts.

sthūla (sthula) (S)
Literally, 'coarse', 'gross', 'bulky', referring to differentiated and conditioned matter.

sthūla-śarīra (sthula-sharira) (S)
The Physical body.

sthūlopadhi (sthulopadhi) (S)
The physical form, i.e., Physical body and Etheric double.

sūkṣma-śarīra (sukshma-sharira) (S)
The fine material body equivalent to the Liṅga-śarīra *q.v.*

sūkṣmopadhi (sukshmopadhi) (S)
The subtile vehicle.

sūtra (sutra) (S)
The second division of the sacred writings (in Hinduism as well as Buddhism), generally addressed to the Buddhist laity.

sūtrātman (sutratman) (S)
Literally, 'the thread of spirit', the sacred 'Thread-Self'—the stream of consciousness–life, which is the fundamental and individual Selfhood of every entity, which, in man, is the immortal Ego, or Individuality, which incarnates one life after the other, and upon which are strung, like beads on a string, his countless personalities.

svadhiṣṭhāna (svadhisthana) (S)
The sacral centre cākra *q.v.*

svapna (S)
The dreaming state.

tamas (S)
The quality of ignorance, darkness, inactivity; also stability, repose, passivity. One of the three guṇas *q.v.* representing inertia.

taṇhā (tanha) (P)
The 'thirst' for material life; the desire to live and to cling to life on this Earth (being the main cause of rebirth or reincarnation). (*See also* tṛṣṇā.)

tanmātras (tanmatras) (S)
The objects of the senses equivalent to vishayas *q.v.*

Tāraka Rāja-Yoga (Taraka Raja-Yoga) (S)
One of the Brahminical Yoga systems for the development of purely spiritual powers and knowledge.

tattva/tattwa (S)
'That', referring to principles in Nature eternally existing; the underlying reality, or essence, behind outward appearances, comparable to the quiddity of European scholastics.

tejas (S)
Fire as a cosmic Element.

tiphereth (H)
Beauty.

Trimūrti (Trimurti) (S)
Literally, 'three faces', or 'triple form'—the Trinity.

tṛṣṇā (trishna) (S)
Literally, 'thirst' and 'longing' for what a man formerly knew and what he wills and desires to know again—things familiar to it and akin to it from past experiences—which draws the man back again to incarnation on the Earth plane. (*See also* taṇhā.)

upādhi (upadhi) (S)
Literally, 'standing in the place of', a veil; hence, that which stands forth as a substitute of something less material than itself. (*See also* vāhana.)

Upaniṣads (Upanishads) (S)
The 'esoteric doctrine', or interpretation of the Vedas *q.v.* from which was later developed the Vedānta *q.v.* system.

vāhana (vahana) (S)
Literally, 'the bearer', 'the carrier', the vehicle of something which enables it to function and manifest itself on a plane hierarchically lower than its own plane. (*See also* upādhi.)

Vāmana (Vamana) (S)
Dwarf.

vānaras/vanaras (S)
A species of ape-like men that existed millions of years ago *alongside humans of our type*, and bearing no relation to the simian or anthropoid primates from which, according to Darwinism, present humanity is supposed to have evolved.

Varāha (Varaha) (S)
Boar.

vasitvā (vasitva) (S)
To command and control anything.

Vedānta (Vedanta) (S)
Literally, 'the End (or Completion) of the Veda'—a mystic system of philosophy which has developed from the efforts of generations of sages to interpret the secret meaning of the Upaniṣads *q.v.*

Vedas (S)
The 'revelation', 'divine knowledge', the most ancient as well as the most sacred of the Sanskrit works.

vidyā (vidya) (S)
Knowledge, generally synonymous with jñāna *q.v.*

vijñāna (vijnana) (S)
Intelligence, the faculty of the Higher Mind.

vijñānamaya-kośa (vijnanamaya-kosha) (S)
The 'Sheath of Intelligence' (lit. 'intelligence-made-sheath'), the Vedantic name for the kośa *q.v.* identical in Theosophical terminology with the Causal Body.

vikarana bhava (S)
Non-instrumental action; pertaining to the spiritual planes and corresponding, in the astral body, to the karmendriyas *q.v.* as the instrument of the connative function of consciousness.

vishaya (S)
The objects of the senses equivalent to tanmātras *q.v.*

Viṣṇu (Vishnu) (S)
Identified as the second Person of the Hindu Trimūrti *q.v.* (Trinity).

viśuddha (visuddha) (S)
The throat cākra *q.v.*

vyavahāra-satya (vyavahara-satya) (S)
Knowledge of the world of appearances obtained through the senses and the intellect.

vyoma (S)
Equivalent to ākāśa *q.v.*, or æther (not ether).

yāma (yama) (S)
'Restraint', or 'forbearance'.

yesōd (yesod) (H)
Foundation.

yetzīrāh (yetzirah) (H)
The Substantial, or Formative World.

Zarathuśtra (Zarathushtra) (A)
The great lawgiver, and the founder of the Zoroastrian religion, variously called Mazdaism, Magism, Parseeism, and Fire-Worship.

Further Reading

This section comprises a representative selection of books, scholarly papers, and electronic resources in support of this three-volume work. The following points should be noted:

1. Subject-specific reference material has been provided in the relevant Endnotes to Volumes I, II, and III and therefore has not been duplicated.
2. References supplied as reference notes to individual chapters to Volumes I, II, and III have been duplicated only in those few cases where the narrative has not warranted sufficient emphasis.
3. A few entries are supported with brief commentary to elucidate their importance.
4. Regarding the several works cited on the *philosophia perennis*, it is necessary to develop the intuitive faculty in order to foster spiritual growth and to deepen understanding of all that this golden tradition stands for. In thus exploring the reading matter listed here, as well as much that is not, it is important to remember that while there are many approaches to, and expositions of, the Wisdom teachings, the teachings themselves are of a unique nature and of an universal scope which remain unchanged, whatever the presentation, albeit some interpretations will necessarily be closer to the spirit of that Wisdom.

Abelson, J., *Jewish Mysticism*, 1913; Kessinger Publishing Co., 2003.

Abu Bakr al-Kalabadhi, *The Doctrine of the Sufis*, trans. A. J. Arberry, Cambridge University Press, 1935.

Adam, D., 'Flickering Light Raises Possibility of Changing "Constant" ', *Nature*, Vol. 412, 2002.

Adams, W. Marsham, *The Book of the Master of the Hidden Places*, London: Search Publishing, 1933.

Aelian, *Historical Miscellany*, trans. N. G. Wilson, Cambridge, Massachusetts: Harvard University Press, 1997.

Aeschylus, *The Complete Greek Tragedies*, ed. D. Grene and R. Lattimore, University of Chicago Press, 1953/1956.

Afford, P., *Therapy in the Age of Neuroscience: A Guide for Counsellors and Therapists*, Routledge, 2020.

Agnew, Z. K., Bhakoo, K. K., and Puri, B. K., 'The Human Mirror System: A Motor Resonance Theory of Mind-Reading', *Brain Research Reviews*, Vol. 54, 2007.

Aharonov, Y. and Bohm, D., 'Significance of Electromagnetic Potentials in the Quantum Theory', *Phys. Rev.*, Vol. 115, No. 3, 1959.

Aiton, E. J., *Leibniz: A Biography*, Bristol and Boston: Adam Hilger, 1985.

Akolkar, V. V., 'Search for Sharada: Report of a Case and its Investigation', *Journal of the American Society for Psychical Research*, Vol. 86, No. 3, July 1992.

Alexander, D., *Is there Purpose in Biology?* Monarch Books, 2018.

Alexander, E., *The Map of Heaven: How Science, Religion, and Ordinary People Are Proving the Afterlife*, New York: Simon & Schuster, 2014.

Allen, R. H., *Star Names: Their Lore and Meaning*, New York: Dover Publications, 1980.

Anderson, R., 'On Novels and Reincarnation Memories', letter in *Journal of the American Society for Psychical Research*, Vol. 87, April 1993.

Arberry, A. J. (ed.), *The Koran Interpreted*, London: Touchstone, 1996.

Arberry, A. J., *Sufism: An Account of the Mystics of Islam*, New York: Dover Publications, 2002.

Aristotle, *Metaphysics*, Vol. 1, Books 1–9, trans. H. Loeb Classical Library, Harvard University Press, 1933.

Armstrong, K., *Muhammed – A Biography of the Prophet*, London: Phoenix Press, 1991.

Arnold, E., *The Light of Asia*, Adyar, India: Theosophical Publishing House, 1997.

Asher, R. A. (ed.), *Encyclopaedia of Language and Linguistics*, Oxford: Pergamon, 1994.

Astin, J. A., Harkness, E., and Ernst, E., 'The Efficacy of "Distant Healing": A Systematic Review of Randomized Trials', *Am. Journal Med.*, Vol. 132, 2000.

Atmanspacher, H., Romer, H., and Walach, H., 'Weak Quantum Theory: Complementarity and Entanglement in Physics and Beyond', *Foundations of Physics*, Vol. 32, 2002.

Attar, Farid ud-din, *The Conference of the Birds*, UK: Pilgrims Book House, 2008.

Augros, R. and Stanciu, G., *The New Biology: Discovering The Wisdom In Nature*, Boston Shambhala, New Science Library, 1988.

Augustine, *The Confessions of St. Augustine*, trans. E. B. Pusey, London: J. M. Dent; New York: E. P. Dutton, 1932.

Aurobindo, Sri, *Hymns to the Mystic Fire*, in *The Complete Works of Sri Aurobindo*, Vol. 16, Sri Aurobindo Ashram Publication Department, 2013.

Aurobindo, Sri, *The Life Divine*, New York: E. P. Dutton, 1949.

Aurobindo, Sri, *The Secret of the Veda*, in *The Complete Works of Sri Aurobindo*, Vol. 15, Sri Aurobindo Ashram Publication Department, 1998.

Ayer, A. J., *The Concept of a Person and Other Essays*, St Martin's Press, 1963.

Bache, C. M., *Diamonds from Heaven*, Park Street Press, 2019.

Backster, C., 'Evidence of a Primary Perception in Plant Life', *Int. Journal of Parapsychology*, Vol. 10, No. 4, 1968.

Bacon, F., *The Advancement of Learning and New Atlantis*, Oxford University Press, 1951.

Bailey, A. A., *A Treatise on Cosmic Fire*, New York: Lucis Press, 1964.

Bailey, A. A., *Discipleship in the New Age*, London: Lucis Press, 1980.

Bailey, A. A., *Esoteric Psychology*, London: Lucis Press, 1981.

Bailey, A. A., *Initiation, Human and Solar*, London: Lucis Press, 1977.

Bailey, A. A., *Letters on Occult Meditation*, New York: Lucis Press, 1973.

Bailey, A. A., *Telepathy and the Etheric Vehicle*, London: Lucas Press, 1956.

Bailey, A. A., *The Externalisation of the Hierarchy*, New York: Lucis Press, 1976.

Bailey, A. A., *The Reappearance of the Christ*, London: Lucis Press, 1969.

Bailey, A. A., *The Seven Rays of Life*, New York: Lucis Publishing Co., 1995. Compilation from all the Alice A. Bailey books of material about the seven rays.

Bailey, A. A., *The Soul: The Quality of Life*, London: Lucis Press, 1974.

Bair, P. and Bair, S., *Living from the Heart: Heart Rhythm Meditation for Energy, Clarity, Peace, and Inner Power*, Tucson, Arizona: Living Heart Media, 2019.

Baker, M. C. and Goetz, S. (eds), *The Soul Hypothesis: Investigations into the Existence of the Soul*, New York: Continuum International Publishing Group, 2011.

Barnett, S. A., *Modern Ethology*, Oxford University Press, 1981.

Barrett, W., Address by the President, *Proceedings of the Society for Psychical Research*, Vol. 18, 1904.

Barrow, J. and Tipler, F., *The Cosmological Anthropic Principle*, Oxford University Press, 1996.

Barrow, J. D. and Webb, J. K., 'Inconstant Constants: Do the Inner Workings of Nature Change with Time?' *Scientific American*, June 2005.

Bartholomae, C., *Die Gathas des Avestas* [The Gathas and the Avestas], Strassburg, 1905.

Bateman, C., *The Mythology of Evolution*, US: Zero Books, 2012.

Bauval, R. and Hancock, G., *Keeper of Genesis*, London: William Heinemann, 2001.

Beauregard, M. and O'Leary, D., *The Spiritual Brain*, New York: HarperOne, 2007.

Bedford, R., *The Defence of Truth*, Manchester: Manchester University Press, 1979.

Behe, M. J., *Darwin's Black Box: The Biochemical Challenge to Evolution*, New York: The Free Press, 1996.

Beloussov, L., 'The Formative Powers of Developing Organisms', in *What Is Life?* ed. H-Peter Dürr, F-A. Popp, and W. Schommers, New Jersey, London, Singapore: World Scientific, 2002.

Bendit, L. J., *The Mirror of Life and Death*, Wheaton, Illinois: Theosophical Publishing House, 1968. Draws upon the knowledge of the psychic Phoebe Payne (who became the author's second wife).

Benor, D. J., 'Survey of Spiritual Healing Research', *Complementary Medical Research*, Vol. 4, 1990.

Benor, D. J., *Healing Research*, Vol. 1, London: Helix Editions, 1993.

Bergson, H., *The Creative Mind*, New York: Philosophical Library, 1946.

Bergson, H., *Creative Evolution*, London: Macmillan, 1911.

Bergson, H., *Introduction to Metaphysics*, New York: Harper, 1949.

Berriman, A. E., *Historical Metrology*, London: Dent; New York: Dutton, 1953.

Bhagavan Das, *The Pranava-Vada of Maharshi Gargyayana*, notes by A. Besant, London & Benares: Theosophical Publishing Society, 1910. The Science of the Sacred Word.

Bhagavan Das, *The Science of Peace*, London & Benares: Theosophical Publishing Society, 1904. An attempt at an exposition of the First Principles of the Science of the Self – Adhyâtma-Vidyâ.

Bhagavan Das, *The Science of the Emotions*, Adyar, Madras: Theosophical Publishing Society, 1924.

Bhattacharya, H. and Das, B., *The Cultural Heritage of India: Vol. 4, The Religions*, Calcutta: The Ramakrishna Mission Institute of Culture, 1993.

Bierman, D. and Scholte, H., 'Anomalous Anticipatory Brain Activation Preceding Exposure of Emotional and Neutral Pictures', *Journal of International Society of Life Information Science*, 2002.

Bilimoria, E., ' "The Last Wonder-Child to Whom the Magi Could do Sincere and Appropriate Homage": How Religion Underpinned Science and Technology', *Journal of the Scientific and Medical Network*, No. 125, 2017.

Bilimoria, E., 'Newton: "The Last Wonder-Child to Whom the Magi Could do Sincere and Appropriate Homage" ', in Ana-Maria Pascal (ed.), *Multiculturalism and the Convergence of Faith and Practical Wisdom in Modern* Society, Hershey, Pennsylvania: IGI Global, 2017.

Bilimoria, E., *The Snake and the Rope: Problems in Western Science Resolved by Occult Science*, Adyar, Madras: Theosophical Publishing House, 2006.

Birge, W. T., 'Probable Values of the General Physical Constants', *Reviews of Modern Physics*, Vol. 33, 1929.

Blaker, G., 'Glancing Back and Forth', in *Wider Horizons: Explorations in Science and Human Experience*, ed. D. Lorimer et al., The Scientific Medical Network, 1999.

Blackmore, S., *Conversations on Consciousness*, Oxford University Press, 2005.

Blackmore, S., *The Meme Machine*, Oxford University Press, 1999.

Bode, Dastur, F. A., *Man, Soul, Immortality in Zoroastrianism*, Bombay: J. C. Tarapore / K. R. Cama Oriental Institute, 1960.

Boehme, J.: *Aurora (1612); Signatura Rerum (1621); The Supersensual Life (1624); Of the Divine Revelation (1624)*; in Rev. W. Law, *The Works of Jacob Behmen, The Teutonic Theosopher*, Vol. 4, English edn, London: M. Richardson, in Paternoster Row, 1764.

Bohm, D. and Hiley, B., *The Undivided Universe*, London: Routledge, 1993.

Bohm, D., *Causality and Chance in Modern Physics*, London: Routledge & Kegan Paul, 1957.

Bohm, D., *Coherence and the Implicate Order*, London: Routledge & Kegan Paul, 1980.

Bohm, D., *Quantum Theory*, New York: Prentice Hall, 1951.

Bohm, D., *The Special Theory of Relativity*, New York: W. A. Benjamin, 1965.

Bohr, N., *Atomic Physics and Human Knowledge*, John Wiley, 1958. Contains an account of Bohr's long struggle with Einstein over the uncertainty principle.

Bohr, N., *Atomic Physics and the Description of Nature*, Cambridge: Cambridge University Press, 1934.

Bondi, H., Bonner, W. B., Lyttleton, R. A., and Whitrow G., *Rival Theories in Cosmology*, Oxford University Press, 1960.

Bondi, H., *Cosmology*, Cambridge University Press, 1960.

Bono, Edward de, *The Use of Lateral Thinking*, Penguin, 1990.

Boseley, S., 'Scandal of Scientists who take Money for Papers Ghostwritten by Drug Companies', *The Guardian*, 7 February 2002.

Bouratinos, E., *Science, Objectivity and Consciousness*, ICRL Press, 2018.

Bowen, P. G., *The Occult Way*, New York: E. P. Dutton & Co., 1978.

Bowen, P. G., *The Sayings of the Ancient One: Wisdom from Ancient Africa*, US: Theosophical Publishing House, 1970.

Bowler, P. J., *Evolution: The History of an Idea*, Berkeley: University of California Press, 1984.

Boycott, B. B., 'Learning in the Octopus', *Scientific American*, Vol. 212, 1965.

Boyle, R., *The Works of Robert Boyle*, ed. M. Hunter and E. B. Davis, 12 vols, UK: Pickering & Chatto, 2000.

Brain–Mind Bulletin: Frontiers of Research, Theory and Practice, 12 July 1982; 3 October 1983, and 30 December 1985.

Braud, W. G. and Schlitz, M., 'Psychokinetic Influence on Electrodermal Activity', *Journal of Parapsychology*, Vol. 47, 1983.

Braud, W. G., 'Human Interconnectedness: Research Indications', *Revision*, Vol. 14, No. 3, 1992.

Braud, W., Shafer, D., and Andrews, S., 'Electrodermal Correlates of Remote Attention: Autonomic Reactions to an Unseen Gaze', *Proceedings of Presented Papers, Parapsychology Association: 33rd Annual Convention*, Maryland: Chevy Chase, 1990.

Brennan, J. H., *Occult Tibet*, US: Llewellyn Publications, 1997.

Bright, W. (ed.), *International Encyclopaedia of Linguistics*, Oxford: Oxford University Press, 1992.

Broad, C. D., *Leibniz: An Introduction*, ed. C. Lewy, Cambridge: Cambridge University Press, 1975.

Broad, W. and Wade, N., *Betrayers of the Truth: Fraud and Deceit in Science*, Oxford University Press, 1985.

Broek, R. van den., and Hanegraaff, W. J., *Gnosis and Hermeticism – From Antiquity to Modern Times*, New York: SUNY Press, 1998.

Broglie, Louis de, *Matter and Light: The New Physics*, New York: Dover Publications, 1939.

Brooke, J. H., *Science and Religion: Some Historical Perspectives*, Cambridge University Press, 1991.

Brooks, M., *13 Things That Don't Make Sense*, London: Profile Books, 2009.

Brother Lawrence, *The Practice of the Presence of God*, US: Martino Fine Books, 2016.

Buber, M., *The Legend of Baal-Shem*, London: Routledge, 2002.

Bucke, R., *Cosmic Consciousness*, New York: University Books, 1961.

Budge, E. A. W., *The Egyptian Book of the Dead*, 1898; repr., New York: Dover, 1967.

Budge, E. A. W., *Egyptian Religion*, New York: Gramercy Books, 1959.

Budge, E. A. W., *The Dwellers on the Nile*, London: The Religious Tract Society, 1926.

Bullmore, E., *The Inflamed Mind*, Short Books, 2018.

Burnet, J., *Early Greek Philosophy*, London: A&C Black, 1930.

Butler, C., *Western Mysticism*, London: Constable & Company, 1922.

Buzsáki, G., *The Brain from the Inside Out*, Oxford University Press, 2019.

Campbell, J., *A Joseph Campbell Companion: Reflections on the Art of Living*, ed. D. Osbon, HarperCollins, 1992.

Campbell, J., *The Hero with A Thousand Faces – The Collected Works of Joseph Campbell*, New World Library, 2012.

Campbell, J., *Transformations of Myth Through Time*, HarperPerennial; illustrated edn, 1990.

Capra, F., *The Web of Life: A New Synthesis of Mind and Matter*, London: HarperCollins, 1996.

Capra, F., *The Turning Point*, Wildwood House, London, 1982.

Cardeña, E., Lynn, S. J., and Krippner, S., *Varieties of Anomalous Experience: Examining the Scientific Evidence*, Washington, DC: American Psychologcal Association, 2000.

Carr, B., 'Worlds Apart? Can Psychical Research Bridge the Gap between Matter and Minds?', *Proceedings of the Society for Psychical Research*, Vol. 59, 2008.

Ch'en, K. K. S., *The Chinese Transformation of Buddhism*, Princeton University Press, 1973.

Chaisson, E., *Cosmic Evolution: The Rise of Complexity in Nature*, Cambridge: Harvard University Press, 2000.

Chalmers, D. J., 'Consciousness and its Place in Nature', in D. J. Chalmers (ed.), *Philosophy of Mind: Classical and Contemporary Readings*, New York and Oxford: Oxford University Press, 2002.

Chalmers, D. J., *The Conscious Mind: In Search of a Fundamental Theory*, Oxford: Oxford University Press, 1996.

Chan, W., *A Source Book in Chinese Philosophy*, Princeton University Press, 1963.

Chandmal, A., *One Thousand Moons: Krishnamurti at Eighty-Five*, New York: Harry N. Abrams, Inc., 1985.

Chandra, A., *The Scientist and the Saint*, Archetype Books, 2018.

Chatterji, J. C., *The Wisdom of the Vedas*, Wheaton: Quest, 1973.

Chaudhuri, H., *Integral Yoga*, London: George Allen and Unwin, 1965.

Chopra, D. and Tanzi, R. E., *Super Genes: Unlock the Astonishing Power of Your DNA for Optimum Health and Well-Being*, New York: Penguin Random House, 2015.

Chopra, D. and Tanzi, R. E., *The Healing Self*, Rider, 2018.

Churton, T., *Gnostic Philosophy*, Rochester, Vermont: Inner Traditions, 2005.

Clowes, E., 'Two Drug Companies Fined £260m for Swindling NHS over "Life-Saving Medicines" ', *Sky News*, 15 July 2021.

Cobb, M., *The Idea of the Brain: A History*, Profile Books, 2020.

Codd, C. M., *The Ageless Wisdom of Life*, Adyar, Madras: Theosophical Publishing House, 1967.

Codd, C. M., *The Technique of the Spiritual Life*, Adyar, Madras: Theosophical Publishing House, 1958.

Cohen, B. and Westfall, R. S. (eds), *Newton*, W. W. Norton & Company, 1995.

Cohen, E. R. and Taylor, B. N., 'The 1986 CODATA Recommended Values of the Fundamental Physical Constants', *Journal of Physical and Chemical Reference Data*, Vol. 17, 1986.

Collins, J., *A History of Modern European Philosophy*, Milwaukee, Wisconin: Bruce Publishing, 1965.

Collins, M., *The Visionary Spirit*, Permanent Publications, 2018.

Collins, Mabel (Mrs Kenningale R. Cook), *The Idyll of the White Lotus: With Commentary by T. Subba Row*, 1884; CreateSpace Independent Publishing Platform, 2017.

Collins, Mabel, *Light on the Path* (incl. essay on *Karma*), London: Reeves & Turner, 1885.

Collins, Mabel, *Through the Gates of Gold: A Fragment of Thought*, Boston: Roberts Brothers, 1887.

Conford, P., *Realising Health*, Cambridge Scholars Press, 2020.

Confucius, *The Analects*, trans. W. E. Soothill, Yokohama: Fukuin Printing Co., 1910; Oxford: Oxford University Press, 1937.

Conniff, R., 'Animal Instincts', *The Guardian*, 27 May, 2006.

Connor, S., 'For the Love of God: Scientists in Uproar at £1 million Religion Prize', *The Independent*, 7 April, 2011.

Conze, E., *Buddhist Meditation*, London: Routledge, 1956.

Cooper, J. M., *The Complete Works of Plato*, Indianapolis: Hackett Publishing Co., 1997.

Copenhaver, B. P. (ed.), *Hermetica*, Cambridge: Cambridge University Press, 1992.

Copenhaver, B., 'Jewish Theologies of Space in the Scientific Revolution: Henry More, Joseph Raphson and Isaac Newton', *Annals of Science*, 37/5, 1978.

Cottingham, J. G., Stoothoff, R., Murdoch, D., and Kenny, A. (eds), *The Philosophical Writings of Descartes*, 3 vols, Cambridge: Cambridge University Press, 1985.

Cottrell, A. (ed.), *The Penguin Encyclopaedia of Ancient Civilizations*, London: Penguin Books, 1980.

Cottrell, I. E., Winer, G. A., and Smith, M. C., 'Beliefs of Children and Adults about Feeling Stares of Unseen Others', *Developmental Psychology*, Vol. 32, 1996.

Cozolino, L., *Why Therapy Works: Using Our Minds to Change our Brains*, W. W. Norton & Co., 2016.

Cramer, J., 'The Transactional Interpretation of Quantum Mechanics', *Reviews of Modern Physics*, Vol. 58, 1986.

Cranston, M., *John Locke: A Biography*, US: Oxford University Press, 1985.

Creel, H. G., *Confucius, the Man and the Myth*, London: Theodore Brun Limited, 1951.

Crick, F., 'Memory and Molecular Turnover', *Nature*, Vol. 312, 1984.

Crick, F., *Of Molecules and Men*, Seattle: University of Washington Press, 1966.

D'Espagnat, B., *Conceptual Foundations of Quantum Mechanics*, US: CRC Press, 1999.

Daily Telegraph, ' "Atheists Just as Ethical as Churchgoers", New Research Shows', 9 February 2010.

Dalai Lama, His Holiness, Tenzin Gyatso, The Fourteenth Dalai Lama, *The Buddhism of Tibet and the Key to the Middle Way*, New York: Harper & Row, 1975.

Dalai Lama, His Holiness, Tenzin Gyatso, The Fourteenth Dalai Lama, *The Opening of the Wisdom Eye*, Wheaton, Illinois: Quest Books, Theosophical Publishing House, 1975.

Dalai Lama, His Holiness, Tenzin Gyatso, The Fourteenth Dalai Lama, *My Land and My People*, ed. D. Howarth, London: Weidenfeld and Nicolson, 1962.

Dalai Lama, His Holiness, Tenzin Gyatso, The Fourteenth Dalai Lama, *The Universe in a Single Atom: The Convergence of Science and Spirituality*, New York: Random House, 2005.

Dalton, K., 'Exploring the Links: Creativity and Psi in the Ganzfeld', *Proceedings of the Parapsychological Association, 40th Annual Convention*, 1997.

Dante, A., *The Divine Comedy*, trans. A. Mandelbaum, introd. E. Montale, US: Everyman's Library, Alfred A. Knopf, 1995.

Darmesteter, J., *Le Zend Avesta*, Annales du Musee Gnimet, 3 vols, Paris, 1892–1893, repr. 1960.

Darwin F., *The Life and Letters of Charles Darwin*, 2 vols, London: John Murray, 1888.

Dasgupta, S., *An Introduction to Tantric Buddhism*, University of Calcutta, 1950.

Dasgupta, S., *History of Indian Philosophy*, 5 vols, Cambridge University Press, 1952–1955.

Dass, R., *Be Here Now*, San Cristobal, New Mexico: Lama Foundation, 1971.

Dass, R., *Be Love Now: The Path of the Heart*, New York: HarperCollins Publishers, 2011.

David-Neel, A., *Initiations and Initiates in Tibet*, London: Rider and Co., 1970.

David-Neel, A., *With Mystics and Magicians in Tibet*, London: Penguin Books, 1931.

Davies, P. and Brown J. (eds), *The Ghost in the Atom*, Cambridge: Cambridge University Press. Versions of different interpretations of the meaning of quantum theory that provide a good example of the perplexity in the understanding of the meaning of quantum mechanics.

Davies, P. C. W. and Brown R., *The Ghost in the Atom*, Oxford: Oxford University Press, 1986.

Davies, P., *Other Worlds*, Dent, 1980.

Davies, P., *The Cosmic Blueprint: New Discoveries in Nature's Creative Ability to Order the Universe*, New York: Simon & Schuster, 1988.

Davies, P., *The Goldilocks Enigma: Why is the Universe Just Right For Life?* London: Allen Lane, 2006.

Davis, H. (trans.), *The Works of Plato*, London: George Bell & Sons, 1894.

Dawkins, R., *The Extended Phenotype*, Oxford University Press, 1982.

de Beer, E. S. (ed.), *The Correspondence of John Locke*, 8 vols, Oxford University Press, 1976.

de Beer, E. S. (ed.), *The Diary of John Evelyn*, Everyman, 2006.

DeConick, A., D., *The Gnostic New Age*, Columbia University Press, 2016.

Dennett, D. C., *Darwin's Dangerous Idea*, New York: Simon & Schuster, 1995.

Dennett, D., *Breaking the Spell: Religion as a Natural Phenomenon*, New York: Viking, 2006.

Descartes, R., *The Philosophical Writings of Descartes*, ed. and trans. J. Cottingham et al., Cambridge University Press, 1985.

Deussen, P., *The Religion and Philosophy of India*: *Vol. 1, Part I, The Philosophy of the Veda*, Leipzig, 1894; *Vol. 1, Part 2, The Philosophy of the Upanishads*, English trans, Edinburgh, 1905.

Dhammapada, trans. S. Radhakrishnan, Oxford University Press, 2007.

Dingwall, E. J., *Ghosts and Spirits in the Ancient World*, London: Kegan Paul, 1930.

Dirac, P., *Lectures on Quantum Field Theory*, New York: Belfer Graduate School of Science, Yeshiva University 1966.

Dirac, P., *Lectures on Quantum Mechanics*, New York: Belfer Graduate School of Science, Yeshiva University, 1964.

Dirac, P., *The Principles of Quantum Mechanics*, Oxford University Press, 1958.

Dobbs, B. J. T., *The Foundations of Newton's Alchemy*, Cambridge: Cambridge University Press, 2009.

Dobbs, B. J. T., *The Janus Faces of Genius: The Role of Alchemy in Newton's Thought*, Cambridge: Cambridge University Press, 1991.

Dobzhansky, T., *Genetics and the Origin of Species*, New York: Columbia University Press, 2nd edn, 1982.

Donnelly, I., *Atlantis, the Antediluvian World*, New York: Dover Books, 1976.

Dossey, L., *Healing Words: The Power of Prayer and the Practice of Medicine*, San Francisco: HarperSanFrancisco, 1993.

Dossey, L., *Meaning and Medicine*, New York: Bantam, 1992.

Dossey, L., *One Mind: How Our Individual Mind Is Part of a Greater Consciousness and Why It Matters*, New York: Hay House, 2013.

Dossey, L., *Recovering the Soul: A Scientific and Spiritual Search*, New York: Bantam, 1989.

Dreyfus, H. L. and Dreyfus, S. E., *Mind over Machine: The Power of Human Intuition and Expertise in the Era of the Computer*, London: Basil Blackwell Free Press, 1986.

Driesch, H., *Mind and Body*, London: Methuen, 1927.

Driesch, H., *The History and Theory of Vitalism*, London: Macmillan, 1914.

Dry, S., *The Newton Papers: The Strange and True Odyssey of Newton's Manuscripts*, US: Oxford University Press, 2014.

Dumoulin, H., *The Development of Chinese Zen after the Sixth Patriarch in the Light of Mumonkan*, trans. R. F. Sasaki, New York: The First Zen Institute of America, 1953.

Duncan, A. J. and Kleinpoppen, H., 'The Experimental Investigation of the Einstein-Podolsky-Rosen Question and Bell's Inequality', in *Quantum Mechanics versus Local Realism – The Einstein-Podolsky-Rosen Paradox*, ed. F. Selleri, New York: Plenum Press, 1988.

Dunne, B. and Jahn, R. (eds), *Being and Biology*, ICRL Press, 2017.

Dupré, L. and Wiseman, J. A. (eds), *Light from Light: An Anthology of Christian Mysticism*, New York: Paulist Press, 2001.

Duquesne, M., *Matter and Antimatter*, trans. A. Pomerans, London: Arrow Books, 1960.

Dvivedi, M. N., *The Yoga Sutras of Patanjali: Sanskrit Text and English Translation*, India: Sri Satguru Publications, 2001.

Dyer, C., *Symbolism in Craft Freemasonry*, UK, Hersham: Lewis Masonic, 2003.

Dyson, F., *Disturbing the Universe*, Harper & Row, New York, 1979.

Earle, J. B. B., 'Cerebral Laterality and Meditaton: A Review of the Literature', *Journal of Transpersonal Psychology*, Vol. 13, No. 2, 1981.

Ebeling, F., *The Secret History of Hermes Trismegistus: Hermeticism from Ancient to Modern Times*, Ithaca: Cornell University Press, 2007.

Eccles, J. C. and Robinson, D. N., *The Human Psyche*, Berlin, Heidelberg, New York: Springer-Verlag, 1980.

Eccles, J. C. and Robinson, D. N., *The Wonder of Being Human*, Boston: Shambhala, 1984.

Eckhart, Meister, *Meister Eckhart*, New York: Harper Torchbook, 1957. A modern translation by R. B. Blakney.

Ecklund, E. H., et al., *Secularity and Science*, Oxford University Press, 2019.

Eddington, A. S., *Science and the Unseen World*, London: George Allen and Unwin, 1930.

Eddington, A. S., *Space, Time and Gravitation*, Cambridge University Press, 1920.

Eddington, A. S., *The Nature of the Physical World*, Cambridge University Press, 1928.

Eddington, A. S., *The Philosophy of Physical Science (The Tarner Lectures, 1938)*, Cambridge University Press, 1939.

Edge, H. T., *Esoteric Key to the Christian Scriptures: And the Universal Mystery Language of Myth and Symbol*, San Diego: Point Loma Publications, 1993.

Editors, *The Chaldean Oracles*, UK, Fintry: Shrine of Wisdom, 1979.

Editors, *The Human Soul in the Myths of Plato*, UK, Fintry: Shrine of Wisdom, 1936.

Eek, Dr. S. and Boris de Zirkoff, *William Quan Judge: A Theosophical Pioneer*, Wheaton, Madras, London: The Theosophical Publishing House, 1969.

Eek, S., *Damodar and the Pioneers of The Theosophical Movement*, Adyar, Madras: Theosophical Publishing House, 1978.

Einstein, A. and Born, M., *The Born-Einstein Letters*, New York: Walker, 1971.

Einstein, A., *Essays in Science*, New York: Philosophical Library, 1934.

Einstein, A., *Ideas and Opinions*, C. Seeling (ed.), New York: Dell Publishing Co., 1973.

Einstein, A., *Relativity: The Special and General Theory*, trans. R. W. Lawson, New York: Henry Holt & Co., 1920.

Eldredge, N., *Time Frames: The Rethinking of Darwinian Evolution and the Theory of Punctuated Equilibria*, New York: Simon & Schuster, 1985.

Eliade, M., *Myths, Dreams and Mysteries*, London: Collins Fontana, 1957.

Eliade, M., *Shamanism: Archaic Techniques of Ecstasy*, New York: Bollingen Foundation, distributed by Pantheon Books, 1964.

Eliade, M., trans. W. R. Trask, *Cosmos and History: The Myth of the Eternal Return*, New York: Harper & Brothers, 1954.

Eliade, M., *Yoga: Immortality and Freedom*, Princeton: Bollingen Foundation, 1970.

Eliot, Sir Charles, *Hinduism and Buddhism: An Historical Sketch*, 4 vols, London: E. Arnold, 1921–1935.

Elliot, E. M., *Medicine and Miracles in the High Desert*, Balboa Press, 2019.

Ellis G., 'The Untestable Multiverse', *Nature*, Vol. 469, 2011.

Ellwood, R., *Finding Deep Joy*, Quest Books, Wheaton, Illinois, 1984.

Ellwood, R., *Finding the Quiet Mind*, Wheaton, Illinois: Quest Books, 1983. This book and the one above above guide the reader step by comfortable step towards a realisation of inner harmony.

Evans-Wentz, W. Y. and Lama Kazi Dawa-Samdup (eds), *The Tibetan Book of the Dead*, Oxford: Oxford University Press, 1957.

Evans-Wentz, W. Y., *The Tibetan Book of the Dead*, Oxford: Oxford University Press, 1927.

Evans-Wentz, W. Y., *Tibetan Yoga and Secret Doctrines*, Oxford: Oxford University Press, 1935.

Evanz-Wentz, W. Y. (ed.), *The Tibetan Book of the Great Liberation: Or the Method of Realizing Nirvana Through Knowing the Mind*, Oxford University Press, 1954.

Everard, Dr., *The Divine Pymander*, Michigan: Wizard Bookshelf, 2000.

Eyles, L., *Strength of the Spirit*, Constable, London, 1930. A thought-provoking novel. The author displays insight into both inner and outer worlds.

Faggin, F., *Silicon: From the Invention of the Microprocessor to the New Science of Consciousness*, Waterside Productions, 2021.

Faivre, A. and Needleman, J. (eds), *Modern Esoteric Spirituality*, New York: Crossroad Publishing Co., 1992.

Faivre, A. and W. J. Hanegraaff, W. J., *Western Esotericism and the Science of Religion*, Leuven, Belgium: Peeters, 1998.

Faivre, A., *Access to Western Esote*ricism, New York: SUNY Press, 1994.

Fanu, James le, *Too Many Pills: How Too Much Medicine is Endangering Our Health and What We Can Do*, Little, Brown, 2018.

Fara, P., *Newton: The Making of Genius*, London: Macmillan, 2002.

Farthing, G., *Exploring the Great Beyond*, Wheaton, Illinois: Quest Books, 1978.

Farthing, G., *When We Die*, London: Theosophical Publishing House, 1968. This book and the one above are based largely upon: H. P. B1avatsky's monumental work *The Secret Doctrine* and *The Mahatma Letters to A. P. Sinnett.*

Fellows, A., *Gaia, Psyche and Deep Ecology: Navigating Climate Change in the Anthropocene*, Routledge, 2019.

Feynman R., *QED: The Strange Theory of Light and Matter*, London: Penguin, 1990. Based on a series of lectures given by Feynman in 1983 to a non-scientific audience. It is a wonderful example of his pictorial way of explaining how quantum physics 'works'.

Feynman, R., *Quantum Electrodynamics*, US: CRC Press, 2018.

Feynman, R., *The Feynman Lectures on Physics, Vol. 1*, Reading, Massachusetts: Addison-Wesley, 1964.

Ficino, M., *The Letters of Marsilio Ficino*, Vol. 1, Shepheard-Walwyn, 2nd ed. 2018.

Fideler, D., *The Pythagorean Sourcebook and Library*, Grand Rapids, Michigan: Phanes Press, 1987.

Firstenberg, A., *The Invisible Rainbow*, Chelsea Green, 2020.

Fischer, J. M. and Mitchell-Yellin, B., *Near-Death Experiences – Understanding Visions of the Afterlife*, Oxford, 2016.

Flew, A. (ed.), *A Dictionary of Philosophy*, London: Macmillan, 1979.

Flinders Petrie, W. M., *A History of Egypt, from the Earliest Times to the XVIth Dynasty*, Norderstedt Hansebooks GmbH 2020.

Flournoy, T., *From India to the Planet Mars*, 1899; Princeton University Press, 1994.

Fortune, D., *Through the Gates of Death*, London: Ariel Press, 2013. Written by a trained psychic, it is full of sound advice, for example the effects upon the departed of excessive mourning and attempts to communicate.

Fox, M., and Sheldrake, R., *The Physics of Angels: Exploring the Realm Where Science and Spirit Meet*, San Francisco: Harper, 1996.

Frawley, D., *Gods, Sages and Kings*, Utah: Salt Lake City: Passage Press, 1991.

Fröhlich, H. (ed.), *Biological Coherence and Response to External Stimuli*, Heidelberg: Springer Verlag, 1988.

Fröhlich, H., 'Long Range Coherence and Energy Storage in Biological Systems', *Int. Journal of Quantum Chemistry*, Vol. 2, 1980.

Fuller, M. (ed.), *The Concept of the Soul*, Cambridge Scholars, 2014.

Fung, Yu-Lan, *A History of Chinese Philosophy*, trans. D. Bodde, 2 vols, Princeton University Press, 1953.

Gardner, E. L., *The Imperishable Body*, London: Theosophical Publishing House, 1948.

Gardner, E. L., *The Play of Consciousness in the Web of the Universe*, Wheaton, Illinois: Theosophical Publishing House, 1987.

Gardner, H., *The Shattered Mind*, New York: Vintage Books, 1974.

Gardner, R., 'Miracles of Healing in Anglo-Celtic Northumbria as recorded by the Venerable Bede and his Contemporaries: A Reappraisal in the Light of Twentieth-century Experience', *British Medical Journal*, Vol. 287, December 1983.

Gattei, S. (ed., trans., and annotated), *On the Life of Galileo*, Princeton University Press, 2019.

Geiger, W. and Windischman, E., *Zoroaster in the Gathas and in the Classics*, trans. Dastur D. P. Sanjana, Leipzig, 1897.

Geldner, K. F. (ed.), *Avesta, the Sacred Books of the Parsis*, Stuttgart: W. Kohlhamme, 1886–1896.

Gibb, H. A. R., *Mohammedanism: An Historical Survey*, London and New York: Oxford University Press, 1949.

Gibran, K., *The Treasured Writings of Kahlil Gibran*, trans. and ed. M. L. Wolf, A. R. Ferris, and A. D. Sherfan, US: Castle Books, 2009.

Gilbert, S. F., Opitz, J. M., and Raff, R. A., 'Resynthesizing Evolutionary and Developmental Biology', *Developmental Biology*, Vol. 173, 1996.

Gilson, E., *From Aristotle to Darwin and Back Again*, University of Notre Dame Press, Indiana: Notre Dame, 1984.

Ginot, E., *The Neuropsychology of the Unconscious – Integrating Brain and Mind in Psychotherapy*, New York, London: W. W. Norton and Co., 2015.

Ginsburg, G., *The Essenes: Their History and Doctrines*, London: Routledge and Kegan Paul, 1864.

Gjertsen, D., *The Newton Handbook*, London and New York: Routledge & Kegan Paul, 1986.

Glatzer, N., *The Judaic Tradition*, New York: Behrman House, 1960.

Gleik, J., *Chaos: Making a New Science*, London: Heinemann, 1988.

Glouberman D., *Into the Woods and Out Again: A Memoir of Love, Madness and Transformation*, Sphinx Books, 2018.

Glover, T. R., *The Conflict of Religions in the Early Roman Empire*, London: Methuen & Co., 1909.

Gober, M., *An End to Upside Down Thinking*, Waterside Press, 2018.

Godwin, J., *The Golden Thread*, Wheaton, Illinois: Quest Books, 2007.

Goff, P., *Galileo's Error: A New Science of Consciousness*, Rider, 2019.

Goldacre, B., 'Backwards Step on Looking into the Future', *The Guardian*, 23 April, 2011.

Goldacre, B., 'Dithering over Statins': Side-effects Label Finally Ends', *The Guardian*, 21 November, 2009.

Goldacre, B., 'Medical Ghostwriters who Build a Brand', *The Guardian*, 18 September, 2010.

Goodrick-Clarke, C. and Goodrick-Clarke, N. (eds), *GRS Mead and the Gnostic Quest*, Berkeley, California: North Atlantic Books, 2005.

Goodson, J. L. (ed.), *William James, Moral Philosophy and the Ethical Life*, Lexington Books, 2018.

Goodwin, B., 'Development and Evolution', *Journal of Theoretical Biology*, Vol. 97, 1982.

Goodwin, B., 'On Morphogenetic Fields', *Theoria to Theory*, Vol. 13, 1979.

Goodwin, B., 'Organisms and Minds as Organic Forms', *Leonardo*, Vol. 22, No. 1, 1989.

Goodwin, B., *How the Leopard Changed its Spots*, London: Weidenfeld & Nicolson, 1994.

Gordon, J. S., *Egypt, Child of Atlantis*, Rochester, Vermont: Inner Traditions, 2004.

Gordon, J. S., *The Path of Initiation*, Inner Traditions, 2013.

Gordon, J. S., *The Rise and Fall of Atlantis*, London: Watkins Books, 2008.

Gorman, P., *Pythagoras*, London: Routledge and Kegan Paul, 1979.

Gorman, P., *Pythagoras: A Life*, London: Routledge and Kegan Paul, 1979.

Goswami, A., *Science within Consciousness: Developing a Science Based on the Primacy of Consciousness*, IONS Research Report CP-7, Sausalito, California: Institute of Noetic Sciences, 1994.

Goswami, A., *The Self-Aware Universe: How Consciousness Creates The Material World*, New York: Tarcher/Putnam, 1993.

Gould, S. J. and Eldridge, N., 'Punctuated Equilibria; The Tempo and Mode of Evolution Reconsidered', *Paleobiology*, Vol. 3, 1977.

Gould, S. J., *Rock of Ages: Science and Religion in the Fullness of Life*, New York: Ballantine, 1999.

Gould, S. J., *Wonderful Life: The Burgess Shale and the Nature of History*, London: Hutchinson, 1989.

Govinda, Lama Anagarika, *Creative Meditation and Multi-Dimensional Consciousness*, Wheaton: Theosophical Publishing House, 1976.

Govinda, Lama Anagarika, *Foundations of Tibetan Mysticism*, New York: Samuel Weiser, 1969.

Govinda, Lama Anagarika, *The Psychological Attitude of Early Buddhist Philosophy*, London: Rider, 1961.

Govinda, Lama Anagarika, *The Way of the White Clouds: A Buddhist Pilgrim in Tibet*, Boulder: Shambhala, 1970.

Grant, J., *Life as Carola*, London: Methuen, 1939. A gripping novel based on memories of a former incarnation.

Graves, R., *The Greek Myths*, London: Penguin Books, 1960.

Gray, J., *Black Mass: Apocalyptic Religion and the Death of Utopia*, London: Allen Lane, 2007.

Gray, J., *Consciousness: Creeping Up on the Hard Problem*, Oxford University Press, 2004.

Gray, J., *The Immortalization Commission: The Strange Quest to Cheat Death*, London: Allen Lane, 2011.

Grayling, A. C., 'Psychology: How we Form Beliefs', *Nature*, Vol. 474, 2011.

Green, A. and Green E., *Beyond Biofeedback*, New York: Delta Books, 1978.

Green, B., *The Elegant Universe: Superstrings, Hidden Dimensions, and the Quest for the Ultimate Theory*, New York: Norton, 1999.

Greene, B., *The Hidden Reality: Parallel Universes and the Deep Laws of the Cosmos*, London: Allen Lane, 2011.

Greenfield, S., *Brain Story: Unlocking Our Inner World of Emotions, Memories, Ideas and Desires*, BBC, London, 2000.

Grey, M., *Return from Death: An Exploration of the Near-Death Experience*, London: Arkana, 1985.

Gribbin, J., *In Search of Schrödinger's Cat – Explaining the Mysteries of Light*, London: Black Swan, 1984. A layperson's guide to how quantum theory emerged.

Gribbin, J., *In Search of the Edge of Time*, London: Black Swan, 1992.

Gribbin, J., *In the Beginning: The Birth of the Living Universe*, New York: Little, Brown & Co., 1993.

Gribbin, J., *Schrödinger's Kittens and the Search for Reality*, London Weidenfeld & Nicolson, 1995.

Griffin, D. R., *Parapsychology, Philosophy and Spirituality: A Postmodern Exploration*, State University of New York Press, 1997.

Griffith, R. T. H., *The Hymns of the Atharva Veda*, 2 vols, Benares: E.J. Lazarus & Co, 1895–1896.

Griffith, R. T. H., *The Hymns of the Rigveda*, 4 vols, Benares: E.J. Lazarus & Co, 1889–1892.

Griffiths, Bede, *Christ in India*, Springfield, Illinois: Templegate Publishers, 1984.

Griffiths, Bede, *The Cosmic Revelation*, Springfield, Illinois: Templegate Publishers, 1983.

Griffiths, Bede, *The Golden String*, Springfield, Illinois: Templegate Publishers, 1980.

Griflin, D. R., *Religion and Scientific Naturalism: Overcoming the Conflicts*, New York, SUNY Press, 2000.

Grinberg-Zylberbaum, J., Delaflor, M., Sanchez-Arellano, M. E., Guevara, M. A., and Perez, M., 'Human Communication and the Electrophysiological Activity of the Brain', *Subtle Energies*, Vol. 3, No. 3, 1993.

Griswold, H. D., *The Religion of the Rigveda*, Oxford University Press, 1923.

Grof, S. and Bennet, H. Z., *The Holotropic Mind*, San Francisco: HarperSanFrancisco, 1993.

Grof, S., *Psychology of the Future: Lessons from Modern Consciousness Research*, Albany, New York: State University of New York Press, 2000.

Grof, S., *The Way of the Psychonaut: Encyclopedia for Inner Journeys*, 2 vols, Multidisciplinary Association for Psychedelic Studies, 2019.

Grossman, N., *The Spirit of Spinoza: Healing the Mind*, Princeton, New Jersey: ICRL Press, 2003.

Grosso, M., *The Final Choice*, White Crow Books, 2017.

Guillaume, A., *Islam*, UK: Pelican, 1956.

Guth, A., *The Inflationary Universe: The Quest for a New Theory of Cosmic Origins*, New York: Perseus Book Group, 1997.

Hall, R. A., *Newton: Adventurer in Thought*, Cambridge: Cambridge University Press, 1996.

Hadot, P., *Philosophy as a Way of Life*, trans. M. Chase, ed. and introd. A. I. Davidson, Blackwell, 1995.

Hagan, J. C. III., *The Science of Near-Death Experiences*, Columbia, Missouri: University of Missouri Press, 2017.

Haldane, J. B. S., *Science and Life: Essays of a Rationalist*, ed. J. Maynard Smith, London: Pemberton Publishing Co., 1968.

Hall, A. R. and Hall, M. B. (eds), *Unpublished Scientific Papers of Isaac Newton*, Cambridge: Cambridge University Press, 1962.

Hall, M. P. (ed.), *The Most Holy Trinosophia of the Comte de St. Germain*, Los Angeles: Philosophical Research Society, 1933.

Hall, M. P., *Reincarnation: The Cycle of Necessity*, Los Angeles: Philosophical Research Society, 1967.

Hall, M. P., *The Adepts in the Western Esoteric Tradition*, 5 vols, Los Angeles: Philosophical Research Society, 1949–1951.

Hameroff, S. R., ' "Funda-Mentality": Is the Conscious Mind Subtly Linked to a Basic Level of the Universe?' *Trends in Cognitive Sciences*, Vol. 2, No. 4, 1998.

Hamilton, A., *The Scalpel and the Soul: Encounters with Surgery, the Supernatural, and the Healing Power of Hope*, New York: Penguin Group, 2008.

Hampton, C., *The Transition Called Death*, Wheaton, Illinois: Quest Books, 1943. 'It is we in the physical world who are really the dead because we are in a world of only three dimensions.' Very informative and easy to read.

Hancock, G., *Fingerprints of the Gods: The Evidence of Earth's Lost Civilization*, New York: Crown Publishers, lnc., 1995.

Hanegraaff, W. J., *New Age Religion and Western Culture*, New York: SUNY Press, 1998.

Hansen, G. M., Schlitz, M., and Tart, C., 'Summary of Remote Viewing Research', in *The Mind Race*, ed. R. Targ and K. Harary, New York: Villard, 1984.

Hanson, V. (ed.), *Karma: The Universal Law of Harmony*, Adyar, London, Wheaton: Theosophical Publishing House, 1975.

Hanson, V. and Linton, G. E., *Readers Guide to The Mahatma Letters to A. P. Sinnett*, Adyar, London, Wheaton: Theosophical Publishing House, 1972.

Hapgood, F., 'Computer Chess Bad – Human Chess Worse', *New Scientist*, Vol. 827, 1982.

Harari, Y. N., *Sapiens: A Brief History of Humanity*, Harper Collins, 2015.

Hardy, A., *The Biology of God*, London: Jonathan Cape, 1975.

Harman, P. M., *Energy, Force and Matter: The Conceptual Development of Nineteenth-Century Physics*, Cambridge University Press, 1982.

Harman, W. and Sahtouris, E., *Biology Revisioned*, Berkeley, California: North Atlantic Books, 1998.

Haroche, S., 'Entanglement, Decoherence and the Quantum/Classical Boundary', *Physics Today*, 1998.

Harrington, J. F., *Dangerous Mystic: Meister Eckhart's Path to the God Within*, Penguin Press, 2018.

Harrison, J., *The Library of Isaac Newton*, Cambridge: Cambridge University Press, 1978.

Harrison, P., *The Territories of Science and Religion*, University of Chicago Press, 2015.

Haug, M., *Essays on the Sacred Language, Writings, and Religion of the Parsis*, Bombay, 1862, ed. E. W. West, London: K. Paul, Trench, Trübner and Co., 1907.

Hawking, S. and Carr, B. J., 'Black Holes in the Early Universe', *Monthly Notices of the Royal Astronomical Society*, Vol. 168, 1974.

Hawking, S. and Ellis, G. F. R., *The Large Scale Structure of Space–Time*, Cambridge: Cambridge University Press, 1973.

Hawking, S. and Mlodinow, L., *The Grand Design: New Answers to the Ultimate Questions of Life*, London: Bantam Press, 2010.

Hawking, S. and Rocek, M. (eds), *Superspace and Supergravity*, Cambridge: Cambridge University Press, 1981.

Hawking, S., 'The Edge of Spacetime', *Am. Sci.*, July–Aug., 1984.

Hawking, S., 'The Existence of Cosmic Time Functions', *Proc. Roy. Soc. A308*, 1968.

Hawking, S., 'The Path Integral Approach to Quantum Gravity' in Hawkings, S. and Israel, W. (eds), *General Relativity: An Einstein Centenary Survey*, Cambridge: Cambridge University Press, 1979.

Hawking, S., *Is the End in Sight for Theoretical Physics?* Cambridge University Press, 1988.

Head, J. and Cranston, S. L. (compiled and ed.), *Reincarnation in World Thought*, New York: Julian Press, 1967.

Hegel, G. W., *The Philosophy of History*, English trans., Canada: Batoche Books, 2001.

Heisenberg, W., 'Development of Concepts in the History of Quantum Theory', *American Journal of Physics*, Vol. 43, No. 5, 1975.

Heisenberg, W., *Physics and Beyond*, New York: Harper & Row, 1971.

Heisenberg, W., *Physics and Philosophy*, New York: Harper & Row, 1985.

Heisenberg, W., *The Physicist's Conception of Nature*, trans. A. J. Pomerans, New York: Harcourt Brace & Company, 1958.

Henry, J. (ed.), *Parapsychology: Research an Exceptional Experiences*, UK: Routledge, 2005.

Hettinger, T. P., 'Misconduct: Don't Assume Science is Self-correcting', *Nature*, Vol. 466, 2010.

Ho, M. W., *The Rainbow and the Worm: The Physics of Organisms*, UK and US: World Scientific Publishing, 1998.

Ho, Mae-Wan and Saunders, P. (eds), *Beyond Neo-Darwinism: An Introduction to the New Evolutionary Paradigm*, London: Academic Press, 1984.

Ho, Mae-Wan, Popp, F. A., and Warnke, U. (eds), *Bioelectromagnetics and Biocommunication*, Singapore: World Scientific, 1994.

Hodson, G., *Reincarnation, Fact or Fallacy*, Adyar, India: Theosophical Publishing House, 1967. A work by a trained psychic.

Hodson, G., *The Kingdom of the Gods*, Adyar, India: Theosophical Publishing House, 1987.

Hoeller, S. A., *Gnosticism: New Light on the Ancient Tradition of Inner Knowing*, Wheaton, Illinois: Quest Books, 2002.

Hoeller, S., *The Gnostic Jung and the Seven Sermons to the Dead*, Wheaton, Illinois: Quest Books, 1982.

Holden, J., Greyson, B., and James, D. (eds), *The Handbook of Near-Death Experiences: Thirty Years of Investigation*, Santa Barbara, California: ABC-CLIO, 2009.

Holding, S. C., Stacey, F. D., and Tuck, G. J., 'Gravity in Mines – An Investigation of Newton's Law', *Physics Review Letters D*, Vol. 33, 1986.

Homer, *Homer's Iliad*, trans. into literal English, Cambridge: J. Hall and Son, 1884.

Homer, *Homer's Odyssey*, ed. W. W. Merry and J. Riddell, Oxford, Clarendon Press, 2nd edn, 1885.

Honorton, C., Berger, R., Varvoglis, M., Quant, M., Derr, P., Schechter, E., and Ferrari, D., 'Psi Communication in the Ganzfeld: Experiments with an Automated Testing System and a Comparison with a Meta-analysis of Earlier Studies', *Journal of Parapsychology*, Vol. 54, 1990.

Hook, R., *The Diary of Robert Hooke MA, MD, FRS, 1672–1680*, foreword by F. Gowland PRS, ed. W. Adams and H. W. Robinson, London: Taylor and Francis, 1935.

Horgan, J., *Rational Mysticism: Dispatches from the Border Between Science and Spirituality*, Boston: Houghton Mifflin, 2003.

Horgan, J., *The End of Science: Facing the Limits of Knowledge in the Twilight of the Scientific Age*, London: Little, Brown, 1997.

Hoyle, F. and Wickramsinghe, C., *Evolution From Space*, London: Paladin Books, 1983.

Hoyle, F., *Of Men and Galaxies*, London: Heinemann, 1965.

Hoyle, F., *The Intelligent Universe: A New View of Creation and Evolution*, Michael Joseph, 1984. The famous astronomer comes round to the view that the Universe must have been created by intelligent design. A copiously illustrated popular account.

Hoyle, F., *The Nature of the Universe*, UK: Harmondsworth, 1963.

Huang-po, *The Zen Teaching of Huang Po on the Transmission of Mind*, ed. and trans. J. Blofeld, New York: Grove Press / Atlantic Monthly Press, 2006.

Hügel, von, *The Mystical Element in Religion as Studied in Saint Catherine of Genoa and Her Friends*, London: J. M. Dent & Co.; New York: E. P. Dutton & Co., 1908.

Hume, D., *Dialogues Concerning Natural Religion*, Oxford: Oxford University Press, 2008.

Hume, R. E. (trans.), *The Thirteen Principal Upanishads*, Oxford: Oxford University Press, 1934.

Humphreys, C. (ed.), *The Wisdom of Buddhism*, London: Michael Joseph, 1960.

Humphreys, C., *Buddhism*, UK: Harmondsworth, 1975.

Humphreys, C., *Concentration and Meditation: A Manual of Mind Development*, UK: Element Books, 1987.

Humphreys, C., *Karma and Rebirth*, London: Curzon Press; US: The Theosophical Publishing House, 1983.

Humphreys, C., *The Field of Theosophy*, London: Theosophical Publishing House, 1966. The Teacher, the Teaching and the Way.

Humphreys, C., *The Seach Within: A Course in Meditation*, London: The Theosophical Publishing House, 1977.

Huxley, A., *The Perennial Philosophy*, London: Chatto and Windus, 1946.

Huxley, F., 'Charles Darwin: Life and Habit', *American Scholar* (Fall/Winter), 1959.

Huxley, T. H., *Methods and Results*, London: Macmillan, 1893.

Iamblichus, *Theurgia, or the Egyptian Mysteries*, trans. A. Wilder, New York: The Metaphysical Publishing Co., 1911.

Iliffe, R., 'Newton, God, and the Mathematics of the Two Books', in *Mathematicians and Their Gods: Interactions between Mathematics and Religious Beliefs*, ed. S. Lawrence and M. McCartney, Oxford: Oxford University Press, 2015.

Iliffe, R., *Priest of Nature: The Religious Worlds of Isaac Newton*, Oxford: Oxford University Press, 2017.

Inge, W. R., Guthrie, W. K. C., and Nairne, J., *The Philosophy of Plotinus*, 2 vols, London: Longmans, Green, 1918.

Iyengar, B. K. S., *Light on Yoga: The Definitive Guide To Yoga Practice*, UK: HarperCollins Publishers, 2001.

Jacob, M. C., *The Secular Enlightenment*, Princeton University Press, 2019.

Jacobi, J. (ed.), *Paracelsus: Selected Writings*, London: Routledge and Kegan Paul, 1951.

Jacolliot, L., *Occult Science in India*, London: W. O. Felt, 1874.

Jahn, R. and Dunne, B., *Margins of Reality: The Role of Consciousness in the Physical World*, Orlando, Florida: Harcourt Brace Jovanovich, 1987.

Jahn, R. G. and Dunne B. J., 'On the Quantum Mechanics of Consciousness, with Application to Anomalous Phenomena', *Foundations of Physics*, Vol. 16, No. 8, 1986.

Jahn, R. G. and Dunne B. J., 'The PEAR Proposition', *Journal of Scientific Exploration*, Vol. 19, No. 2, 2005.

James, E. O., *Comparative Religion*, London: Methuen & Co., 1938.

James, W., *The Varieties of Religious Experience*, New York: Macmillan, 1961.

Jammer, M., *The Conceptual Development of Quantum Mechanics*, Mc-Graw-Hill, 1966.

Jammer, M., *The Philosophy of Quantum Mechanics*, John Wiley, 1974.

Janiak, A., *Newton as Philosopher*, Cambridge: Cambridge University Press, 2008.

Jeans, J., *The Growth of Physical Science*, Cambridge: Cambridge University Press, 1951.

Jensen, L. A., *Rethinking Darwin: A Vedic Study of Darwinism and Intelligent Design*, The Bhaktivedanta Book Trust, 2011.

'John Maynard Keynes: Newton, the Man', http://www-groups.dcs.st-and.ac.uk/history/Extras/Keynes_Newton.html.

John of the Cross, *Ascent of Mount Carmel*, trans. and ed. E. A. Peers, London, 1946; New York: Dover Publications, 2008.

John of the Cross, *Dark Night of the Soul*, trans., ed., and introd., E. A. Peers, 1953; US: The Newman Press, 1959.

Johnson, K. P., *Initiates of Theosophical Masters*, New York: SUNY Press, 1995.

Johnson, K. P., *The Masters Revealed: Madame Blavatsky and the Myth of the Great White Lodge*, New York: SUNY Press, 1994.

Jones, et al., 'A Randomized Control Trial of the Effects of Remote, Intercessory Prayer on Outcomes in Patients Admitted to the Coronary Care Unit', *Arch. Intern. Med.*, Vol. 159, 1999.

Jones, C. P., *Philostratus, The Life of Apollonius of Tyana*, London: Loeb Classical Library, 1989.

Jones, R. M., *Studies in Mystical Religion*, London: Macmillan and Co., 1909.

Jones, R., *Physics as Metaphor*, Minneapolis, Minnesota, University of Minnesota Press, 1990. Examines the way physicists think about the world, and questions commonplace assumptions about the relationships between models, and reality.

Joseph, H. W. B., *Lectures on the Philosophy of Leibniz*, ed. J. L. Austin, Oxford, Clarendon Press, 1949.

Josephson, B. D. and Pallikari-Viras, F., 'Biological Utilization of Quantum Nonlocality', *Foundations of Physics*, Vol. 21, 1991.

Josephson, B., ' "Beyond Quantum Theory: A Realist Psycho-biological Interpretation of Reality" Revisited', *Biosystems*, Vol. 64, 2002.

Jowett, B. (trans.), *Plato's Republic and Other Works*, London: Anchor Press, 1973.

Joye, S., *The Electromagnetic Brain*, Rochester, Vermont: Inner Traditions, 2020.

Judge, W. Q., *Echoes of the Orient: The Writings of William Quan Judge*, compiled by D. Eklund, Pasadena, 4 vols, California: Theosophical University Press, 2009–2011.

Judge, W. Q., *Letters That Have Helped Me*, Pasadena, California: Theosophical University Press, 1981.

Judge, W. Q., *The Ocean of Theosophy*, 1893; US: Wildside Press, 2007.

Jung, C. G., *Analytical Psychology: Its Theory and Practice*, London: Routledge and Kegan Paul, 1970.

Kaegi, A., *The Rigveda: The Oldest Literature of the Indians*, US: Boston, Ginn, 1886.

Kahn, C. H., *Pythagoras and the Pythagoreans*, Cambridge, Massachusetts: Hackett Publishing Co., 2001.

Kak, S., Penrose, R., and Hameroff, S. (eds), *Quantum Physics of Consciousness*, Cambridge, Massachusetts: Cosmology Science Publishers, 2011.

Kastrup, B., *Brief Peeks Beyond: Critical Essays on Metaphysics, Neuroscience, Free Will, Skepticism, and Culture*, Winchester, UK: Iff books, 2015.

Kastrup, B., *More Than Allegory: On Religious Myth, Truth, and Belief*, Winchester, UK: Iff books, 2016.

Kealey, T., *The Economic Laws of Scientific Research*, London: Macmillan, 1996.

Keightley, T., *The Mythology of Ancient Greece and Italy*, London: Whittaker and Co., 1838.

Keith, A. B., *The Religion and Philosophy of the Veda and the Upanishads*, 2 vols, Cambridge, Massachusetts, 1925.

Keller, E. F., *A Feeling for the Organism: The Life and Work of Barbara McClintock*, New York: W. H. Freeman, 1983.

Kelly, E. F., Kelly, E. M., Crabtree, A., Gauld, A., Grosso M., and Greyson, B., *Irreducible Mind: Toward a Psychology for the 21st Century*, Lanham, Maryland: Rowman & Littlefield, 2007.

Kersten, H., *Jesus Lived in India*, England: Element Books, 1994.

Khoury, M. J., Evans, J., and Burke, W., 'A Reality Check for Personalized Medicine', *Nature*, Vol. 464, 2010.

Kiernan, V., 'Gravitational Constant is Up in the Air', *New Scientist*, 29 April 1995.

Kingsland, W., *The Real H. P. Blavatsky*, London: John M. Watkins, 1928.

Kingsley, P., *Catafalque – Carl Jung and the End of Humanity*, 2 vols, Catafalque Press, 2018.

Kirsch, I., 'Not All Placebos are Born Equal', *New Scientist*, 11 December 2010.

Kirsch, I., *The Emperors New Drugs: Exploding theAntidepressant Myth*, London: Bodley Head, 2009.

Kitto, H. D., *The Greeks*, Penguin Books, 1969.

Koch, C., *The Feeling of Life Itself: Why Consciousness is Widespread But Can't be Computed*, MIT Press, 2019.

Koenig, H., *Medicine, Religion and Health: Where Science and Spirituality Meet*, West Conshohocken, Pennsylvania: Templeton Foundation Press, 2008.

Koestler, A. and Smythies, J. R. (eds), *Beyond Reductionism*, London: Hutchinson, 1969.

Koestler, A., *The Ghost in the Machine*, London: Hutchinson, 1967.

Kovacs, B. J., foreword by A. Baring, *Merchants of Light*, Kamlak Centre, 2019.

Krauss, L. M., 'Cosmological Antigravity', *Scientific American*, 1999.

Krauss, L. M., 'The End of the Age Problem and the Case for a Cosmological Constant Revisited', *Astrophysical Journal*, Vol. 501, 1998.

Kreiger, M., *Doing Physics*, Bloomington, Indiana, Indiana University Press, 1992. Clearly and forcefully shows the extent to which physics is not just based on, but *is* a system of analogies and metaphors.

Kreitzer, M. J. and Riff, K., 'Spirituality and Heart Health', in Devries, S. and Dalen, J. E. (eds), *Integrative Cardiology*, New York: Oxford University Press, 2011.

Kretzman, N. and Stump, E. (eds), *The Cambridge Companion to Aquinas*, Cambridge: Cambridge University Press, 1993.

Krishnamurti, J. and Bohm, D., *The Ending of Time: Thirteen Dialogues between J. Krishnamurti and David Bohm*, San Francisco: Harper & Row, 1985.

Krishnamurti, J., *Commentaries on Living: From the Notebooks of J. Krishnamurti*, ed. D. Rajagopal, 3 vols, Wheaton, Illinois: Theosophical Publishing House, 1967.

Krishnamurti, J., *Freedom from the Known*, ed. M. Lutyens, US: Harper & Row, 1969.

Krishnamurti, J., *The Awakening of Intelligence*, London: Victor Gollancz, 1991.

Krishnamurti, J., *The Only Revolution*, ed. M. Lutyens, London: Gollancz, 1970.

Krishnamurti, J., *The Urgency of Change*, ed. M. Lutyens, New York: Harper & Row, 1970.

Kubler-Ross, E., *On Death and Dying*, London: Souvenir Press, 1982. Near-death experiences.

Kuhn, T. S., 'Energy Conservation as an Example of Simultaneous Discovery', in M. Clagett (ed.), *Critical Problems in the History of Science*, University of Wisconsin Press, 1959.

Kuhn, T. S., *The Structure of Scientific Revolutions*, 1962; 2nd ed., University of Chicago Press, 1970.

Kunz, F. L., 'On the Symmetry Principles', in *Order in the Universe*, New York: The Foundation for Integrative Education, 1967.

Kunz, F. L., 'The Reality of the Non-material', *Main Currents in Modern Thought*, December, 1963.

Lao Tzu, *Tao Te Ching*, trans. S. Addiss and S. Lombardo, UK: Hackett Publishing Co., 1993.

Laplace, P. S., *A Philosophical Essay on Probabilities*, 1819; repr. New York: Dover, 1951.

Lashley, K. S., 'In Search of the Engram', *Symposium of the Society for Experimental Biology*, Vol. 4, 1950.

Lashley, K. S., *Brain Mechanisms and Intelligence*, Chicago University Press, 1929.

Laszlo, E. and Biava, P. M., *Information Medicine*, Healing Arts Press, 2019.

Laszlo, E., *How Can We Build a Better World*, Waterside Books, 2020.

Laszlo, E., *Reconnecting to the Source*, St Martins Essentials, 2020.

Latham, J., 'The Failure of the Genome', *The Guardian*, 18 April, 2011.

Latour, B., *Politics of Nature: How to Bring the Sciences into Democracy*, Harvard University Press, 2009.

Latour, B., *Science in Action: How to Follow Scientists and Engineers Through Society*, Harvard University Press, 1987.

Lau, D. C., *Lao Tzu: Tao Te Ching*, London: Penguin Classics, 1963.

LaViolette, P., *Beyond the Big Bang: Ancient Myth and the Science of Continuous Creation*, Rochester, Vermont: Park Street Press, 1995.

LaViolette, P., *Subquantum Kinetics: A Systems Approach to Physics and Cosmology*, US, Alexandria: Starlane Publications, 2003.

Leclerc, I. (ed.), *The Philosophy of Leibniz and the Modern World*, Nashville, Tennessee: Vanderbilt University Press, 1973.

Leeder, J. S. and Spielberg, S. P., 'Personalized Medicine: Reality and Reality Checks', *Annals of Pharmacotherapy*, Vol. 43, 2009.

Leibniz Selections, ed. P. P. Wiener, New York: Charles Scribiner's Sons, 1951.

Leibniz, G. W., *Discourse on Metaphysics and The Monadology*, ed. G. R. W. Montgomery, New York: Dover Publications, 2005.

Leibniz, G. W., *Leibniz Philosophical Writings*, ed. G. H. R. Parkinson, London: Dent, 1973.

Leibniz, G. W., *Logical Papers: A Selection*, trans. G. H. R. Parkinson, Oxford, Oxford University Press, 1966.

Leibniz, G. W., *Philosophical Papers and Letters*, ed. L. E. Loemker, 2nd ed. Springer, 1989.

Lemaitre, G., *The Primeval Atom: An Essay on Cosmogony*, New York: Van Nostrand, 1950.

Lemesurier, P., *The Great Pyramid*, Dorset, UK: Element Books, 1987.

Leonardo, da Vinci, *The Notebooks of Leonardo da Vinci*, compiled and ed. J. P. Richter and R. C. Bell, 2 vols, New York: Dover Publications, 1970.

Leslie, J. (ed.), *Physical Cosmology and Philosophy*, New York: MacMillan, 1990.

Leslie, J., *Universes*, London and New York: Routledge, 1989.

Lester Smith, E., 'Science and the Real', the Blavatsky Lecture, 1963, London: The Theosophical Society.

Lester Smith, E., *Intelligence Came First*, Wheaton, Illinois: Quest Books, 1975. Intelligence, consciousness and life are the primal realities, not matter.

Let Newton Be! A New Perspective on his Life and Works, ed. J. Flauvel, et al., US: Oxford University Press, 1994.

Levi, E., *The Key of the Mysteries*, London: Rider and Co., 1969.

Levitin, D., *Ancient Wisdom in the Age of the New Science: Histories of Philosophy in England, c. 1640–1700*, Cambridge: Cambridge University Press, 2015.

Lewin, R., 'Is Your Brain Really Necessary?', *Science*, Vol. 210, 1980.

Liana Saif (guest ed.), 'Islamic Esotericism', *Correspondences: Journal for the Study of Esotericism*, 2019.

Libet, B., 'Can Conscious Experience Affect Brain Activity?', *Journal of Consciousness Studies*, Vol. 10, 2003.

Libet, B., 'Do we have Free Will?', *Journal of Consciousness Studies*, Vol. 6, 1999.

Libet, B., 'Reflections on the Interaction of the Mind and Brain', *Progress in Neurobiology*, Vol. 78, 2006.

Lichtheim, M., *Ancient Egyptian Literature*, 3 vols, Berkeley: University of California Press, 1973.

Lilley, D., *Healing the Soul: Volume One – The Lives of Samuel Hahnemann and William Lilley; Volume Two – The Archetype and the Psyche*, Saltire Books, 2018.

Lindorff, D., *Jung and Pauli – The Meeting of Two Great Minds*, Wheaton, Illinois: Quest Books, 2004.

Lipton, B., *The Biology of Belief: Unleashing the Power of Consciousness, Matter & Miracles*, UK: Hay House 2011.

Locke, J., 'Of Study', in *The Educational Writings of John Locke*, ed. J. L. Axtell, Cambridge, Cambridge University Press, 1968.

Locke, J., *An Essay Concerning Human Understanding*, ed. P. H. Nidditch, Oxford: Oxford University Press,1975.

Locke, J., *Of the Conduct of the Understanding*, ed. P. H. Nidditch. Oxford: Clarendon Press,1975.

Locke, J., *Some Thoughts upon Education*, ed. J. Yolton, Oxford: Oxford University Press,1989.

Lohrey, A., *The Evolution of Consciousness*, ICRL Press, 2018.

Lommel, P. van., 'About the Continuity of our Consciousness', *Advances in Experimental Medicine and Biology, Adv Exp Med Biol.*, 2004.

Lommel, P. van., *Consciousness Beyond Life: The Science of the Near-Death Experience*, HarperCollins Publishers, 2010.

Long, W., *How Animals Talk*, New York: Harper, 1919.

Lorimer, D., *A Quest for Wisdom: Inspiring Purpose on the Path in Life*, Aeon Books, 2021.

Lorimer, D., *Resonant Mind: Life Review in the Near-Death Experience*, White Crow Books, 2017.

Lovelock, J. E., *The Ages of Gaia*, London: W. W. Norton, rev. ed. 1995.

Lovelock, J., *Gaia: A New Look at Life on Earth*, Oxford University Press, 1979. Persuasive hypothesis that conditions favourable to life are maintained in the environment by the 'Earth Goddess' Gaia.

Lucretius, *Lucretius On the Nature of Things*, trans. C. Bailey, Oxford: Clarendon Press, 1948.

Lutyens, E., *Candles in the Sun*, London: Rupert Hart-Davis, 1957.

Lutyens, M., *Krishnamurti: The Years of Awakening*, London: Rider, 1984.

Lutyens, M., *Krishnamurti: The Years of Fulfillment*, London: Rider, 1985.

Macdonell, A. A., *History of Sanskrit Literature*, London: William Heinemann, 1928.

Macdonell, A. A., *Vedic Mythology*, Strassburg: Verlag Von Karl J. Trübner, 1897.

Mackey, S. A., *The Mythological Astronomy of the Ancients Demonstrated*, London: Hurst & Clarke, 1826.

Malhotra, R., Holman, M., and Ito, T., 'Chaos and Stability of the Solar System', *Proceedings of the National Academy of Sciences US*, Vol. 98, 2001.

Manuel, F. E., *A Portrait of Isaac Newton*, Boston, Massachusetts: Da Capo Press, 1990.

Manuel, F. E., *The Religion of Isaac Newton*, Oxford: Oxford University Press, 1974.

Marsh, M., *A Matter of Personal Survival: Life after Death*, Wheaton, Illinois: Quest Books, 1985. A study of survival with convincing and plausible evidence.

Marshall, P., *The Shape of the Soul: What Mystical Experience Tells Us about Ourselves and Reality*, Rowan & Littlefield, 2019.

Mascaró, J., *The Upanishads*, UK: Harmondsworth, 1965.

Massignon, L., *Passion d'al-Hosayn-Ibn-Mansour al-Hallaj: martyr mystique de l'Islam exécuté a Bagdad le 26 Mars 922* [Passion of al-Hosayn-Ibn-Mansour al-Hallaj: mystical martyr of Islam, executed in Baghdad on March 26, 922], 2 vols, Paris: P. Geuthner, 1922.

Matthews, C. and Matthews, J., *The Western Way: A Practical Guide To The Western Mystery Tradition: The Hermetic Tradition*, Vol. 2, Law Book Co. of Australasia, 1986.

Matthews, C. and Matthews, J., *Western Way: The Native Tradition: A Practical Guide To The Western Mystery Tradition*, Vol. 1, Law Book Co. of Australasia, 1985.

Max Müller, F. (ed.), *The Sacred Books of the East*, 50 vols, Oxford: Clarendon Press, 1879–1910.

Max Müller, F. and Oldenberg, H., *Vedic Hymns*, Oxford, Clarendon Press, 1891–97.

Max Müller, F., *Six Systems of Indian Philosophy*, 1902; London: Longmans, Green, 1919.

Maxwell, J. C., *A Dynamical Theory of the Electromagnetic Field*, ed. T. F. Torrence, Edinburgh: Scottish Academic Press, 1982.

Maxwell, N., *Science and Enlightenment – Two Great Problems of Learning*, Springer, 2019.

Mayr, E., *The Growth of Biological Thought*, Harvard University Press, 1982.

McCrone, J., 'Power of the Paranormal: Why it Won't Surrender to Science', *New Scientist*, 2004.

McFadden, J. and Al-Khalili, J., *Life on the Edge: The Coming of Age of Quantum Biology*, New York: Crown Publishers, 2014.

McGrath, A., *The Territories of Human Reason*, Oxford: Oxford University Press, 2018.

McGuire, J. E., 'Space, Infinity and Indivisibility: Newton on the Creation of Matter', in *Contemporary Newtonian Research*, ed. Z. Bechler, Cambridge: Cambridge University Press, 1982.

McLachlan, H., *Sir Issac Newton: Theological Manuscripts*, Liverpool at the University Press, 1950.

McLeish, K., *Children of the Gods*, London: Longmans, 1983.

McLeish, T., *The Poetry and Music of Science*, Oxford: Oxford University Press, 2019.

McMullin, E., 'Galileo on Science and Scripture', in *The Cambridge Companion to Galileo*, ed. P. Machamer, Cambridge: Cambridge University Press,1998.

Mead, G. R. S., *Apollonius of Tyana*, London: Theosophical Publishing Society, 1901.

Mead, G. R. S., *Echoes from the Gnosis*, Wheaton, Illinois: Quest Books, 2006.

Mead, G. R. S., *Fragments of a Faith Forgotten*, 1960; CreateSpace Independent Publishing Platform, 2016.

Mead, G. R. S., *Orpheus*, New York: Barnes and Noble, 1965.

Mead, G. R. S., *Pistis Sophia*, London and New York: Theosophical Publishing Society, 1896.

Mead, G. R. S., *The Subtle Body*, London: Stuart and Watkins, 1919.

Mead, G. R. S., *Thrice Greatest Hermes*, Boston: Weiser Books, 2001.

Medawar, P. B., *Induction and Intuition in Scientific Thought*, London: Methuen, 1969.

Medler, E., *The Colours of Virtue*, St Ursin Press, 2020.

Mehta, P. D., *Early Indian Religious Thought*, London: Luzac & Co., 1956.

Meister Eckhart, *Sermons and Tractates*, trans. from F. Pfeiffer's Collection by C. de B. Evans, 2 vols, London: J. M. Watkins, 1947.

Menas, K. and Nadeau, R., *The Conscious Universe: Part and Whole in Modern Physical Theory*, New York: Springer Verlag, 1990.

Menas, K., 'Non-locality, Foundational Principles and Consciousness', *Noetic Journal*, Vol. 2, 1999.

Menas, K., *Bell's Theorem, Quantum Theory and Conceptions of the Universe*, Dordrecht, Holland: Kluwer, 1989.

Mercola, Dr J., *EMF*D: 5g, Wi-Fi & Cell Phones Hidden Harms And How To Protect Yourself*, Hay House, 2020.

Michelson, A. A., 'The Relative Motion of the Earth and the Luminiferous Ether', *American Journal of Science*, Vol. 22, 1881.

Midgley, M., *Are You an Illusion?* Acumen Press, 2014.

Midgley, M., *Evolution As A Religion*, London: Routledge, 2002.

Midgley, M., *What is Philosophy For?* Bloomsbury Academic, 2018.

Milner, D., *Kosmos: An Evolutionary–Wholistic Account of Creation*, US: Ozark Mountain Publishing, 2012.

Milton, J. and Wiseman R., 'Does Psi Exist? Lack of Replication of an Anomalous Process of Information Transfer', *Psychological Bulletin*, Vol. 125, 1999.

Milton, J., 'Should Ganzfeld Research Continue to be Crucial in the Search for a Replicable Psi Effect?', *Journal of Parapsychology*, Vol. 63, 1999.

Mitchell, E. D., et al., *Psychic Exploration: A Challenge for Science*, New York: G. P. Putnam's Sons, 1974.

Mitchell, E. D., *The Way of the Explorer: An Apollo Astronaut's Journey through the Material and Mystical Worlds*, Norwalk, CT: The Easton Press, 1996.

Mitchell, E., 'Nature's Mind: The Quantum Hologram', *International Journal of Computing Anticipatory Systems*, Vol. 7, 2000.

Mitchell, G., *Developing the Mind with Biofeedback*, London: Biofeedback Workshops, 1979.

Mitchell, M., *Complexity: A Guided Tour*, New York: Oxford University Press.

Moncrieff, J., *The Myth of the Chemical Cure: A Critique of Psychiatric Drug Treatment*, London: Palgrave Macmillan, 2009.

Monier-Williams, Sir Monier, *Indian Wisdom*, London: Luzac & Co., 1893.

Monk, M., 'A Hierarchy of Consciousness from Atom to Cosmos', *Integral Review*, Vol. 16, No. 2, August 2020.

Monk, M., 'Scientist, Poet and Mystic: Complementary Ways of Knowing and Being', *Journal of the Scientific and Medical Network*, 2021/1.

Monod, J., *Chance and Necessity*, London: Collins, 1972.

Monod, J., *Le Hasard et la Nécessité – Essai sur la Philosophie Naturelle de la Biologie Moderne* [Chance and Necessity – Essay on the Natural Philosophy of Modern Biology], Paris: Editions du Seuil, 1970.

Monroe, R., *Journeys Out of the Body*, New York: Doubleday, 1971.

Moody, R. A., *Life after Life*, London: Mockingbird, 1976; New York: Bantam, 1981.

Moody, R. with Perry, P., *Glimpses of Eternity: Sharing a Loved Ones Passage from This Life to the Next*, New York: Guideposts, 2010.

Moody, R., *Life after Life: The Investigation of a Phenomenon – Survival of Bodily Death*, US: Stackpole Books, 1976.

Moorjani, A., *Dying to Be Me: My Journey from Cancer, to Near Death, to True Healing*, New York: Hay House, 2012.

More, H., *An Antidote Against Atheism; Or, an Appeal to the Naturall Faculties of the Minde of Man, Whether There Be Not a God*, London: printed by J. Flesher, for William Morden, bookseller in Cambridge, 1655.

More, H., *Divine Dialogues Concerning Sundry Disquisitions & Instructions Concerning the Attributes of God and His Providence in the World*, 1668; London: printed and sold by Joseph Downing, 1713.

More, H., *The Immortality of the Soul, So Farre Forth as It Is Demonstrable from the Knowledge of Nature and the Light of Reason*, printed by J. Flesher, for William Morden Bookseller in Cambridge, 1659.

Morris, S. C., *Life's Solution: Inevitable Humans in a Lonely Universe*, Cambridge University Press, 2003.

Muir, J., *Original Sanskrit Texts on the Origin and History of the People of India, their Religion and Institutions*, 5 vols, London, Trübner, 1858–1870.

Muldoon, S. J. and Carrington, H., *The Projection of the Astral Body*, London: Rider, 1963.

Muller, E., *A History of Jewish Mysticism*, Oxford: East and West Library, Phaidon Press, 1946.

Munowitz, M., *Knowing: The Nature of Physical Law*, Oxford University Press, 2005.

Murphet, H., *Hammer on the Mountain*, Madras, Wheaton, London: Theosophical Publishing House, 1972. Life of Henry Steel Olcott (1832–1907).

Murphet, H., *When Daylight Comes*, Madras, Wheaton, London: Theosophical Publishing House, 1975. Biography of Helena Petrovna Blavatsky.

Murphy, G. and Ballou, R. O. (eds), *William James on Psychical Research*, London: Chatto and Windus, 1961.

Murray G., *Five Stages of Greek Religion*, London: Watts & Co., 1946.

Murray G., *The Rise of the Greek Epic: Being a Course of Lectures Delivered at Harvard University*, Oxford: Oxford University Press; 4th edn, 1934.

Murti, T. R. V., *The Central Philosophy of Buddhism*, London: Allen & Unwin, 1955.

Nasr, S. H., *The Islamic Intellectual Tradition in Persia*, London: Curzon Press, 1996.

Naydler, J., *In the Shadow of the Machine*, Temple Lodge, 2018.

Naydler, J., *Shamanic Wisdom in the Pyramid Texts*, Rochester, Vermont: Inner Traditions, 2005.

Naydler, J., *Temple of the Cosmos: The Ancient Egyptian Experience of the Sacred*, Rochester, Vermont: Inner Traditions, 1996.

Neff, M. K., *Personal Memories of H. P. Blavatsky*, London: Rider and Co., 1937.

Nelkin, D. and Tancredi, L., *Dangerous Diagnostics: The Social Power of Biological Information*, University of Chicago Press, 1994.

Nelson, J. E., *Healing the Split*, Albany, New York: SUNY Press, 1994.

Nelson, R. D., *Connected: The Emergence of Global Consciousness*, ICRL Press, 2019.

Newman, W. R., *Newton the Alchemist: Science, Enigma and the Quest for Nature's 'Secret Fire'*, Princeton and Oxford: Princeton University Press, 2019.

Newton, ed. I. B. Cohen and R. S. Westfall, London and New York: Norton, 1995.

Newton, I., *Observations upon the Prophecies of Holy Writ, particularly the Prophecies of Daniel, and the Apocalypse of St. John*, London: W. Innys and R. Manby, 1733; Echo Library, 2007.

Newton, I., *The Chronology of Ancient Kingdoms Amended*, London: J. Tonson, J. Osborn, and T. Longman, 1728; published online, June 2006, https://www.newtonproject.ox.ac.uk/view/texts/diplomatic/THEM00184.

Nicholson, D. J. and Dupré, J., *Everything Flows*, Oxford University Press, 2018.

Nicholson, R. A., *Rumi, Poet and Mystic*, London: George Ellen & Unwin, 1950.

Nicholson, R. A., *Studies in Islamic Mysticism*, Cambridge University Press, 1921.

Nicholson, R. A., *The Mystics of Islam*, London: Routledge, Kegan & Paul, 1914.

Nielsen, C., 'Post-mortem Consciousness: Views of Psychotherapists and their Influence in the Work with Clients', PhD thesis, University of Chester, 2019.

Noble, D., *The Music of Life: Biology Beyond the Genome*, Oxford University Press, 2006.

Noe, A., *Out of Our Heads: Why You Are Not Your Brain, and Other Lessons from the Biology of Consciousness*, New York: Hill & Wang, 2009.

Northrop, F. S. C., *The Meeting of East and West: An Inquiry Concerning World Understanding*, New York: The Macmillan Co., 1949.

O'Neill, J. J., *Prodigal Genius: The Life of Nikola Tesla*, New York: Ives Washburn, Inc. 1944.

Odeberg, H., *3 Enoch: or, the Hebrew Book of Enoch*, Cambridge: Cambridge University Press, 1928.

Odeberg, H., *The Fourth Gospel: Interpreted in its Relation to Contemporaneous Religious Currrents in Palestine and the Hellenistic–Oriental World*, B. R. Grüner Publishing Company, 1974.

Oldenberg, H., *Buddha, His Life, His Doctrine, His Order*, trans. W. Hoey, London and Edinburgh: Williams Norgate, 1882.

Olsen, S., *The Golden Section: Nature's Greatest Secret*, New York: Walker & Company, 2006.

Oppenheimer, J. R., *Science and the Common Understanding*, Oxford University Press, 1954.

Oreskes, N. and Conway, E. K., *Merchants of Doubt: How a Handful of Scientists Obscured the Truth on Issues from Tobacco Smoke to Global Warming*, New York: Bloomsbury Press, 2010.

Oschman, J. L., *Energy Medicine: The Scientific Basis*, London: Harcourt, 2001.

Ostriker, J. P. and Steinhardt, P. J., 'The Quintessential Universe', *Scientific American*, January 2001.

Otto, R., *Mysticism, East and West: A Comparative Analysis of the Nature of Mysticism*, trans. B. L. Bracey and R. C. Payne, US: Wipf and Stock, reissue edn, 2016.

Otto, R., *The Idea of the Holy*, trans. J. W. Harvey, Oxford University Press, 1923.

Pagels, H. R., *The Cosmic Code*, London: Michael Joseph, 1983.

Pahnke, W. N. and Richards, W. A., 'Implications of LSD and Experimental Mysticism', in Tart, C. T., *Altered States of Consciousness*, New York: Wiley, 1969.

Pais, A., *Subtle Is the Lord: The Science and the Life of Albert Einstein*, foreword by R. Penrose, US: Oxford University Press, 2005.

Palmer, T., *The Science of Spirit Possession*, Cambridge Scholars Publishing, 2nd edn, 2019.

Panda, N. C., *Māyā in Physics*, Delhi: Motilal Banarsidass Publishers, 1991.

Panogopoulos, D. K., 'Comparing DNA Damage Induced by Mobile Telephony and Other Types of Man-Made Electromagnetic Fields', from Mutations Research Reviews in *Mutation Research*, Vol. 781, 2019.

Paracelsus – Selected Writings, foreword by C. G. Jung, ed. and introd. J. Jacobi, trans. N. Guterman, Princeton University Press, 1979.

Parnia, S. with Young, J., *Erasing Death*, HarperOne, 2014.

Pauli, W. and Jung, C. G., *Atom and Archetype: The Pauli/Jung Letters 1932–1958*, Princeton University Press, 2001.

Peake, A., *The Hidden Universe: An Investigation into Non-Human Intelligences*, Watkins Publishing, 2019.

Pearce, J. C., *The Biology of Transcendence: A Blueprint of the Human Spirit*, Rochester, New York: Park Street Press, 2002.

Peebles, P. J. E., *Principles of Physical Cosmology*, Princeton University Press, 1993.

Peers, E. A., *Studies of the Spanish Mystics*, 3 vols, London: Sheldon Press; New York: Macmillan, 1927–1960.

Pelgrin, M., *And a Time to Die*, Wheaton, Illinois: Quest Books, 1962. A man dying of cancer struggles right to the end to discover his inner self. Intensely personal, moving and inspiring.

Penfield, W. and Roberts L., *Speech and Brain Mechanisms*, Princeton University Press, 1959.

Penfield, W., *The Mystery of the Mind*, Princeton University Press, 1975.

Penrose, R., *Cycles of Time: An Extraordinary New View of the Universe*, London: Bodley Head, 2010.

Penrose, R., *Shadows of the Mind: A Search for the Missing Science of Consciousness*, Oxford University Press, 2000.

Penrose, R., *The Emperor's New Mind: Concerning Computers, Minds, and the Laws of Physics*, New York: Oxford University Press, 1989.

Penrose, R., *The Large, the Small and the Human Mind*, Cambridge: Cambridge University Press, 1997.

Perlas, N., *Humanity's Last Chance*, Temple Lodge, 2018.

Philo, *The Works of Philo*, Peabody, Massachusetts: Hendrickson Publishers, 1993.

Pisano, G. P., *Science Business: The Promise, the Reality and the Future of Biotech*, Harvard Business School, Boston, Massachusetts, 2006.

Planck, M., *The Philosophy of Physics*, trans. W. H. Johnston, London: George Allen & Unwin, Ltd., 1936.

Plato, *The Dialogues*, trans. and ed. B. Jowett, 5 vols, Oxford University Press, 3rd edn, 1892.

Plato, *The Republic*, trans. B. Jowett, New York: Dover Books, 2000.

Plato, *Timaeus and Critias*, trans. D. Lee, London: Penguin Classics, 1971.

Plotinus, *Select Works of Plotinus*, trans. T. Taylor, introd. G. R. S. Mead, London: 1895.

Plotinus, *The Enneads*, trans. S. MacKenna, London: Faber & Faber, 1956.

Plummer, L. G., *From Atom to Kosmos*, Point Loma, California: Theosophical University Press, 1940. A Theosophical study in evolution.

Plummer, L. G., *The Mathematics of the Cosmic Mind*, Adyar, London, Wheaton: Theosophical Publishing House, 1970. A study in mathematical symbolism.

Polanyi, M., 'Life Transcending Physics and Chemistry', *Chemical and Engineering News*, 1967.

Polanyi, M., *Personal Knowledge*, London: Routledge & Kegan Paul, 1958.

Polanyi, M., *The Tacit Dimension*, University of Chicago Press, 2009.

Polkinghorne, J. C., *The Quantum World*, Penguin Books, 1990.

Popper, K., *Conjectures and Refutations*, London: Routledge & Kegan Paul, 1969.

Porritt, J., *Hope in Hell*, Simon & Schuster, 2020.

Powell, A., *Conversations with the Soul*, Muswell Hill Press, 2018.

Powell, A., *The Way of the Soul*, Muswell Hill Press, 2018.

Presti, D. E. with Greyson, B., Kelly, E. F., Kelly, E. W., and Tucker, J. B., *Mind Beyond Brain*, Columbia University Press, 2019.

Pribram, K. H., 'Transcending the Mind–brain Problem', *Zygon*, Vol. 14, 1979.

Pribram, K. H., *Languages of the Brain*, US: Englewood Cliffs, Prentice Hall, 1971.

Prigogine, I. and Isabelle S., *Order Out of Chaos: Man's New Dialogue With Nature*, New York: Bantam Books, 1984.

Prigogine, I., *From Being to Becoming*, San Francisco: Freeman, 1980.

Prigogine, I., *From Being to Becoming: Time and Complexity in the Physical Sciences*, San Francisco: W. H. Freeman & Co., 1980.

Principe, L., *The Aspiring Adept: Robert Boyle and His Alchemical Quest*, Princeton University Press, 2000.

Proclus, *Commentary on the Timaeus of Plato*, UK, Westbury: Prometheus Trust 1998.

Psaltis, L., *Dynamics of the Psychic World*, Adyar, Wheaton, London: Theosophical Publishing House, 1972. Excerpts from H. P. Blavatsky's writings on magic, mediumship, psychism, and the powers of the spirit.

Ptolemy, *Tetrabiblios*, trans. F. E. Robbins, London: Heinemann (Loeb Classical Library no. 435), 1980.

Purucker, G. de, *Fountain–Source of Occultism*, ed. G. F. Knoche, Pasadena, California: Theosophical University Press, 1974.

Purucker, G. de, *Fundamentals of the Esoteric Philosophy*, London: Rider & Co., 1947.

Purucker, G. de, *Golden Precepts of Esotericism*, 1943; 3rd edn as *Golden Precepts*, San Diego: Point Loma Publications, 1971.

Purucker, G. de, in collaboration with K. Tingley, *H. P. Blavatshy: The Mystery*, San Diego: Point Loma Publications, 1974.

Purucker, G. de, *Man in Evolution*, Point Loma, California: Theosophical University Press, 1977.

Purucker, G. de, *Studies in Occult Philosophy*, Covina, California: Theosophical University Press, 1945.

Purucker, G. de, *The Esoteric Tradition*, 2 vols, Point Loma, California: Theosophical University Press, 1973.

Purucker, G. de, *Wind of the Spirit*, San Diego: Point Loma Publications, 1971. A selection of talks on Theosophy as related primarily to human life and human problems.

Purucker, G. de., *Galaxies and Solar Systems*, San Diego, California: Point Loma Publishing, 1987.

Purucker, G. de., *Hierarchies and the Doctrine of Emanations*, San Diego, California: Point Loma Publishing, 1987.

Purucker, G. de., *Invisible Worlds and Their Inhahitants*, San Diego, California: Point Loma Publishing, 1987.

Pythagoras, *The Golden Verses of Pythagoras, and other Pythagorean Fragments*, compiled F. M. Firth, introd. A. Besant, London & Benares: Theosophical Publishing Society, 1905.

Quatrefages, A. de, *Histoire Générale des Races Humaines* [General History of Human Races], Paris: A. Hennuyer, 1889.

Radhakrishnan, S. and Muirhead, H., *Contemporary Indian Philosophy*, New York and London: The Macmillan Company/George Allen & Unwin Ltd, 1927.

Radhakrishnan, S., et al. (eds), *History of Philosophy, Eastern and Western*, 2 vols, London: George Allen & Unwin, 1953.

Radhakrishnan, S., *Indian Philosophy*, 2 vols, London, 1927.

Radhakrishnan, S., *The Principal Upanishads*, London: George Allen & Unwin, 1953.

Radin, D. L. and Nelson, R. D., 'Evidence for Consciousness-related Anomalies in Random Physical Systems', *Foundations of Physics*, Vol. 19, 1989.

Radin, D., *Conscious Universe: The Scientific Truth of Psychic Phenomena*, New York: HarperCollins Publishers, 1997.

Radin, D., *Entangled Minds: Extrasensory Experiences in a Quantum Reality*, New York: Simon & Schuster, 2006.

Radin, D., *Real Magic: Ancient Wisdom, Modern Science, and a Guide to the Secret Powers of the Universe*, Harmony Books, 2018.

Radin, D., *Supernormal: Science, Yoga, and the Evidence for Extraordinary Psychic Abilities*, New York: Random House, 2013.

Radin, D., *The Conscious Universe: The Scientific Truth of Psychic Phenomena*, San Francisco: HarperEdge, 1997.

Rae, A., *Quantum Physics: Illusion or Reality*? Cambridge: Cambridge University Press, 1986.

Rees, M., *Before the Beginning: Our Universe and Others*, London: Simon & Schuster, 1997.

Rees, M., *Our Final Century: The 50/50 Threat to Humanity's Survival*, London: Arrow, 2004.

Reiche, E. M. V., Nunes, S. O. V., and Morimoto, H. K., 'Stress, Depression, the Immune System and Cancer', *Lancet Oncology*, Vol. 5, 2005.

Rendell, P., *Introduction to the Chakras*, UK: Aquarian Press, 1974.

Rescher, N., *G. W. Leibniz's Monadology*, London: Routledge, 1991.

Reynolds, B. (ed.), *Embracing Reality: The Integral Vision of Ken Wilber*, New York: Penguin, 2004.

Riordan, M. and Schramm, D., *The Shadows of Creation*, Oxford: Oxford University Press, 1993.

Rishabhchand, *The Integral Yoga of Sri Aurobindo*, Sri Aurobindo Ashram Press, 1959.

Rizzolatti, G., Fadiga, L., Fogassi, L., and Gallese, V., 'Resonance Behaviors and Mirror Neurons', *Archives Italiennes de Biologie*, Vol. 137, 1999.

Robinson, O., *Pathways Between Head and Heart*, O Books, 2018.

Rolt, C. E., *Dionysius the Areopagite: On the Divine Names and the Mystical Theology*, London: Forgotten Books, 2018.

Ross, MacDonald, G., *Leibniz*, New York and Oxford, Oxford University Press, 1992.

Royal Society, *Knowledge, Networks and Nations: Global Scientific Collaboration in the 21st Century*, Royal Society Policy Document 03/11, London, 2011.

Rubik, B., 'The Biofield Hypothesis: Its Biophysical Basis and Role in Medicine', *The Journal of Alternative and Complementary Medicine*, Vol. 8, No. 6, 2002.

Russell, B., *A Critical Exposition of the Philosophy of Leibniz*, Cambridge: Cambridge University Press, 1900.

Russell, B., *History of Western Philosophy*, London: George Allen and Unwin Ltd., 1946.

Russell, B., *Mysticism and Logic and Other Essays*, London: George Allen and Unwin Ltd., 1959.

Russell, P., *The Awakening Earth*, London: Routledge and Kegan Paul, 1982. An eminently optismistic view of the future when world government is run by practical mystics.

Sabom, M. B., *Recollections of Death: A Medical Investigation*, New York: Harper & Row, 1982.

Sacks, O., *The Man Who Mistook His Wife for a Hat*, London: Duckworth,1985.

Sági, M. with Sági, I., *Healing with Information: The New Homeopathy*, O Books, 2018.

Sarton, G., 'Introductory Essay', in J. Needham (ed.), *Science, Religion and Reality*, New York: Braziller, 1955.

Satprem, *Sri Aurobindo or the Adventure of Consciousness*, Mysore, India: Mira Aditi Centre, 2000.

Saunders, P., *An Introduction to Catastrophe Theory*, New York: Cambridge University Press, 1980.

Schaffer, S., 'Newton's Comets and the Transformation of Astrology', ed. P. Curry, in *Astrology, Science and Society: Historical Essays*, Woodbridge, UK: The Boydell Press, 1987.

Schelling, F. von, *Ideas for a Philosophy of Nature*, Cambridge University Press, 1988.

Schilpp, P. A. (ed.), *Albert Einstein: Philosopher–Scientist*, The Library of Living Philosophers, Vol. 7, Cambridge University Press, 1949.

Schimmel, A., *The Mystery of Numbers*, New York: Oxford University Press, 1993.

Schlegel, Friedrich von, *Die Philosophie der Geschichte* [The Philosophy of History], trans. J. B. Robertson, 1846; London: H. G. Bohn, 1957.

Schlegel, von, *Ueber die Sprache and Weisheit der Inder* [On the Language and Wisdom of the Indians], 1808; Wentworth Press, 2018.

Schmidt, S., Erath, D., Ivanova, V., and Walach, H., 'Do You Know Who Is Calling? Experiments on Anomalous Cognition in Phone Call Receivers', *Open Psychology Journal*, Vol. 2, 2009.

Schmidt, S., Schneider, R., Utts, J., and Walach, H., 'Distant Intentionality and the Feeling of being Stared At: Two Meta-analyses', *British Journal of Psychology*, Vol. 95, 2004.

Schmitt, C. B., 'Perennial Philosophy: From Agostino Steuco to Leibniz', in *Journal of the History of Ideas*, 27, 1966.

Schmitt, R. [also cited as Schmitt, A.] and Westergaard, N. L. (eds), *Zendavesta or the Religious Books of the Zoroastrians; Volume I: The Zend Texts*, Germany: Dr. Ludwig Reichert Verlag, rev. edn, 1993.

Schmitt-Biggeman, W., *Philosophia Perennis: Historical Outlines of Western Spirituality in Ancient, Medieval and Early Modern Thought*, Springer, 2004.

Scholem, G. S., *Major Trends in Jewish Mysticism*, London: Thames and Hudson, 1955.

Scholem, G. S., *On the Kabbalah and Its Symbolism*, 1965; US: Random House Inc, rev. edn, 1996.

Schubert, K., *The Dead Sea Community: Its Origins and Teachings*, trans. J. W. Doberstein, London: Adam and Charles Black, 1959.

Schuon, F., *The Transcendent Unity of Religions*, Wheaton, Illinois: Quest Books, 1984.

Schwartz, S. A., Woollacott, M. H., and Schwartz, G. E. (eds), *Is Consciousness Primary?* Academy for the Advancement of Postmaterlist Sciences, 2020.

Schwarzschild, B., 'Very Distant Supernovae Suggest that the Cosmic Expansion is Speeding Up', *Physics Today*, Vol. 51, No. 6, 1998.

Schwegler, A., *A History of Philosophy in Epitome*, trans. J. H. Seelye, 1871; University of Michigan Library, 2005.

Scott, Sir Walter (ed. and trans.), *The Hermetica: The Writings Attributed to Hermes Trismegistus*, 1924–36; UK: Solos Press, 1993.

Scott, Sir Walter (trans.), *Asclepius III*, London: Solos Books, 1992.

Searle, J., 'Consciousness and the Philosophers', *New York Review of Books*, 6 March, 1997.

Searle, J., *The Rediscovery of the Mind*, Cambridge, Massachusetts: MIT, 1992.

Sepher Yetzirah, The Book of Formation, by Rabbi Akiba ben Joseph, trans. K. Stenring, introd. A. E. Waite, New York: Ktav Publishing House, 1970.

Seyffert, O., *A Dictionary of Classical Antiquities: Mythology, Religion, Literature & Art*, rev. and ed. H. Nettleship and J. E. Sandys, London: Swan Sonnenschein & Co., rev. edn with additions, 1984.

Shah, I., *The Sufis*, London: Octagon Press, 1977.

Shah, I., *Oriental Magic*, London: Octagon Press, 1956.

Shankara, *Crest-Jewel of Discrimination*, trans. Swami Prabhavananda and C. Isherwood, New York: New American Library, 1970.

Shearer, A., *The Story of Yoga: From Ancient India to the Modern World*, Hurst & Co., 2020.

Sheldrake, M., *Entangled Life*, Bodley Head, 2020.

Sheldrake, R. and Smart, P., 'Experimental Tests for Telephone Telepathy', *Journal of the Society for Psychical Research*, Vol. 67, 2003a.

Sheldrake, R. and Smart, P., 'Testing for Telepathy in Connection with E-mails', *Perceptual and Motor Skills*, Vol. 101, 2005.

Sheldrake, R. and Smart, P., 'Videotaped Experiments on Telephone Telepathy', *Journal of Parapsychology*, Vol. 67, 2003b.

Sheldrake, R., *Ways To Go Beyond*, Coronet, 2019.

Shermer, M., *The Believing Brain: From Ghosts and Gods to Politics and Conspiracies – How We Construct Beliefs and Reinforce them as Truths*, New York: Times Books, 2011.

Sherrington, C., *Man on his Nature*, Cambridge: Cambridge University Press, 1940.

Silverman, S., 'Placebos are Getting More Effective. Drugmakers are Desperate to Know Why', *Wired Magazine*, 24 August, 2009.

Singer, P., *Ethics in the Real World*, Princeton University Press, 2016.

Singh, S. and Ernst, E., *Trick or Treatment? Alternative Medicine on Trial*, London: Corgi Books, 2009.

Sinnett, A. P., *Incidents in the Life of Madame Blavatsky*, New York: J. W. Bouton; London: George Redway, 1886.

Skrbina, D., 'Panpsychism as an Underlying Theme in Western Philosophy', *Journal of Consciousness Studies*, Vol. 10, 2003.

Slater, V. W., *Hatha Yoga*, London: Theosophical Publishing House, 1966.

Slater, V. W., *Raja Yoga*, London: Theosophical Publishing House, 1965.

Smith, A., *The Mind*, London: Hodder and Stoughton, 1984.

Smith, E. L. (ed.), *Intelligence Came First*, Wheaton, Illinois: Theosophical Publishing House, 1975.

Smith, E. L., *Our Last Adventure*, London: Theosophical Publishing House, 1986.

Smith, M., *Jesus The Magician*, London: Aquarian Press, 1978.

Smith, M., *Rabi'a the Mystic*, Cambridge University Press, 1928.

Smolin, L., *The Trouble With Physics: The Rise of String Theory, The Fall of a Science, and What Comes Next*, London: Allen Lane, 2006.

Smuts, J. C., *Holism and Evolution*, London: Macmillan, 1926.

Smythies, J. R., *The Walls of Plato's Cave: The Science and Philosophy of Brain, Consciousness and Perception*, UK: Avebury, 1994.

Snobelen, S. D., 'Isaac Newton, Heretic: The Strategies of a Nicodemite', *The British Journal for the History of Science*, Vol. 32, Issue 04, December 1999.

Sophocles, *The Tragedies of Sophocles*, trans. Sir Richard C. Jebb, Cambridge University Press, 1904.

Sparks, T., *The Power Within – Becoming, Being and the Holotropic Paradigm*, London: Muswell Hill Press, 2016.

Spence, L., *The History of Atlantis*, London: Senate Books, 1995.

Spierenberg, H. J., *H. P. Blavatsky on the Gnostics*, San Diego, California: Point Loma Publishing, 1994.

Spierenberg, H. J., *The Buddhism of H. P. Blavatsky*, San Diego, California: Point Loma Publishing, 1991.

Spierenberg, H. J., *The New Testament Commentaries of H. P. Blavatsky*, San Diego, California: Point Loma Publishing, 1987.

Spierenberg, H. J., *The Vedanta Commentaries of H. P. Blavatsky*, San Diego, California: Point Loma Publishing, 1992.

Spinoza, Benedict de, *Ethics*, London: Penguin Classics, 2004.

Spinoza, Benedict de, *The Chief Works of Benedict de Spinoza*, trans. and introd. R. H. M. Elwes, 2 vols, London: George Bell and Sons, 1891.

Squire, L. R., 'Mechanisms of Memory', *Science*, Vol. 232, 1986.

Sri Ram, N., *An Approach to Reality*, Adyar, Madras: Theosophical Publishing House, 1968.

Sri Ram, N., *Thoughts for Aspirants*, Wheaton, Illinois: Theosophical Publishing House, 1972.

Stapp, H. P., *A Report on the Gaudiya Vaishnava Vedanta Form of Vedic Ontology*, Berkeley: Bhaktivedanta Institute, 1994.

Stapp, H. P., *Mind, Matter, and Quantum Mechanics*, New York: Springer, 1993. A weighty exposition of the mystery of mind and matter.

Stapp, H. P., *Mindful Universe: Quantum Mechanics and the Participating Observer*, Heidelberg: Springer, 2007.

Steane, A., *Science and Humanity*, Oxford University Press, 2018.

Stephenson, L. M., 'A Possible Annual Variation of the Gravitational Constant', *Proceedings of the Physical Society*, Vol. 90, 1967.

Stevenson, I., 'Birth Marks and Birth Defects Corresponding to Wounds on Deceased Persons', *Journal of Scentific Exploration*, Vol. 7, 1993.

Stevenson, I., *Where Reincarnation and Biology Intersect*, Westport, Connecticut: Praeger Publishers, 1997.

Stewart, M., *Patterns of Eternity*, Floris, 2011.

Stewart, M., *Symbols of Eternity: Landmarks for a Soul Journey*, Floris, 2011.

Stier, K., 'Curbing Drug-company Abuses: Are Fines Enough?', *Time*, 30 May 2010.

Strawson, G., 'Realistic Monism: Why Physicalism Entails Panpsychism', *Journal of Consciousness Studies*, Vol. 13, 2006.

Subba Row, T., *Esoteric Writings*, 1895; Adyar: Theosophical Publishing House, 1931.

Subba Row, T., *Notes on the Bhagavad Gita*, Point Loma, California: Theosophical University Press, 1934.

Susskind, J., *Future Politics*, Oxford University Press, 2020.

Suzuki, D. T., *Essays in Zen Buddhism*, 3 vols, London: Rider, 1953.

Suzuki, D. T., *On Indian Mahayana Buddhism*, ed. E. Conze, New York: Harper & Row Publishers, 1968.

Taimni, I. K., *Science and Occultism*, Theosophical Publishing House, 1974.

Taimni, I. K., *The Science of Yoga*, Wheaton, Illinois: Theosophical Publishing House, 1975.

Targ, R, and Harary, K., *The Mind Race*, New York: Villard Books, 1984.

Tarnas, R., *The Passion of the Western Mind*, New York: Harmony Books, 1991.

Taylor, R., 'A Gentle Introduction to Quantum Biology', *Consciousness and Physical Reality*, Vol. 1, No. 1, 1998.

Taylor, S., *Spiritual Science*, Watkins, 2018.

Tegmark, M., 'The Multiverse Hierarchy', in Carr (ed.), *Universe or Multiverse?* Cambridge University Press, 2007.

Teilhard de Chardin, P., *The Phenomenon of Man*, New York: Harper & Row, 1959.

Teresa, of Avila, *The Interior Castle*, trans. Benedictines of Stanbrook, Cosimo Classics, 2007.

Teresa, of Avila, *The Life of Saint Teresa of Avila by Herself*, trans. J. M. Cohen, UK: Harmondsworth, 1957.

The Chymistry of Isaac Newton, Indiana University, http://webapp1.dlib.indiana.edu/newton/.

The Correspondence of Robert Boyle, eds M. Hunter et al., 6 vols, London: Routledge, 2001.

The Correspondences of Isaac Newton, eds H. W. Turnbull, J. F. Scott, A. R. Hall, and L. Tilling, 7 vols, Cambridge: Cambridge University Press, 1959–77.

The Mathematical Papers of Isaac Newton, 8 vols, ed. D. T. Whiteside, Cambridge: Cambridge University Press, 1967–81.

The Newton Project, https://www.history.ox.ac.uk/newton-project.

Thom, R., *Mathematical Models of Morphogenesis*, UK: Ellis Horwood, 1983.

Thomas Aquinas, *The 'Summa Theologica' of St. Thomas Aquinas*, 10 vols, trans. literally, Fathers of the English Dominican Province, 2nd and rev. edn, London: Burns Oates and Washbourne, 1920–1922.

Thomas, E. J., *The History of Buddhist Thought*, London: Kegan Paul, Trench, Trubner & Co.; New York: A. A. Knopf, 1933.

Thomas, E. J., *The Life of the Buddha as Legend and History*, London: Routledge & Kegan, 1949.

Thomas, E. J., *The Perfection of Wisdom*, London: John Murray, 1952.

Thurman, R. (ed.), *The Life and Teachings of Tsong Khapa*, Dharamsala: Library of Tibetan Works and Archives, 1982.

Tiller, W. A., 'Subtle Energies in Energy Medicine', *Frontier Perspectives*, Vol. 4, No. 2, 1995.

Tingley, K., *The Wisdom of the Heart: Katherine Tingley Speaks*, San Diego: Point Loma Publications, 1978.

Tobert, N., *Cultural Perspectives on Mental Wellbeing: Spiritual Interpretations of Symptoms in Medical Practice*, Jessica Kingsley Publishers, 2017.

Tolle, E., *The Power of Now: A Guide to Spiritual Enlightenment*, US: New World Library, 1999.

Tompkins, P., *Secrets of the Great Pyramid*, London: Allen Lane, 1973.

Trew, C., 'Theosophy and the Changing Outlook in Science', the Blavatsky Lecture, 1943, London: The Theosophical Society.

Tucker, J. B., *Return to Life: Extraordinary Cases of Children Who Remember Past Lives*, New York: St. Martin's Griffin, 2013.

Tudge, C., *The Great Re-Think*, Pari Publishing, 2020.

Turner, K. A., *Radical Remission: Surviving Cancer Against All Odds*, New York: HarperCollins Publishers, 2014.

Tweedie, I., *The Chasm of Fire*, London: Element Books, 1979.

Tyberg, J., *Sanskrit Keys to the Wisdom Religion*, Theosophical University Press, 1943.

UK Government, *Healthy Lives, Healthy People*, HM Stationery Oflice, London, 2010.

Ullman, D., *Homeopathy: Medicine for the 21st Century*, Berkeley, California: North Atlantic Books, 1988.

Ullman, M. and Krippner, S., *Dream Studies and Telepathy: An Experimental Approach*, New York: Parapsychology Foundation, 1970.

Underhill, E., *Mysticism: A Study in the Nature and Development of Man's Spiritual Consciousness*, London: Methuen & Co,, 1952.

Utts, J. and Josephson, B., 'The Paranormal: The Evidence and its Implications for Consciousness', from *Times Higher Education Supplement*, special section on Consciousness linked to Tucson II conference, 'Toward a Science of Consciousness', April 1996.

Velikhovsky, I., *Earth in Upheaval*, London: Abacus, 1956.

Vickers, B., *In Defence of Rhetoric*, Oxford: Clarendon Press, 1989.

Virgil, *The Aeneid*, trans. A. S. Kline, CreateSpace Independent Publishing Platform, 2014.

Vithulkas, G., *The Science of Homeopathy*, New York: Grover Press, 1980.

Von Neumann, J., *The Conceptual Foundations of Quantum Mechanics*, Princeton University Press, 1955.

Wachtmeister, Countess Constance, *Reminiscences of H. P. Blavatsky and the Secret Doctrine*, 1893; Adyar, Wheaton, London: Theosophical Publishing House, 1976.

Wackermann, J., Seiter, C., Keibel, H., and Walach, H., 'Correlations between Brain Electrical Activities of Two Spatially Separated Human Subjects', *Neuroscience Letters*, Vol. 336, 2003.

Waddington, C. H., 'Fields and Gradients', in *Major Problems in Developmental Biology*, ed. Michael Locke, New York: Academic Press, 1966.

Waddington, C. H., *The Ethical Animal*, London: George Allen and Unwin, 1960.

Waite, A. E., *The Holy Kabbalah*, London: Williams and Norgate, 1929.

Waite, A. E., *The Occult Sciences*, 1891; repr. London: Kegan Paul, 1972.

Walach, H., *Secular Spirituality*, Springer, 2015.

Wallace, A. R., *Miracles and Modern Spiritualism*, London: 3rd edn, George Redway, 1896.

Wallace, A. R., *The Scientific Aspect of the Supernatural: Indicating the Desirableness of an Experimental Enquiry by Men of Science into the Alleged Powers of Clairvoyants and Mediums*, London: F. Farrah, 1866.

Wallace, A. R., *The Taboo of Subjectivity*, Oxford University Press, 2000.

Wallace, B. A., *Mind in the Balance: Meditation in Science, Buddhism and Christianity*, New York, Columbia University Press, 2009.

Wallace, R. K. and Benson H., 'The Physiology of Meditation', *Scientific American*, Vol. 226, 1972.

Wansbrough, J., *Quranic Studies*, Oxford: Oxford University Press, 1977.

Warraq, I., *The Quest for the Historical Muhammad*, New York: Prometheus Books, 2000.

Warren, W. F., *Paradise Found: The Cradle of the Human Race at the North Pole*, Amsterdam, the Netherlands: Fredonia Books, 2002.

Watson, L., *Supernature*, London: Coronet Books (Hodder & Stoughton), 1974.

Weber, R., 'Field Consciousness and Field Ethics', in K. Wilber (ed.), *The Holographic Paradigm and Other Paradoxes*, Boulder: Shambhala, 1982.

Weber, R., 'The Good, the True, the Beautiful: Are they Attributes of the Universe?' *Main Currents in Modern Thought*, Vol. 32, November 1975.

Weber, R., 'The Physicist and the Mystic – Is a Dialogue between them Possible?' Interview with David Bohm, *ReVision Journal*, Spring 1981.

Weber, R., 'The Reluctant Tradition: Esoteric Philosophy East and West', *Main Currents in Modern Thought*, Vol. 31, March–April, 1975.

Weber, R., 'The Tao of Physics Revisited', A conversation with Fritjof Capra, *ReVision Journal*, Vol. 4, No. 1, Spring 1981.

Weber, R., 'What is Insight?' An interview with Krishnamurti, *Revision Journal*, Spring 1980; and in Jayakar, P. and Patwardhan, S. (eds), *Within the Mind*, Madras: Krishnamurti Foundation of India, 1982.

Wegner, D., *The Illusion of Conscious Will*, Cambridge, Massachusetts: MIT, 2002.

Weil, S., *Selected Essays 1934–1943*, Wipf and Stock, 2015.

Weizsäcker, Carl Friedrich von, *The Unity of Nature*, trans. F. J. Zucker, New York: Farrar, Strauss & Giroux, 1980.

West, A., *Serpent in the Sky: The High Wisdom of Ancient Egypt*, Wheaton, Illinois: Quest Books, 1993.

Westfall, R. S., 'Unpublished Boyle Papers Relating to Scientific Method', *Annals of Science*, Vol. 12, 1956.

Wheeler, J. A., 'Bits, Quanta, Meaning', in *Problems of Theoretical Physics*, ed. A. Giovannini, F. Mancini, and M. Marinaro, Italy: University of Salerno Press, 1984.

Wheeler, J. A., 'Quantum Cosmology', in *World Science*, ed. L. Z. Fang and R. Ruffini, Singapore: World Scientific, 1987.

Whiston, W., *The Works of Flavius Josephus: Antiquities of the Jews*, London: T. Nelson and Sons, 1883.

White, J., *A Practical Guide to Death and Dying*, Wheaton, Illinois: Quest Books, 1980. Intended as a guide-book.

Whitehead, A. N., *An Enquiry Concerning the Principles of Natural Knowledge*, Cambridge University Press, 1919.

Whitehead, A. N., *Modes of Thought*, New York: Macmillan, 1968.

Whitehead, A. N., *Process and Reality: An Essay in Cosmology*, New York: Free Press, 1978.

Whitehead, A. N., *Religion in the Making*, Cambridge University Press, 1926.

Whitehead, A. N., *Science and the Modern World*, Cambridge: Cambridge University Press, 1928.

Whitehead, A. N., *The Interpretation of Science, Selected Essays*, ed. A. H. Johnson, US, Indianapolis: Bobbs-Merrill, 1961.

Whiteman, J. M. H., *Old & New Evidence on The Meaning of Life: The Mystical World-view and Inner Contest*, Colin Smythe Ltd., 1986.

Wigner, E. P., 'Two Kinds of Realty', *The Monist*, 1964.

Wilber, K. (ed.), *The Holographic Paradigm and Other Paradoxes*, Boulder, Colorado: Shambala, 1982.

Wilber, K., *Eye to Eye: The Quest for the New Paradigm*, New York: Doubleday, 1983.

Wilber, K., *No Boundary: Eastern and Western Approaches to Personal Growth*, Boulder and London: Shambhala, 1981.

Wilford, Col. J., *Asiatic Researches*, 10 vols, London: Royal Asiatic Society, 1806.

Wilhelm, R. and Jung C., *The Secret of the Golden Flower: A Chinese Book of Life*, London: Routledge & Kegan Paul, 1975.

Wilkins, H. T., *Secret Cities of Old South America: Atlantis Unveiled*, London Rider, 1952.

Willis, A., 'Immortality Only 20 Years away Says Scientist', *Daily Telegraph*, 22 September 2009.

Wilsdon, J., Wynne, B., and Stilgoe, J., *The Public Value of Science: Or How to Ensure That Science Really Matters*, London: Demos, 2005.

Wiseman, R., *Paranormality: Why We See What Isn't There*, London: Macmillan, 2011.

Wiseman, R., Smith, M., and Milton, J., 'The "Psychic Pet" Phenomenon: A Reply to Rupert Sheldrake', *Journal of the Society for Psychical Research*, 2000.

Wolters, C. (trans. and introd.), *The Cloud of Unknowing and Other Works*, London: Penguin Books, 1978.

Woodroffe, Sir John [Arthur Avalon], *Shakti and Shâta*, London: Luzac & Co., 1918.

Woodroffe, Sir John [Arthur Avalon], *The Serpent Power: The Secrets of Tantric and Shaktic Yoga*, Dover Publications, 2000.

World Health Organization, *Acupuncture: Review and Analysis of Reports on Controlled Clinical Trials*, World Heath Organization, Geneva, 2003.

Yarker, J., *The Arcane Schools*, Belfast: W. Tait, 1909.

Yonge, C. D. (trans.), *The Works of Philo Complete and Unabridged*, Massachusetts: Hendrickson Publishers, 1993.

Young, E., 'Rewriting Darwin: The New Non-genetic Inheritance', *New Scientist*, 9 July 2008.

Young, J. Z., *Doubt and Certainty in Science*, Oxford, 1951.

Zaehner, R. C., *Mysticism, Sacred and Profane*, Oxford University Press, 1957.

Zaehner, R. C., *The Dawn and Twilight of Zoroastrianism*, London: Weidenfeld and Nicolson, 1961.

Zajonc, A., *Catching the Light: The Entwined History of Light and Mind*, New York: Bantam Books, 1993.

Zeiger, B. F. and Bischof, M., 'The Quantum Vacuum and its Significance in Biology', Germany, Neuss: Paper presented at The Third International Hombroich Symposium on Biophysics, August 20–24, 1998 (mimeograph).

Zohar, The, trans. H. Sperling and M. Simon, 5 vols, London: The Soncino Press, 1933.

Zukav, G., *The Dancing Wu Li Masters: An Overview of the New Physics*, New York: William Morrow and Company, 1979.

Zukav, G., *The Seat of the Soul*, New York: Simon & Schuster, 1989.

General Index

Protocol:

1. Page numbers are prefixed by the Volume number, for example: I.84, II.170, III.205. Volume and page numbers in italics indicate figures and tables.
2. Titles of works and articles are italicized.
3. In most cases a comma after the first word, or words in a main or sub-entry, indicate the term, or word, of the main entry. For example: Lanka, Battle of III.9—means, Battle of Lanka; traffic accident, road (post-mortem energy field of) II.83—means, post-mortem energy field of road traffic accident.
4. A word in a main entry followed by *q.v.* means that the word in question is an entry in its own right. For example: afterglow (spiritual experiences *q.v.*) III.200—means, 'spiritual experiences' is also an index entry in its own right.

1st–Macrocosm III.123, *III.124*
2nd–Microcosm III.123, *III.124*
3rd–Microcosm III.123, *III.124*

aṣṭāṅga III.190–1
aberrant neural pathways II.90
abode, spiritual III.184, III.248
as above, so below *see* Hermetic Axiom
Absolute I.184, I.238, I.294, II.20, III.118, III.119
  and Galileo Commission Report III.329
  and Newton III.142
  two facets of III.145
ABSOLUTE consciousness I.242
Absolute IS III.120
absolute knowledge III.119
Absolute Motion III.144
absolute motion II.208–9
absolute nature III.151, III.352–3, III.365
Absolute Negation III.145
Absoluteness I.263, II.175
abstract and scientific level II.8
abstract formula (Stanzas *q.v.*) III.74
abstraction III.72
abstract thought (significance of) III.1
abuse, of nature's secret powers III.296
The Abyss III.64
  see also Sephirothic Tree
academia III.59, III.273
Academy of the Worldly Sapience III.311
accident I.70, I.87, I.136, I.137, I.171
accidental changes I.56, I.57, I.58
acclaim, international II.123
accountability (human traits *q.v.*) II.88–90
'The Achieving of the Philosopher's Stone' II.59
A-consciousness I.171–2, I.323
acoustic software II.122
Across the Frontiers (Heisenberg) I.337
action-at-a-distance I.109, I.110, I.111, I.213
Action for Happiness (AfH) I.xlii
active characteristic II.5
active governing principle III.146
active organs III.201
active principle II.11, II.34, II.137
active spiritual agencies III.245
activity (system) II.7
actors II.106
  see also personality
the actual (Aristotle *q.v.*) III.220
  see also Aristotelian philosophy
actuality (Schiller, Friedrich von *q.v.*) III.60, III.226, III.372
acupuncture I.320
Adam and Eve I.269, III.38
Adam Kadmon/Qadmon I.265, III.61, III.155
Adepts II.52, II.166, III.125, III.130
adepts I.209, I.211, I.212–13, I.246, I.252, I.291–2, III.210, III.277
  alchemical II.58, II.59
  definition I.210

adepts (continued)
  and Devachan II.75
  highest III.186
  and Māyāvi-rūpa II.56–7
  Rosicrucian Brotherhood III.14–15
Ādi plane II.162
Advaita Vedānta I.271
advanced individuals III.165
advanced souls II.75
adventurers (when close to death) II.55
Aeneid III.47
Æther II.209–10, III.46, III.94, III.95
affective brain III.43
Affinity, Law of II.79
after-death communications (ADCs) II.63, II.94–6
after-death states II.24–5
afterglow (spiritual experiences *q.v.*) III.200
afterlife I.57, I.266, II.91–2, II.93
agami (karma *q.v.*) III.127
Agathon II.9, II.175, II.178, III.48
ageless wisdom III.91
agency III.162, III.173, III.342
agents I.243, I.342, II.89, III.159, III.163, III.178
Ahaṁkāra III.111, III.112, III.156
Ahriman I.267, I.268, II.174, III.13
Ahura-Mazda I.267, I.268, II.172, II.174
Ain III.61
Ain Soph III.61
Ain Soph Aur III.61
air II.210
Ākāśa I.153, II.28, II.52, III.39, III.82, III.94, III.95
ākāśa II.209–10
Akashic field I.153, II.197
Akashic Record/Chronicle I.71, I.153, III.209
Akem-Mainyu I.267–8
Ālaya III.96, III.97
Alayic III.96
alchemical adepts II.58, II.59
alchemical marriage III.14
alchemical metaphoric expressions II.59
Alchemists I.209
alchemy I.xxxix, I.140, I.262, III.14–15, III.25, III.90, III.205
  European I.280
  and Jung I.245
  and Newton I.231, II.3, II.125, III.312
alcohol III.197
Alcott, Dr William A. III.208
Alef Trust III.293
Alexander, Eben I.15, I.88, I.220, II.91, III.162, III.318, III.351
Alexander the Great I.269
algebra (triple constitution of man *q.v.* and septenary constitution of man *q.v.*, rationale for) II.18
Algeo, John I.283
Alger, William Rounsville I.287
algorithms II.130
Alice in Wonderland III.117
Alighieri, Dante I.218, I.219, II.25, II.63, II.65–6, II.70, III.16
Allah's Wisdom II.34
allegorical figures III.17
  see also divine principles
allegorical terms III.15
  see also alchemy; Philosopher's Stone
allegories I.180, I.190, I.282, III.1–2, III.51, III.55, III.106
  and the Bible I.189, III.4, III.38
  of cave III.253, III.377
  and Purgatory II.66
All-Knowingness I.xlvii
All-That-Is III.356
Allwood, Julian III.327
Altar of Burnt Incense III.252
  see also Tabernacle of Moses
Altar of Burnt Offerings III.252
  see also Tabernacle of Moses
altered states of consciousness I.66, I.87, I.93, I.145, I.217, I.308
alternative universes III.85–6
altruistic motives II.25
Altwegg, Kathrin I.107
Alvarado, Carlos I.85, I.118
Amaru Muru (South America, Mysteries *q.v.*) I.277
Amazon (treatment of employees) I.4
ambition, unsatisfied II.78
ambitious people III.294
Ameghino, Carlos III.233
Amen III.107
Amenti II.65
Americas (Mystery centre) II.3
American Geophysical Union III.222
American Heart Journal III.42
American Indians I.199, I.272–4
American Mysteries I.272–8
American televangelists I.290–1
Amesha Spentas II.53
Ammonius Saccas I.239

amoebae   I.135, I.136
Anacalypsis (Higgins)   I.284
Analogeticists   I.239
analogous principles   III.70
analogue   III.36, III.38, III.184, III.366
analogy   I.12, I.18, I.40, I.154, II.70, III.2, III.3,
      III.72–3, III.74, III.75, III.80
   anatomical   III.38
   and car   II.119
   computationalist master   II.120–5
   consciousness and its forms   I.145, I.154–5,
      III.147
   and correspondence   I.248
   death and rebirth   III.70
   definition   III.71
   and Fourth Principle   I.239
   and Hermetic Axiom   III.83
   and human principles   III.78
   with Iśvara   III.370
   law of   II.126
   and Newton   I.231, I.250
   with physical sight   III.249
   post-mortem   II.78–9
analytical approach   I.166–7, I.254, *I.255*, III.366
Ānanda   III.106
Ānandamaya-kośa   II.52, II.170
Anandatwa   III.111
anatomical analogy   III.38
anatomical maps   *II.21*, III.287
anatomical symbolism   III.33
anatomy   II.1, II.2, II.100
Anaxagoras   II.2, II.176–7
ancestors   III.247, III.325
ancestral germinal cell   III.247
Ancient (Ageless) Wisdom   I.xxxix, III.11, III.64,
      III.253
see also *philosophia perennis*
Ancient Freemasonry (Higgins)   I.188
Ancient Greek drama   I.191
ancient lore   III.183
ancient mysteries   I.262–82
ancient records   III.50, III.284
ancient religions   III.47
ancient sources   II.221
ancient wisdom   I.xxxviii–xxxix, III.39
   see also *philosophia perennis*
The Ancient Wisdom (Besant)   II.153
Andean mystical brotherhood   I.277
Anderson, Philip   I.116, I.317, I.319, I.320
Andes   I.276, I.276–7
Andrews, George   III.206

androids   II.140
   see also computationalists; robots
android software   II.141
Angra-Mainyush   I.267–8, II.172, II.174
anima   I.235
animal behaviour   III.223, III.243
animal cunning   II.89–90
animal desires, seat of   II.24
Animal kingdom   II.110
animal kingdom   III.245
animal life   II.184
animal nature   II.38, II.89, II.109, III.185
animals   II.108–10, II.172, II.178, II.196, II.216,
      II.231
   body   II.xvii
   and Dawkins   II.176
   love between   III.244
   and signs of the zodiac   III.24
   and Third Eye   III.183
animal sacrifice   III.18, III.19
Animal soul   II.17, II.19, II.38, II.45, II.79, *II.108*,
      II.175
   and Empedocles and Aristotle   II.177
   and Manas   II.176
   and Taimni System   II.162
   and transformer   II.202
   and Zohar   II.73
animal telepathy   I.79
animal world   II.184
Anima Mundi   II.28, III.97
anima mundi   II.209–10
animate life   II.184
animating principle   III.97
anna   II.170
Annals of Psychiatry and Clinical Neuroscience
      III.43
Annamaya-kośa   II.35, II.170
annihilation of consciousness   II.76
Anoia   I.324, I.326, II.39, II.170, II.175–6, III.12,
      III.109, III.112
anomalous monism   I.30
antaḥkaraṇa   II.48, II.80, II.86–90, II.172,
      II.215–17, III.6
Antahkaranic connection   II.90, II.97
antecedent probabilities   I.113–14
An Anthology (Whitehead)   I.333
The Anthropic Cosmological Principle (Barrow and
      Tipler)   I.339
anthropic principle   III.240–2
'The Anthropic Principle and the Structure of the
      Physical World' (Carr and Rees)   I.338

anthropocentric outlook III.235
anthropocentric phantasies III.99
anthropogenesis I.5, I.240, I.298, III.101
anthropoid primates III.236
anthropomorphism I.326
Anthropos III.129
Anthroposophical Society I.lxxx, II.148, II.219
Anthroposophists II.183
Anthroposophy I.42, I.122, II.182–5, II.219
antibiotics I.lviii–lix
antiquity
  of man III.216, III.229–35
  Mystery Schools of I.262–82
antiseptics in surgery II.131
aṇu III.107
Anu Gītā II.27
Anupādaka plane II.162
ape-like men III.236
apes I.137, II.108, II.110, III.236, III.324
apex (human constitution *q.v.*) II.43, II.204
apex (symbol of) III.4
Apis I.267
Apocalypse I.199
apophatic theology I.292–3, III.280
apostolic relics III.17–18
apparitions II.63, II.80–4, II.150
appearance III.83, III.106, III.108, III.119, III.290, III.291, III.350
  and Gandhi III.265
  manifested III.141
  of the mental world III.167
  and Mind III.369
  outward I.297, II.xviii, III.295
  and shadows III.142
Arabian alchemy III.25
Arabic language II.3, II.5
arbiter of truth (standpoint of scientific materialsm *q.v.*) II.133
Arcane School I.lxxx, II.148
arcane teachings I.160
archæology III.216, III.232–4
Archæus III.179
Archangel Michael II.53
Archangels II.53, III.72
archetypal forces III.5
Archetypal Man III.35, III.60–1, III.155, III.237
Archetypal plane III.26, III.96
archetypal sphere I.274
archetypal world/realm III.26, III.123
Archetype I.264
archetypes I.265, I.278, III.235
Archimedes III.364
Archimedes' principle II.71
Architect III.89
see also Chaldean Kabala
'Are Superluminal Connections Necessary?' (Stapp) I.338
argumentation, computers II.117–20
Arhat Esoteric School II.168
Ariadne III.6, III.16
Ariadne's thread III.72
Aristotelian method I.229, I.235
Aristotelian philosophy I.196
Aristotle I.203, I.222, I.251–2, I.270, II.177, III.72, III.220
  doctrines I.143
  Four Causes I.40
  Metaphysics I.202
  on purpose I.xix
arms (scientific innovation) III.267
army II.247
  see also karma; skandhas; elementals
arousal, premature, of latent powers *q.v.* III.193
arrhythmia III.41
arrogance II.221
  see also humility
arsenic I.240, I.241, I.356
art I.280, II.135, III.15, III.327
artificial insemination III.336
artificial intelligence (AI) II.113, II.116, II.139, III.337–8
artists II.100, III.46, III.119–20
Aryan Root Race I.286
Aryans I.292
ascending frequencies I.148
ascending stages III.223
ascent (consciousness *q.v.* and spirituality *q.v.*) II.217, III.122, III.192
ascetic life III.208
Ashmole, Elias I.190
Aspect, Alain I.111, I.339
Aspects III.174
aspects
  of consciousness II.17
  Cosmic Elements III.168
  emanational descent III.155
  of human principles III.121
  ONE REALITY III.172
  of reality III.330
aspirants II.203, III.198
aspiration III.38, III.242, III.248
The Association for Skeptical Investigation I.50

assumptions III.51, III.276, III.282, III.318, III.353
unsupported I.321, III.137, III.306, III.307
Assyrian bull-man III.49
Aston, Francis I.98
The Astonishing Hypothesis: The scientific search for the soul (Crick) I.8, I.352
the Astral II.39, II.42
Astral body II.18, II.27–8, II.47, II.54, II.165, III.125
  and Blavatsky II.149
  and post-classical Theosophy II.153
  and Steiner II.184
and Sūtras III.112, III.113, III.114
astral counterparts III.127, III.197–8
astral duplicate II.81
Astral Form II.52
astral life II.64
Astral Light II.28, III.94–5, III.97
astral light III.209–10
Astral-Mental II.41–2
Astral-Physical II.42
Astral plane III.94, III.96, III.199
astral planes I.175
astral projection I.89
astral shadow II.178
astral soul III.36
astral substance III.94
astrobiology I.106–7, III.23
astrological correspondences II.178
astrological Zodiac III.24
astrology I.265, II.175, III.22, III.25, III.29, III.256
astronauts II.88
astronomers III.7, III.92
Astronomia Magna or the Whole Sagacious Philosophy of the Macrocosm and Microcosm (Paracelsus) I.250
astronomy III.22, III.23
Aswatha Tree III.64–5, *III.65*
atheism II.xv, II.224
atheists III.245, III.271
ATHMAN = BRAHMAN (Schrödinger *q.v.*) II.198
Atkins, Peter I.55, I.91, II.74, II.94, III.269
Atlantean Root Race I.286, III.183
Atlanteans I.199
Atlantis I.108
Atlas II.139, *II.139*
Ātma II.9, II.23, II.30, II.38, III.161, III.164–5, III.315
  and Agathon II.175
  and Ānandamaya-kośa II.52
  and Auric Envelope III.97
  and Buddhi II.22, II.41, II.227
  and classical Theosophical literature II.151
  king (chess) III.13
  and lamp III.11–12
  meaning II.20, II.39
  and Saptaparṇa III.56, III.58
  and Sephirothic Tree III.63
  and Supreme Deity III.48
  and Tāraka Rāja-Yoga II.170
  and temple (simile) II.200
  and three Egos II.46
  and Wisdom III.59
Ātma-Buddhi II.73, II.176
Ātma-Buddhi-Manas II.105, III.13
Ātman II.9, II.20, III.6, III.125
Atmic radiance II.154
Atmic vehicle II.162
atmosphere
  Auschwitz and Birkenau II.85
  of debauched places II.81
atmospheric haze III.253, III.254
Atmu II.9
Atom III.107, III.109, III.111, III.112, III.113
atomic theory I.270
atoms I.95, I.98, III.2, III.107, III.131, III.161, III.177
attention III.xvii, III.xix, III.106, III.110
Attraction towards SPIRIT *q.v.* (Puranic philosophy) III.112
  see also III.103
attractors I.72, I.346
attributes II.38, III.36, III.113, III.370
attunement I.234, II.106
Atzīlūth III.63
Augoeides II.53, II.59
Aum III.107
Aun Weor, Samael II.164–5
aura electricities III.112–13, III.114
aural perception III.135
auras II.81, II.154, III.203
the Auric III.96
Auric Body III.125
Auric Egg II.51–2, II.151, III.96
Auric Envelope II.47, II.51, III.97, III.247
auric field II.165
Aurobindo, Śrī I.99, I.217, I.346, I.348, II.186, *II.187*
Auschwitz II.55, II.85
  see also Avītchi

Australian Aboriginal tribes II.87
australopithecines I.57, III.236
Austria II.183
authenticated cases of sensed presence *q.v.* II.57
see also Māyāvi-rūpa
authoritarians (class of human beings *q.v.*) III.334
authority I.322, II.189, II.218–25, II.219, III.302, III.318
Autobiography of a Yogi (Yogananda) II.202, III.102
autogenic development I.5
autopoiesis I.58
Autopoiesis and Cognition (Maturana and Varela) I.351
Avalokiteshvara II.2
Avatars I.270, I.271–2
Ave Maria (Schubert) II.118
Avidyā III.109
avidyā II.203, III.49
Avītchi II.78, II.84–6
see also Eighth Sphere
awakening of latent faculties and latent powers *q.v.* II.164, III.190, III.256
awareness, clouding III.xviii
axiom of completeness III.358, III.362
ayahuasca I.262, III.198
Ayer, Sir Alfred Jules III.309
see also logical positivism; Vienna School
Aztec people I.273, I.276, III.18

baby (and umbilical life-support) II.88
Bacchic Rites I.263
Bacchus I.263
Bach, Johann Sebastian I.218, II.130
Bach-y-Rita, Paul I.161
Bacon, Francis I.219, II.63, III.60, III.216, III.302, III.303
Bacon, Roger III.72
bad archaology III.232
Bad Pharma (Goldacre) I.49
bad science II.221, III.338
bad Theosophy II.221
Bailey, Alice I.lxxx, II.148, II.162, II.166
Bain, Alexander II.231, III.56, III.244
balanced outlook (need of in philosophers *q.v.*) II.30
Baldwin effect I.52
Barborka, Geoffrey II.220
The Bardo Thödol I.89
Barenboim, Daniel II.165
barrenness (materialistic theories on mind *q.v.* and consciousness *q.v.*) II.127
Barrett, Sir William III.316
Barrow, John I.339, III.241
baryonic matter II.xvii
base II.36
see also upādhis
Basic and Clinical Neurocardiology III.41
basic substance III.80, III.147
Basios, Vasileios III.269
Bateson, William I.347
Bat House I.275
bats (symbol of) I.200
Battle of Lanka III.9
see also Rāma; Sīta
BBC Young Musician of the Year competition I.9
B-consciousness I.171–2, I.323
beasts (Biblical symbol) III.108, III.109
Beatrice III.16
Beauty I.300
beauty III.187
BECOMING (evolution *q.v.*) III.117
becoming III.221, III.289
bees (simile) III.137
Beethoven, Ludwig van I.218, II.100, II.121, II.219, III.5, III.15–16, III.52, III.257
Choral Symphony II.120, II.122
Elegischer Gesang II.99
Eroica Symphony, smashing compact disc recording of (analogy) I.17
on the mind III.261
Ninth Symphony II.230–1
behaviour (brain states *q.v.*) II.119
behavioural sciences I.83
behaviourism I.29
Behe, Michael I.353
Being I.202, II.20, II.162, III.82, III.152, III.288
being II.129, II.136, III.221, III.289, III.320
Being & Biology: Is consciousness the life force? (Dunne and Jahn) I.356
From Being to Becoming (Prigogine) I.351
Being You: A new science of consciousness (Seth) I.357
Being You: The inside story of your inner universe (Seth) III.315
Beiträge zur Descendenzlehre (Weismann) I.347, III.247
Bekenstein, Jacob I.341
beliefs I.67–8, II.7, II.221, II.223, III.279, III.280, III.281

mistaken II.110
power of III.352
and pseudoscience III.30
belief systems II.209, III.308
Bell, Alissa I.342
Bell, John I.110–11, I.336
Bell's inequality I.111
Bembine Table of Isis III.22, III.24–8, *III.25*
Bembo, Cardinal III.25
benchmark (for comparison of diverse systems) II.221
Benveniste, Jacques I.49
Bergson, Henri I.172
Berkeley, Bishop III.351
Berkeley, George I.34
Bernoulli, Daniel III.278
Berry, Adrian I.85
Besant, Annie I.lxxxi, I.lxxxiii, I.16, I.256, II.7, II.148, II.151, II.153–6, II.220, III.78, III.81
  comparing the mind to a mirror III.148
  and Inner Group, Esoteric Section III.121
  Occult Chemistry I.98
  and the poor II.165
  Second International President, Theosophical Society II.219
  A Study in Consciousness III.163
  on thoughts I.165
Besant System II.153–6, *II.157*
Besso, Michael I.133
betrayal II.123
'Beyond Darwin's Paradigm' (Wyller) I.355
Beyond Natural Selection (Wesson) I.352
'Beyond the Laboratory' (Rees) III.276
Bezos, Jeff III.321
Bhagavad Gītā I.270, I.287, I.296, II.225
bhaktī III.227
bhūtas III.145–6, III.160–1
bias I.84, I.85, I.86, III.xxi
Bible I.175, III.4, III.17, III.38, III.121, III.239
  Days of Creation III.74
  New Testament III.104–20
  and Newton III.284–5
'biblical' status II.131
Big Bang II.228, III.85, III.92, III.262, III.310
big calculator (computers *q.v.*) II.140
bigotry (Anderson on) I.317
'billiard ball' notion (classical physics *q.v.*) II.126
'billions of watts' (Kriya *q.v.* Yoga) II.202, II.203
Bīnāh III.63
biochemical activity II.118
bioelectric fields I.102
Biological Anomalies (Corliss) III.228
biological computer II.112
biological inheritance I.78
biological locus of memory I.76
biological machines I.lxii, III.xvii, III.235
biology I.345–57, II.xvi, II.132, III.37, III.317
  blended with meta-biology III.248
  Cartesian reductionist approach II.xvii
  developmental I.70, I.73, I.149
  and epigenetics I.105
  and the establishment I.220
  and evolution I.52, II.109, III.246
  holistic III.278
  human III.336
  and junk DNA I.106
  and living cell I.81
  modern developmental III.177
  molecular I.8, I.75, I.135, III.309
  and phenomenon of life III.237
  and reductionism I.69
  and vitalism III.176
The Biology of Belief (Lipton) I.355
Biology Revisioned (Harman and Sahtouris) I.354
Biology Today: An issues approach (Minkoff and Baker) I.355
bionic implants III.337
bionts III.222
Biophotonics and Coherent Structures (Bischof) I.354
biophysics III.42
biosphere III.222–3
Biot, Jean Baptiste III.206
birds (symbol of) I.200
bird, mystical I.200, III.84
  see also Kalahaṃsā
Birkenau II.85
  see also Avītchi
birth II.64, II.89, III.7, III.83, III.185, III.187
birth-instinct II.97
birth marks I.101
birthright, man's wisdom *q.v.* and knowledge *q.v.* II.174
Bischof, Marco I.354
bishops (chess *q.v.*) III.13
black arts III.272–3
  see also black magic
black-body problem I.332
The Black Cloud (Hoyle) I.107
black holes III.207
black king (chess *q.v.*) III.13, III.14

black magic I.199, I.200–1, I.202, I.275, I.282, III.45, III.210
see also Left-Hand Path
Blake, William III.xix–xx
Blaker, George I.lxxxiv
Blavatsky, H. P. I.93, I.153, I.166, I.300, II.220, III.56, III.209–10
on Absolute Motion III.144–5
and Adepts II.166
on adepts I.246
on Anaxagoras II.176
on Antaḥkaraṇa II.86
on Astral body II.149
on astrological Zodiac III.24
on the Augoeides II.53
on Auric Egg II.52
and Bailey II.162
on blending of science and metaphysics I.235
on the brain III.39–40
on Buddhi II.22
on Buddhi-Manas II.41
and consilience I.320
'A Dialogue Between the Two Editors' II.150–1
on difference between animals and men II.108
on drugs III.197
emissary of Adepts III.130
on eternal truth II.191
on evil I.268
on evolution I.242, III.244
and First Fundamental Proposition III.105
formed Esoteric Section III.121
on foundation and apex (human constitution) II.43
and four-part rule (applying the Hermetic Wisdom) I.248
on 'Gods' (reference to Newton) II.77
on good and evil II.202–3
on great Illusion III.117
and Guénon I.208
on hell II.84
on Higher Self II.227
on Individuality and personality II.200–1
Inner Group Teachings of H. P. Blavatsky I.209
Isis Unveiled I.liii, II.107
and Jñāna Yoga I.165
on Kāma II.26
on law of Analogy III.70
on learning the formula (applying Hermetic Wisdom) III.73
on life-principles III.55–6
on Liṅga-Śarīra II.28, II.29
and macrocosm II.205
on magic I.281–2
and Mahātmās I.212
on Manas II.23
on materialism III.304
on material–spiritual divide I.174
on Māyāvi-rūpa II.54
on metaphysics II.4, III.262
and method of consilience I.232
'The Mysteries of the Hebdomad' III.66
on Mystery Schools I.217
and Mystery Teachings I.179, I.284–5
need to look beyond physical matter II.136
on nervous ether III.178
on number 7 III.67
on onion skins II.10
on permanent Individuality II.105–6
on *philosophia perennis* III.284
on Plato I.264
on Prāṇa II.27
Psychic and Noetic Action II.59–60, II.198
The Secret Doctrine I.xlvii, I.15, I.283, II.166, III.30
and septenary constitution III.77
on septenary law III.99
and slander I.219
and solitude III.210
on soulless beings II.89
on Stanzas III.74
on symbolism III.19
on the Theosophical Society I.lxxxii, I.lxxxiii
on thread doctrine I.236
on the universe III.81, III.82
on upādhi II.37
on Upper Triad II.20
on vehicles of expression III.296–7
vociferous attacks on II.134
The Voice of the Silence I.222, III.xxi–xxii
on water (molecules) I.175
writing to Besant II.155–6
Blavatskyites II.155
blending, Buddhi-Manas II.23
blind belief I.67, I.192, I.220
blind faith (Christian orthodoxy) II.80
blindness II.120–1, III.186, III.188–9
blind programmer II.117, II.118
blinds I.205–6, I.209
bliss II.70, II.76, II.102
blood II.42, III.43, III.177, III.178, III.317–18

blueprint I.52, I.106, I.244, I.265
blurring of categories II.127
  see also category errors; Walshe
Boar III.303–4
Boar Avatar III.303
Boar's Head III.303
Bodhi Tree III.64–5, *III.65*
Bodily Activities (Jinarâjadâsa System *q.v.*) II.160
bodily dress (simile) II.102
  see also Yogananda
Body II.17, II.164
body I.3, I.266, II.xviii, *II.108*, II.135, III.46–7, III.125
  animal II.xvii
  collective and generalized term II.11
  and Divine Forces III.127
  dwelling place of man's divine nature III.252
  and earth I.278
  earthly III.130
  electro-chemical interactions III.136
  emotional and the mental II.153
  energetic III.113
  of ethereal substance III.183
  and evolution III.245
  feels real enough but unreal thing II.29–30
  headless III.262
  immortal III.247, III.338
  left and right side III.44–5
  of man III.37
  and mind I.39
  mortal I.324
  natural and spiritual II.32
  new, karmically conditioned psycho-physical II.80
  parent (as host) III.223
  and planes III.94
  and Plato I.324
  and Plutarch II.177
  and Principles of Man II.19
  role and function in man I.326–7
  and Saint Paul (teaching) II.178
  of Sattva Buddhi III.113
  and Self III.110
  and soul III.361
  spiritual III.316
  and Steiner II.183
  terminology of II.1
  thoughts and emotions can affect III.192
  see also human body; out-of-body experience (OBE); physical body; Physical body; subtle bodies
body language II.129
body-mind-spiritual traditions I.140
body of consciousness II.183
Body of desire II.52
body of evidence on psychic communication *q.v.* II.94
  see also Crookall
Body of Experience III.357–8
body of mind III.113
Bohm, David I.110, I.323, I.337–8, I.339, I.351, III.281, III.295
  and hidden variables theory I.80
  and implicate order I.251
Böhme, Jakob I.209
Bohr, Niels I.98, I.109, I.111, I.320, III.309
bola III.233, *III.233*
bondage II.97, II.99
Bondi, Hermann I.335
'A book for burning?' II.131–2
book knowledge II.171
Book of Life II.71
Book of Revelation I.199
'Book of the Apocalypse' III.303
Book of the Dead I.175, III.59
Book of the Keys II.73
'The Book of the Mat' I.274
Book of Thoth III.25
book-worship II.219
Born, Max I.334, III.283
borrowed light III.254
  see also heart; intellect
Bortoft, Henri I.42
Bose, Sir Jagadis Chandra III.201
Boston Dynamics II.139
Boström, Niklas II.116
Botticelli, Sandro II.66, II.71, II.86
bottled-up waves I.37
bottom-up approach I.16, I.32, I.54, I.55, I.105, I.345
  Aristotlean I.229
  and scientific paradigm I.331
bottom-up process III.146
boundaries II.43–7, III.289
Bourbourg, Abbé Charles-Étienne Brasseur de I.279
Bowen, Commander Robert III.78
Bowen Notes III.70–1
Boycott, Brian I.76
Boyle, Robert I.51, II.210
Brahmā II.228, III.147, III.173, III.174
Brahmā Caitanya III.156

Brahmacarya III.185
Brahman II.9, II.20, II.228, III.147, III.370
Brahmanical eschatology II.80
Brahmanical Schools I.213
Brahmanism III.38, III.227
Brahmā-Vidyā I.183
Brahmins I.216, I.270, I.272
brain III.xvii, III.33, III.34, III.44, III.179, III.195
  acts as a whole I.164
  and Æther III.46
  affective III.43
  atypical states III.196
  base III.182
  and Blavatsky III.39–40
  cavities III.39–40
  centre of III.182
  clinical death of I.15
  and computationalists II.138
  and computers I.328, II.59, II.112–13, III.272
  and consciousness I.139, I.145–7, III.xviii, III.109, III.357–65
  and creativity I.170, I.172
  dark energy of III.115
  divided II.122–5
  Einstein's *I.135*
  and electromagnetic waves III.377
  evolution of II.129
  and eyes III.201
  and filter model II.137
  function *III.45*
  and fungi III.223
  and ghost III.351
    see also neuroscience; Alexander, Eben
  hallucinates conscious reality III.315
  and Higher Self II.199
  infection I.15
  instrumentality of III.153
  and intelligence I.132, I.134–6
  is the front-door II.60
  left- and right-brain thinking I.165
  and left eye III.79
  left temporo-parietal junction II.55
  link between the superior and inferior worlds III.38
  and Marsh and Al-Khalili I.17
  mechanisms III.112
  and meditation I.163, III.203
  and memory I.70–1, I.76–7, III.95
  and mental health III.275
  mental perceptions of II.60
  and mind I.xlvi, I.11, I.16, I.18, I.32, I.55, I.149, I.154, II.197, III.36
  and the Mysteries I.179
  and near-death experiences I.87–8
  neurological mechanisms III.279
  and neurology III.311
  and neuron assemblies II.xvi
  and neuroscience III.162, III.306–7
  and Novella and Shermer I.12
  objectively measurable III.136
  once thought static is now regarded as 'plastic' I.105
  and pineal gland and pituitary body III.182
  processes II.186
  and psychedelic drugs III.196
  quality III.256
  in the realm of physical matter III.146
  refracts the light of consciousness III.165
  rhythms III.71
  scans III.314
  and secret doctrine III.46
  and sensation III.135–6, III.137
  signals III.267
  and Sperry I.83
  and spinal column II.181
  and stroke victims II.128
  structure can be dissected II.115
  thought producer I.10
  threshold III.165, III.255
  transceiver/transducer I.78
  two hemispheres of II.23
  and upādhi II.37
  and Vogt I.9, I.38
The Brain II.xvi
brain cells I.70
brain damage II.119
brain-equals-computer II.112
Brain–Heart Interactions III.41
brain intellect II.177
brain in the gut III.41
brain-light III.256
brain-minds, gross II.77
brain movements II.199
brain-only consciousness I.145–7
brain pathways I.163
brain plasticity I.77, I.160–3, II.128–9
'Brain Reactions' III.162
brain research II.199
brain states II.117, II.119–20
The Brain That Changes Itself (Doidge) I.161

The Brain: The story of you (Eagleman) III.305–6
brain waves II.45
Brasseur de Bourbourg, Abbé Charles-Étienne I.279
Braun, Werner von I.133
breakouts II.85
  see also consciousness; Avītchi; *Harry Potter and the Prisoner of Azkaban*
breath II.178
breathing out II.228
breathing practices I.262
Brennan, Barbara Ann II.165
Brewster, Sir David III.279
bridge II.48, II.63, II.86, II.87, II.90, II.172, II.216
bridge of mind II.23
bridle (animal behaviour *q.v.*) II.109
A Brief History of Time (Hawking) III.109
Briggs, Robert I.349
Bright Air, Brilliant Fire: On the matter of the mind (Edelman) I.8, I.352
bright light III.165, III.253
brih II.228
British Radionics Association II.166
Broad, Charlie Dunbar I.113–14
Broglie, Louis de I.45, I.96–7, I.333
broken heart (dying of) III.42
brotherhood, universal II.153
Brotherhood of the Seven Rays I.277, I.280
Brothers of the Shadow III.333, III.334
Brown, Rosemary II.74
Browning, Robert I.3, II.xv
Bruno, Giordano I.218–19
Brunton, Paul I.lxxxi, I.17, I.99, I.218, I.260, II.220, III.33, III.257
  on animal and man opposing each other on spine III.182, III.185
  on the body II.29, II.30
  on cunning III.294
  on death III.341
  on divinity III.252
  on drugs III.194
  and instrument and user II.138
    see also Leggett; Walshe
  on karmic debts I.295
  in King's Chamber I.309, III.50, III.129
  on knowledge and principles III.296
  on Kuṇḍalinī I.262
  on materialism III.307–8
  on meditation III.204, III.253
  on the mind II.1, II.136–7
  and *philosophia perennis* II.219
  and Ramana Maharshi III.118
  on science and superstition III.30, III.318–19
  on scientific and occult methods I.233
  on sectarianism II.190
  The Spiritual Crisis of Man III.275
  on truth II.14, II.146, III.257
Buddha I.190, I.272, II.90, II.167, III.18, III.110
Buddhas II.167
Buddhi II.43, II.46, II.52, II.170, III.111
  and Ālaya III.97
  and Alayic III.96
  with Ātma II.227
  and Auric Body III.125
  and classical Theosophical literature II.149
  and Higher Manas II.68
  meaning II.22, II.167
  queen (chess) III.13
  and Saptaparṇa III.58
  and Upper Triad II.23
Buddhic Body II.154
Buddhi-Manas II.23, II.41, *II.42*, III.112
Buddhism II.167, III.17, III.102, III.356
Buddhist Sūtras I.192
Budge, Sir Ernest Alfred Wallis III.190
budh II.167
Budha II.167
builded up constitution *II.11*
building blocks II.16
bull I.267, III.18
Bulwer-Lytton, Edward III.198
Burbidge, Geoffrey I.340
Burnett, Dean III.275
Burnier, Dr Radha II.7
Burr, Harold Saxton I.82
Burtt, Edwin Arthur I.xviii, I.46, I.51
Butterfly III.304
butterfly (symbol of) II.68, III.304
butterfly effect I.lx

Cagliostro, Comte di I.218
Cahill, Reginald T. II.208–9
cākras I.148, II.165, II.166, III.190, III.191–3, *III.193*
calculus (scientific breakthrough) I.79, III.149
California Institute of Technology (Caltech) III.267
calm dignity (response to scientific attacks) II.134
caloric III.180
Camazotz I.275

Cameron, David I.4
cAMP (cyclic adenosine monophosphate) I.135
Camus, Albert III.xx
canalized development I.72
Canavero, Sergio III.339
canons of scientism I.121
  see also scientism
capacity (human mind *q.v.* versus computers *q.v.*) II.129
capital punishment (psychic implications of) II.81
  see also Kāma-rūpa
Capra, Fritjof I.353, II.125
carbon I.241
Cardeña, Etzel I.86, I.141, I.142
cardiology III.41, III.43
Carell, Alexis I.348
Carnatic tradition III.80
Carr, Bernard I.102, I.338, I.342, III.4, III.85, III.241, III.353
Carrel, Alexis III.177
carrier II.29, II.37
  see also Physical body; vāhana
Carrington, Hereward I.90
'car soul' II.119
Carter, Brandon I.336, III.241
Cartesian coordinates III.363
Cartesian reductionist approach I.51, I.53, I.229, II.xvii
Case, Paul Foster I.280, I.281
Cases of the Reincarnation Type (Stevenson) I.101
Cassini, Giovanni Domenico III.23
Castillejo, David I.303, I.305–6
'The Casting of the Molten Sea' II.59
castles (chess *q.v.*) III.13
cataclysms I.277
catalyst III.162–3
cataphatic approach I.293
categorical thinking II.123–4
categories
  blurring of II.127
  memory I.163–4
category errors II.3, II.8, III.340
Cathars I.209, III.313
Catholic Church I.209, I.269, I.273
Causal Body II.41, II.51, II.54, II.165, III.112, III.113, III.174–5
  and Besant System II.154
  and classical Theosophical literature II.150
  meaning II.47, II.52–3
  and post-classical Theosophy II.153
causal closure I.24, I.26–7, I.32, I.46, I.49, I.50, I.137
causality I.40, I.44, I.45, I.109, I.110, II.166
causal realms III.84–5
causation I.47, I.326, III.71, III.306
  and correlation I.173
  formative I.73, I.74, I.345, I.351
causative field II.28
Causeless Cause I.237
causes I.137, I.303, II.67, III.36, III.71, III.136, III.250
  chain of II.79
  One unchanging I.306
  and planes II.78
  primary III.77
  and realm of the invisible I.304
  and upādhi II.36
Cazzamali, Ferdinando III.377
Ceaseless Motion III.144
celebrity scientists I.77, III.313
celestial 'double' II.53
celestial spheres III.22, III.23
cells II.60, III.42, III.47, III.247, III.289
cellular memory III.41, III.375
cement II.200, II.201
  see also glue
Central America
  conquest of I.273
  Mysteries I.274–5, I.278–9, I.280
central source of esoteric learning II.188
  see also Sūtrātman; *philosophia perennis*
Central Spiritual Sun III.253
centre of gravity (Fourth Way teaching *q.v.*) II.181
  see also Ouspensky; Gurdjieff
centres
  of consciousness II.181, III.38–9, III.86, III.164, III.172, III.224
  of operation II.2
  three II.178, *II.180*, II.181
centrifugal forces in nature *q.v.* II.174
  see also Angra-Mainyush
centripetal forces in nature *q.v.* II.174
  see also Spento-Mainyush
cerebral baggage III.191
cerebral cortex III.162, III.307
cerebral mechanisms II.45, II.59–60, III.136
ceremony I.191, I.192, I.193
CERN I.54, III.310
Chadwick, Sir James I.98

chain of causes II.79
Chain of Globes III.93
Chaitin, Gregory III.352
Chaldean astrology III.25
Chaldean Kabala III.89, *III.90*, III.91
Chaldeans III.64–5
Chaldean universe III.26
challenge, reigning orthodoxy II.134
Chalmers, David I.xviii, I.28, I.29, I.146, I.352, III.40
chance I.40, I.47, I.54, I.55, I.66, I.70, III.239, III.240
  and creativity and genius I.11
  and gene mutation I.9, I.72
  and natural selection I.58
  and scientific materialism I.136
  and the universe I.54
Chandogya Upaniṣad III.147
Chaney, Earlyne I.277
change III.117, III.142, III.149, III.220
  brain states II.119
  guided pathway of I.71
  of phase II.64
Chaos I.271
Chaos-Theos-Kosmos III.65
character/characteristics II.112, II.118, III.98, III.201
  distinguishing III.200
  essential III.218
  inheritance of acquired I.75
  transmission of III.247
Chardin, Pierre Teilhard de I.52, I.346, I.350, III.43
Charles, Prince of Wales III.273
charm (warning against) II.89
  see also animal cunning; soulless beings; soul-eclipse
Chartres Cathedral III.7
chastity III.185
Le Chatelier's principle III.90–1
chelas I.270–1
chemical III.289
  see also ELEMENT; CONSCIOUSNESS
'The Chemical Basis of Morphogenesis' (Turing) I.349
chemical catalyst III.162–3
The Chemical Marriage III.14
The Chemical Wedding III.14
chemistry III.176, III.177, III.180, III.237, III.269
Cherokee Indians II.26
chess (symbol of) III.13–14
chi II.27, III.176, III.180
Chidākāśa III.141
chief vehicles and centres of operation (consciousness *q.v.*) II.2
child II.79–80, II.88, II.90
childhood experiences II.90
children of flesh III.185
Children Who Remember Previous Lives (Stevenson) I.102
CHiram Abiff III.14, III.190
Chiron III.49
Chit III.106, III.144
Chitta III.111, III.113
CHKDSK II.129
choice I.269, I.271, I.296, I.340, II.34, II.48, III.352
  and responsibility III.12
  of words II.35
Chopin, Frédéric II.55, II.71, II.100, II.101, III.149
Choral Symphony (Beethoven) II.120, II.122
chorus II.120, II.230
chreodes I.71, I.72, I.346
Christ I.217, I.304, II.69, II.70, II.90, III.xix, III.202–3
  crucifixion I.218
  and Nous I.326
Christian Gospels I.192
Christianity I.208, I.217, I.245, II.172, III.4
  and Archangels II.53
  and blinds I.209
  and the Devil III.323
  dogma about creation III.242
  esoteric dimension of III.36
  mystic II.164
  vicarious atonement, doctrine of II.80
Christian Mysteries I.264
Christian Science I.lxxx, I.288
Christos I.270, II.2, II.79
The Chronology of Ancient Kingdoms Amended (Newton) I.205–6
chrysalis II.68
Chuang-tzu III.116–17
the Church I.326
Churchianity III.130
Churchland, Patricia I.30
Churchland, Paul I.30
'Church of Scientism' I.119–21
The Chymical Wedding of Christian Rosenkreutz I.206

cinema pictures III.118
see also MAHĀMĀYĀ; Māyā; māyā
circadian rhythm III.182
circles, seven concentric (planes of Kosmos *q.v.*) III.87
circuits (historical labyrinth *q.v.*) III.7–8
circular argument III.241–2, III.288
circumference (symbol of) III.4
city (different views of) III.249
civilization II.205, III.37, III.243
'civilized' man III.18
clairvoyance I.86, II.154, II.156
clarity, inner III.363
classes, of human beings III.334
Classical Islam II.58
classical physics I.22, I.95, I.96, I.109, I.133, I.318
classical Theosophical literature II.148–51
classical Theosophy II.146, *II.152*, II.189, II.220
classification II.14, II.151, II.154, II.155, II.162
  septenary constitution of man II.149, II.196
classroom of life II.75
Clauser, John I.111
Cleather, Alice Leighton III.121
climate crisis III.327
clinical medicine III.41–3
cloak (simile for surface meaning) III.284
  see also the exoteric, definition of
clock time II.75
clockwork universe I.xlv
closed mind II.221
closedness of the physical I.39
closed system of thought III.118
'closeness' (to source) III.83
closing of the eyes/mouth I.207
The Closing of the Scientific Mind (Gelernter) II.113
clothing II.32, II.102
clouds III.253
coded instructions II.115, II.129
code of conduct III.121
coexistence III.236
coffin III.13
cognition II.45
cognitive bias I.84
cognitive habits I.163
cognitive processes III.42, III.160
cognitive science II.199, III.135–6, III.337
cognitivism II.113
Cognizance, Subject of I.48
Coleridge, Sir Paul III.274
The Collected Writings (Blavatsky) I.236
'The Collection of Written Leaves' I.274
collective memory I.78, I.352
collective psyche II.126
collective term II.10, II.11
collective unconscious theory I.71
Collins, Mabel II.150–1
Collins, Philip II.140
colour I.35, II.118–19, II.120, III.39–40, III.86
  and human principles III.77–9, *III.79*
  and neural correlate III.135
coloured rays (simile) II.189
combat II.139
  see also robots; dehumanization
combination (human constitution *q.v.*) II.106
  see also Higher Triad; Lower Quaternary
Comet 67P I.107
COMING (evolution *q.v.*) III.117
common high purpose III.149
common humanity II.90
common meaning III.286
common origin III.108, III.285
common purpose III.153
common sense I.46–7, I.112, I.170, II.141, III.243
common source III.286
common thread I.302, II.181, II.204
communication III.274
  and Antaḥkaraṇa II.88
  between Personal ego and Higher Ego II.89
communion III.178, III.274
commutation of forces II.231
companion globes III.93, *III.93*
comparative approach/study II.3–4, II.7, II.218
comparison with occult teaching on human constitution *q.v.* II.186
  see also Wilber; Aurobindo; modern psychology
competence, without comprehension III.337–8
complementary medicine II.164
complementary principles II.74
complex bodies III.xvii, III.242
complex interactions of inorganic components III.291
complexity III.163, III.164, III.166
complexity theory I.149, I.355
complex unit circle III.357–8, *III.357*
complex vehicles III.221, III.291
components
  computer II.129, II.130
  three II.12
composite entity II.105, II.106, III.92–3

composition of man II.1, II.2–14, II.34, II.155, II.205, III.287
compound III.110, III.162
compound nature III.66, III.284
comprehension, and competence III.337–8
computational fluid dynamics III.365
computationalism II.113
computationalist argumentation II.112
computationalist master analogy II.120–5
computationalists II.129, II.138
computer-brain interface III.272
computers II.112, II.118, II.124, II.128–30, II.138–41
complexity of III.166
definitions II.113–14
idea that 'brain equals computer' is highly misleading II.59
conative functions of consciousness III.160
concave lens II.189
concepts I.1, I.67, I.164, II.7, II.222, II.223, III.xx, III.242, III.280, III.282
about God III.51
and the brain III.343
and Brunton II.1
of physics III.350
conceptual map III.167
conceptual objects III.114
conceptual order I.317
concert pianist III.198–9
concordance between esoteric traditions I.245
concretion III.72
see also Hermetic Axiom; analogy
condemnation II.131
see also Sheldrake; Maddox; heretical views
condition, human II.100, II.135
conditioned state III.271
conditioned things III.110
conditioned universe III.172
cone (symbol of) III.4
Confessio Fraternitatis I.194, I.208, I.212, I.280
confirmation/confirmatory bias I.84
'Confirmation of the Existence of an Ancient Worldwide Wisdom Religion' (Walder and Bilimoria) III.355
conflict II.221
conflicting systems III.284
confusing terminology II.1–2, III.247
confusion III.9, III.287, III.293, III.309, III.338
conjectures by some Theosophists *q.v.* II.222
conjunction
of Manas and Buddhi III.189, III.202
two streams of consciousness III.161
connectedness of scientific knowledge I.318
connection II.63, II.89, II.123, III.xx
between Cosmos, Nature, and man III.255
between the eyes with the brain, mind, and soul-nature III.201
pineal gland and the genitalia III.185
conscience II.109
conscience-bestowing connection II.89
conscious and sapient life III.240, III.241
conscious awareness II.203, III.305–6
Conscious being III.237
conscious causation I.40
conscious experience III.115
conscious human cell III.248
conscious mind III.136
Consciousness III.80, III.370
Consciousness III.353, III.369
Cosmic III.87
evolution of III.242
and Father Mind *III.27*
Integrated III.148, III.167
and Jinarâjadâsa System II.160
mystery of III.342
pure III.161
radiance of III.253
realm of III.238
and Schrödinger II.229
States of II.44, II.204
Supreme III.362, III.363, III.365, III.370
supreme III.176
undifferentiated and pure Light III.254
Universal III.86–7, III.172, III.217
universal II.73, III.221
see also A-consciousness; B-consciousness; Divine Consciousness
consciousness III.41, III.70, III.288–91, III.293, III.331
annihilation of II.76
and apparitions II.80
ascent in III.192
aspects and states II.17
and Astral Light III.95
awakening II.164, III.288
beyond the brain II.197
bottom-up and top-down approaches III.146
and cākras III.192
centres II.181, III.38–9, III.86, III.164, III.172, III.224

consciousness (continued)
and cerebral cortex III.307
and chess III.13
cognitive functions of III.160
conative functions of III.160
conjunction of two streams of III.161
conveyors of II.160
elastic term I.143–4
elevated III.92, III.108
eliminating II.119
embodied III.223
emergence of II.131
epiphenomenon of brain mechanisms II.138
etymology and historical perspective I.144
evolution of III.263, III.304, III.327
evolving III.295
exists apart from the body III.130
expression of III.163
extinction of II.65, III.312
faculties of III.190
fountainhead of III.40
fragmented III.322
and Galileo Commission Report III.329
genesis in the West I.144
gradually freed from encumbrance of the brain III.165
hard problem of III.135, III.163
see also hard problem of consciousness
highest and divinest III.184
and human brain III.357–65
and ideas III.116
and impediments of the mechanism III.164
individual units of III.236–7
innumerable forms of III.140
and involutionary and evolutionary cycles III.161, III.183
irreducibility of III.307
is a phenomenon I.144
key factor in understanding quantum phenomena III.164
landmark developmental stages III.187
levels I.145, III.xix–xx, III.78, III.249, III.256
linear III.249
and matter III.237, III.276
and mental images III.152
and mind and matter III.140
modern usage I.144
modes of II.196, III.87
mystery of II.45, II.140, III.40
nature of II.224, III.329
neural correlate of III.112–13
and neuroscience III.351
and neuroscientific diktat on II.xvi
not generated by the brain III.xviii
passive III.204
see also drugs
personal II.73
physical basis and mechanism for II.199
and physical brain III.109
and pineal gland III.182
powers of II.45
primacy of II.198, III.120, III.271, III.291
pure III.235
quality of III.110, III.335
and quantum processes II.126, III.164
raising III.248–55
rays III.39
residual II.81
and Root Races III.375
of the sages of India and Egypt III.59
same III.288
science of III.43, III.136
and seers III.186
self-caricature III.314, III.315
and self-expression III.10
sleeping II.164–5
software program II.115
and sound III.159
spectrum of I.145–51, I.154–5
spiritual II.22
stream of II.73, II.76, III.149
and structure for experience III.357
terms of III.71, III.72
through vehicles II.161
traits of II.85
transfer of II.32, II.77
two dimensional III.249
two theories of III.314
underlying III.295
understanding of II.100
undivided III.xx
unfoldment and functioning of III.101, III.175
and vehicles III.137, III.166
wellspring of III.42
see also states of consciousness
Consciousness and the Universe (Penrose) III.164
Consciousness Explained (Dennett) II.114–15
Consciousness: Key problems in philosophy (Weisberg) I.39
Consciousness–Matter III.145, III.78
conscious percept (neuroscience) III.136
conscious point of view III.287

conscious power III.319
conscious Principles III.159, III.168
conscious self III.235
Conscious Soul II.164
consilience I.xl, I.232, I.316, I.319–20, II.93
consistency II.93, III.xx
consistent reports II.56
consonance II.188
constellations, zodiacal III.31
constitution of man *I.325*, II.1, II.7, *II.21*, *II.31*, II.162, III.28, III.37, III.252, III.254
  and analogy III.36
  and nature II.10–14, II.34
  and Principles of Man II.149
  and Steiner II.184–5, *II.185*
  twofold III.35, III.38
constitution of the universe III.28
'construct' man II.195
Consultant Psychiatrist (McGilchrist *q.v.*) II.122
contemplation II.101, III.5, III.11, III.19, III.206
contemporary mystery teachings I.260, I.282–5, I.308
contemporary scientific cosmology III.86, III.240
contemporary scientific terms III.122
contradictions II.218
  see also fundamentalists
contrasting methodologies II.59
control of desire *q.v.* II.26
  see also Kāma
controlled use, psychedelic drugs III.195
controlling agent III.163
conundrums III.134, III.135, III.243
conventional science III.303
  see also mainstream science
convergence I.319, III.271
converging experiments II.36
convex lens II.189
Cook, Captain James I.68
Cooke, George Willis I.293
Cooper, Dr Callum E. II.95
Copernicus, Nicolaus I.51
co-primacy of Spirit *q.v.* and Matter *q.v.* III.329
  see also Galileo Commission Report; First Fundamental Proposition/axiom
core, deepest and innermost II.9
core classification II.155, II.170
Corinthians II.32
Corliss, William Roger III.228
corporeality, material objects I.34
corporeal plane III.122
Corpus Hermeticum I.247, I.252, I.254, I.264–5
correct image III.247
correct thinking I.300
correlates III.136, III.141
correlation II.93, III.47, III.120, III.122, III.306
  and causation I.173
  of consciousness III.168
  definition III.71
correspondences I.239, I.244, I.250, III.80, III.121
  with Adept teachers III.130
  astrological II.178
  cākras III.192
  definition III.71
  and Divine Principle II.20
  human body to evolution III.222
  with human principles II.151, III.78–9, III.98
  and *Inner Group Teaching of H.P. Blavatsky* I.209
  law of III.122
  to levels of descent III.154
  and planes III.83
  and post-mortem states of consciousness II.25
  Principle of I.247–8, I.251–4, I.326
  and principles III.167
  sensory input II.120
  unitary consciousness III.168
Unmanifest Worlds and the Manifest Worlds III.61
within man's his own nature III.252
Cosmic Background Explorer (COBE) mission I.340
cosmic birth I.252, I.253, III.83
cosmic blueprint I.244
The Cosmic Blueprint (Davies) I.354
Cosmic Consciousness III.87
cosmic consciousness I.132, I.151
Cosmic Electricity II.223
cosmic electricity III.97
Cosmic Elements III.114, III.148, III.154–5, III.156–9, III.168
cosmic ether II.210
cosmic evolution III.74
cosmic force III.31
cosmic Gaia III.265
Cosmic Ideation III.146, III.151, III.152, *III.153*
cosmic influences III.179
Cosmic Logos III.152
cosmic mind I.52–3
cosmic origins III.262

cosmic pendulum I.268
Cosmic Principles III.74–5, *III.75*
Cosmic seed *I.253*
Cosmic slumber III.75
Cosmic Space I.80
cosmic standpoint III.286
cosmic system III.52
Cosmocreators *III.27*
cosmogenesis I.108, I.298, III.82
cosmogony *I.253*, I.270, I.305, I.306, II.39, III.61, III.108
cosmology I.332–43, II.228, III.86, III.92, III.238, III.240
Cosmos III.22, III.80, III.82, III.83, III.255, III.288
  definition III.84
  plains of III.13
cosmos III.74, III.75, III.82, III.84, III.91, III.112, III.253
The Cosmovision of the Incas (Soria) I.276, I.280
counsel III.106, III.194
counselling II.96
counterbalance to life on Earth *q.v.* II.70
  see also Devachan
counterfeit of genuine spiritual experiences *q.v.* III.200
counterpart II.6, II.37
courage II.134
COVID-19 I.140, III.329
cowardice III.171
Cox, Brian III.319
Cranston, Sylvia I.100
Crawford, Dr Jackson I.102
Creation I.271, I.279, III.107
creation III.38, III.61, III.77, *III.103*, III.104
  emanational emergence III.141
  insubstantiality of III.117
  of the raw material III.173
creationist–fundamentalists I.244
creationists III.239–40
Creative Evolution (Bergson) I.172
Creative Evolution (Goswami) I.137, I.355
creative freedom II.141
creative ideation III.123
creative people III.185
creative poles III.185
The Creative Process in the Individual (Troward) I.300
Creative Word III.13
creativity I.11, I.170, I.172, III.119, III.205, III.255
Creator III.174
  see also Trimūrti; logos; Brahmā
Creator God III.240
creatures III.253
credibility II.93
creed II.146
Cremo, Michael I.352, III.228–30, III.234, III.235, III.236, III.238, III.248
crest III.303
Cretan Labyrinth III.7–8
Crick, Francis I.8, I.105, I.345, I.349, I.352, II.199, III.305, III.307
crimes II.203, III.41
criminality II.89, II.90
criminals II.75
crisis II.95, II.133, III.263
criticism
  by establishment scientists III.230
  of neo-Darwinism III.228
Crone, Patricia I.xviii
Crookall, Robert II.92–4
Crookes, Sir William I.120, II.36, II.207, II.223, III.171, III.172, III.316
crop circles I.207
the Cross *III.145*, III.145
cross I.206, III.77
crossing, antahkaranic bridge II.88–9
crude substance III.242
cryonics III.272, III.335–6, III.338–9
Cryonics Institute III.335
crypt (Great Pyramid *q.v.*) II.84
crystallized Idea III.35
Csikszentmihalyi, Mihaly II.139
CUBE (symbol of) III.65
Cube unfolded (symbol of) III.65–7, *III.67*
cult
  computationalist II.126
  of rationalism II.125
cultural evolution III.245
culture II.183, II.188, III.18, III.35, III.196, III.242
  and mind II.122, II.124
cunning II.89–90, III.294
Curie, Marie I.95, I.117
Curie, Pierre I.95, I.117–18
currents (mental) III.149–53
cyborg technology III.338
cycle of necessity II.174
cycles II.76–7, II.78
cyclical processes III.98, III.225, III.227
cyclical time III.234

cyclicity I.240, I.294, I.306, I.307, I.340, III.3, III.29
eternal *III.27*
cyclic journey II.97
'A Cyclic Model of the Universe' (Steinhardt and Turok) I.341
Cyclops III.183
cymatics III.78

Da'at III.64
Daedalus; or, Science and the Future (Haldane) I.348, III.336
Daemon est Deus inversus I.268
Daena II.172
Daisetsu Suzuki I.218
daivīprakṛti II.209–10, II.211
Dalai Lama I.163, I.296
Dalton, John III.2
damaging misperception about scientific thought III.276
DaMonte, John II.166
dangers of accelerated spiritual progress II.202, III.78, III.191, III.199, III.210
dangers, of symbolism misinterpreted/misused III.16–18
dangers, of statistics *q.v.* III.282
Dangma's open Eye III.186
Dante I.218, I.219, II.25, II.63, II.65–6, II.70, III.16
'Dante—Ptolemaic Cosmology— The Labyrinth' (Bilimoria) III.7
dark cell (symbol in Beethoven's *Fidelio q.v.*) III.16
dark energy II.xvii, III.115
darker regions, of consciousness *q.v.* II.84
dark face, of science *q.v.* III.277
dark forces II.89
dark matter II.xvii, III.310
Darkness III.13, III.105, III.111
darkness III.44–5
Dart, Raymond I.348
Darwin, Charles I.51, I.56, I.58, I.136–8, II.222, III.219, III.224, III.257, III.278
in defence of III.244–5
The Descent of Man in Relation to Sex I.346, III.242
and Gould I.57
Darwinian ape III.236
Darwinian theory I.3, I.55, I.56–8, II.110, III.65, III.219–20, III.242–5
and Blavatsky II.134
and bola III.233
on complex forms of matter III.240
limitations III.122
and Nagel I.48, I.115, II.131
and neuroscience III.307
on origin of man III.227–8
and *philosophia perennis* III.225
Darwinism: An Exposition Of The Theory Of Natural Selection – With Some of Its Applications (Wallace) I.347
Darwin's Black Box: The biochemical challenge to evolution (Behe) I.353
Darwin's Dangerous Idea (Dennett) I.353
Dass, Ram III.196
data processing II.129
Davidson, Donald I.30
Davidson, Richard I.163
Davies, Dame Sally I.lix
Davies, Paul I.240, I.354, III.109, III.176
da Vinci, Leonardo II.110, II.125, II.135
Dawkins, Peter I.116
Dawkins, Richard I.2, I.66, I.320–1, I.350, III.220, III.245, III.295
on the Bible III.17
on God III.311
on lumbering robots II.117–18
and Medawar II.176
Day of Brahmā II.77, III.234
see also manvantara
Days of Creation III.74
dead-letter interpretation II.69, II.155, II.218, III.17, III.19
Deadly Medicines and Organised Crime (Gøtzsche) I.49
dead matter III.289, III.290
dead ritual III.185
deafness (Helen Keller *q.v.* and Beethoven *q.v.*) II.120–1, II.122
death II.63, II.65–8, II.76, II.93, II.97–9, III.178, III.368
and Antaḥkaraṇa II.216
and computers II.130
fear of III.200
The Mathnawi on II.xiv
medical definition of II.xiv
and Mozart II.100, III.340–1
and photographs III.201
premature II.75
recent II.59
shadow of I.172, II.74
and sleep II.70

death (continued)
sudden and violent II.81–2
survival after I.14–15
transition II.91, II.101–2
two II.64
of vitalism III.176
see also brain, clinical death of
Death and the Maiden (Schubert) II.100
deathbed apparitions II.83
A Death in the Desert (Browning) I.3
death struggle II.68
debasement, of spirit into forms III.65
debauched places, atmosphere of II.81
debts, karmic I.295
decay III.110, III.317
deceptive mind (Novella, Steven *q.v.*) I.12, I.30
deductive arguments III.73
deductive method I.230, I.235
deeper principle at work (ignored by mainstream science *q.v.*) III.250
deeper questions III.110, III.262
'The DeepScience of NeuroCardiology' (Mukhopadhyay and Relan) III.43
defects (spiritual aspirants *q.v.*) III.293
defence mechanisms, of mainstream science *q.v.* I.322
A Defence of Poetry (Shelley) III.327–8
deficiencies, mainstream scientific paradigm III.xvii
degeneration (psycho-mental) II.73
dehumanization II.139
Deity III.34, III.173, III.311
deity II.125
de la Warr, George II.166
Delphic Oracle I.xxxviii
delusions I.309, II.56, II.99, II.100, III.293, III.311
Dembski, William I.355
DeMeo, James II.207, II.213
demerit, of incarnation II.76
Demikhov, Vladimir III.339
Demiurge *III.27*
demiurge III.238
Demiurgic power III.46
Demiurgus I.263
Democritus I.270
demons III.9
Dennett, Daniel I.30, I.353, II.114–15, II.117
Dense (Physical) Body II.164
depersonalization II.139
deposition II.36
see also upādhi(s)
depraved men II.108
depression II.9, III.12, III.196–7, III.272, III.337
deprivation II.120
Deśā III.107
Descartes, René I.27, I.32, I.51, II.126, III.184
descent II.217, III.122, III.123, III.126, *III.128*, III.167, III.237
The Descent of Man in Relation to Sex (Darwin) I.346, III.242, III.244
description, and the described III.143, III.370–1
The Description of the Human Body (Descartes) II.126
deserving candidates (awakening latent powers *q.v.* in) III.181
see also pineal gland
design III.92, III.126
desire II.25, II.26, II.52, II.79, II.171
bondage of III.6
of the heart III.114
and mind III.58
natural, love-driven III.185
Desire body II.154, II.164
Desire-driven thought II.168
desire nature II.81
Desire principle II.18, II.19, II.23, II.24, II.42
and Besant System II.155
and classical Theosophical literature II.151
'join' the immortal and mortal parts of man II.200, II.201
and Mind Principle II.202
Desire World II.164
d'Espagnat, Bernard I.111, I.113, I.338
destination, of the physical body II.96
destiny II.205, III.261, III.269, III.291, III.293, III.326
destruction, premature II.89
deterioration, inner III.194, III.197
determinism I.5, I.96, I.109
'Determinism and Free Will' (Schrödinger) II.198
deterministic characteristic II.135
deterministic paradigm I.41, I.44, I.104, I.108, I.331
Deucalion (symbol of) III.9
Deunov, Peter I.217, I.219, I.266, II.58, III.187, III.188
Devachan II.68, II.70–4, II.75, II.78, II.216
devachanee II.73
Devachanic Entity II.52

devachanic experience II.78–9
devachanic state II.78, III.125
devachanic store II.75
Devā Eye III.182, III.187
Devanagari II.3
Devatās III.159
developmental biologists I.346
developmental biology I.70, I.73, I.149, III.177
developmental psychology II.186
developmental stages III.98, III.375
Devil I.268, I.269, II.174, III.323
devolution I.242–3, III.219, III.235–8, III.248, III.254, III.256
devotion II.219, III.227, III.313
Dhāraṇā III.191
Dhyāni-Chohans *III.27*, III.72, III.130
Diabolos I.268
diagrams, limitations III.5, III.93
dialectics I.47
dialogue (counter dogmas *q.v.* and conflict *q.v.*) II.189, II.221
'A Dialogue Between the Two Editors' (Blavatsky and Collins) II.150–1
Dialogues with Scientists and Sages: The search for unity (Weber) I.186–7, I.339
diamonds, rough (Devachan *q.v.*) II.70
dichotomies I.295, II.1, II.2, II.7–8, II.190, III.43, III.163
Dicke, Robert I.336
dictators
  characteristics of III.9
  exclamatory utterances of III.35
didactic attitude II.44
diet, abstemious in III.208
different dimensions II.70
differentiation III.144, III.145, III.167, III.225
diffusion I.73
digital afterlife III.315
dignity II.127
dimensions
  higher II.154, III.93, III.249
  of intentionality II.165
  of reality III.4
  of space II.5
Diogenes III.11
Dionysiac Rites I.263
Dionysian Mysteries I.180, I.213
Dirac, Paul I.133, I.334
directed effort III.242
direct knowing II.22, III.205
direct knowledge II.41
direct perception II.22
dirty filters (simile for diminution of spirit *q.v.* by brain *q.v.*) III.165
Dirven, Anny I.87
disagreement, between science and Theosophy II.221
disciple III.304
disciplines, contemplative III.11
disciplining, lower nature II.90
disconnection, between classical and quantum physics I.318
'Discourse on Metaphysics' (Leibniz) I.33
discoveries II.126, II.223, III.262, III.278–9, III.284
discrete ecological unit III.222
disease I.lviii, III.49, III.174
diseases of meaning III.273–4
disorder in pituitary body *q.v.* III.197
  see also psychedelic drugs; *Knowledge of the Higher Worlds*
dissecting software II.115
  see also computationalists; Dennett
dissection III.363
dissemination, after-death communications research II.94
dissolute persons, aura of II.81
dissolution, of universes or 'world periods' *q.v.* II.77
dissonance II.188
distilled wisdom II.146
distinctions III.111, III.142
  between hearing and listening III.xix
  between machine/mechanic, instrument/performer II.126
  between the 'map' and the 'territory' III.150
  of meaning III.84
  between seeing and looking III.xix
  between soul and spirit II.107
distribution centre I.284
diverse sources II.146
diversity I.294, III.55, III.86, III.223, III.334
divided nature of thought II.123
La Divina Commedia (Dante) II.25, II.63, II.66, *II.67*, II.70
the Divine II.39, II.41, III.80, III.118, III.152–3, III.226
  as generating centre I.301
  and New Thought I.289
the divine III.36, III.120
Divine awareness III.46
Divine Being III.9

divine Beings III.130
divine brain II.122
divine caprice III.187
Divine command III.46
Divine Consciousness I.xlvii, I.xlviii, I.xlix, I.183, I.184, I.251, III.80, III.101, III.147, III.240, III.279
basic substance III.147
and emanation III.134
Ideas in III.109
and integration III.371
and macrocosm III.120
and manifestation III.141
origin of physical man III.248
reflected in human consciousness III.70, III.82
and spiritual prototypes *III.27*
unknown multi-dimensions of III.365
divine consciousness III.235
Divine Design III.92
divine desire of creating happiness and love II.26
Divine Ego II.53, II.215, II.216, III.254, III.255, III.256
divine element III.244
Divine Ethics I.183
Divine Fire II.196
The Divine Flame (Hardy) I.53
Divine Forces I.xlix, I.liii, II.204
divine forces II.45, III.120, III.162, III.171, III.172, III.175–6, *III.175*
Divine Grace I.165
Divine Handicraft I.liii, III.127
Divine handiwork III.92
Divine hierarchies I.xlix
divine husband II.73
Divine Ideas III.109
Divine Ideation I.liii, III.127, III.146, III.148, III.151, III.153, *III.153*
origin in III.148, III.152
Divine instrument III.80
divine instrument III.172
Divine Intellect I.247
Divine Intelligence I.xlix
divine intelligence II.29
Divine interest III.46
Divine Justice of Karma II.203
Divine Knowledge I.183, III.364–5
Divine Law III.89
divine laws II.34, II.165
divine light II.216
divine man III.105
divine mandate III.71–4
Divine Messenger III.303, III.304
Divine Mind I.239, I.247, I.301, I.303, I.327, III.92, III.362
Ideas in III.107, III.108, III.109
and individual mind III.148–9, III.153–4, III.167
and personal self II.90
and third current III.151
divine Mind II.97, II.216
Divine Nature I.327, III.127, III.129
divine nature III.11, III.252, III.257
Divine Negative Principle III.243
Divine Numbers III.371
divine Omniscience III.286
divine origin III.243, III.257
divine parent source II.89
divine perception II.22
Divine Perfection II.196
Divine Plan (man *q.v.*, the image of) III.38
divine plan (evolution *q.v.*) III.122
Divine plane III.87
Divine Positive Principle III.243
Divine Power I.290, I.298, III.37
divine presence III.271
Divine Principle II.20
divine principles III.17, III.271
divine projection II.29
Divine Providence (Deunov) II.58
divine purpose II.29
The Divine Pymander I.264
Divine Quartet III.194
Divine Science I.183
Divine Self II.18, II.19, II.20, II.195, II.196, III.315
and Ātma II.227
and lamp III.11–12
and Supreme Deity III.48
and three Egos II.46
and transpersonal psychology II.188
Divine Spirit I.266, II.99, II.164
Divine–Spiritual (the Monad *q.v.*) II.41
Divine Substance II.209
Divine Thought I.289, I.327, III.226, III.236, III.362
Divine vitality III.46
Divine Wisdom I.xxxix, I.xlix, I.184, I.327, II.225
divine wisdom II.7–8
Divinity I.238, I.251, III.34, III.46, III.202, III.271

divinity I.204, I.221, I.267, I.326, II.77, II.117, II.224, III.329
and Gandhi II.xv
and Ramanujan III.208
and stars III.269
divisions, man's constitution and nature II.14
divorce II.73, II.127
DNA I.74–5, I.137, I.240, I.241, I.356, III.176, III.289
junk I.106
Dobbs, Betty Jo Teeter I.231
Dobzhansky, Theodosius I.348
The Doctrine of Synthesis II.164
Doctrine of the Eye I.193, I.194
Doctrine of the Heart I.193, I.194
doctrines II.146
dog III.6
dogmas I.51, I.58, I.121, II.189, II.190, II.210, III.185, III.304, III.306
brain = mind I.12
Christian I.208, I.245, I.326
and Darwin's natural selection theory III.317
and materialism I.53, I.67
molecular biology I.105, I.115
neurocentric III.315
saying by Christ I.326
theology of evolutionary scientism III.244
dogmatic people II.221
dogmatic theology II.218
Dogs That Know When Their Owners are Coming Home (Sheldrake) I.79
Doidge, Norman I.161
domestic houses (simile for human body *q.v.*) II.202, *II.203*
domination II.106, II.115
doors II.60, III.64, III.253, III.352
The Doors of Perception (Huxley) III.195
doppelgänger II.54
Der Doppelganger (Schubert) II.56
Dossey, Larry I.356
double II.150
see also Liṅga-śarīra
double-blind methodology I.84
double-helix structure, DNA I.349, III.176
dove of truth III.261
Dowding, Lord II.82
drama, and symbolism III.5
dream body II.57
dream consciousness II.24–5
dream landscape II.70
dreamless sleep II.68, III.256
dream-life III.87
dreams II.74, II.102, III.116–17, III.312
lucid I.87, I.90–1, II.53, II.56
of physical birth III.129
Dreams of a Final Theory (Weinberg) I.317, III.268
dream state II.53, II.75, II.97
Dream Time I.78
dṛṣṭi III.186
Driesch, Hans I.70, I.71, I.72, I.347, I.348
Drown, Ruth II.166
drugs I.262, I.308, III.34, III.195–9
induced experience III.200, III.204
overdoses II.83
Druidic Schools I.213
Druidic traditions III.10
Drummond, Henry I.302
Duad III.371
duad III.66
dual constitution II.16, II.17
dual embrace (Janus *q.v.* Faces of science) III.264
dual functions *II.13*, II.107
dualism I.72, III.156, III.289
dualistic religion II.172
dualist notion II.125
duality II.18, III.144, III.145
dual make-up *II.13*
dual nature II.38, II.123
Dumskulls (Blavatsky on mental sluggards) II.222
Dunne, Brenda I.356
Dunselman, Ron III.197–8
Duplantis, Jesse I.290
Dupré, John I.69, I.356
duration II.76, II.77, III.142
Dürr, Hans-Peter I.353
dust of the Earth (human constitution *q.v.*) III.131
duties II.79, II.91
Dweller on the Threshold III.198
dying III.165, III.221
see also death
dying young (Devachan *q.v.*) II.75
Dying to Wake Up (Parti) I.15, I.88–9
dynamical systems I.41, I.43
Dyson, Freeman I.243, I.244, I.340, II.224, III.206–7

eagle, symbol of I.194, I.212
Eagleman, David III.305–6

ears II.142, III.46, III.135
Earth II.29, III.10, III.234, III.289, III.361
  Myalba II.100
  and seven planes III.87
  six principal components I.241
earth II.177, III.56
earthbound afterlife II.82
earthbound man II.81
Earth Chain III.93
earthiness III.18
Earth life II.75
earthly body III.130
earthly desires III.6
earthly existence II.30, II.196, III.6
earthly garment II.73
earthly realm III.238
earthly things II.69
earthly wedlock (*Book of the Keys q.v.*) II.73
Earth Mother I.280
East
  and ageless wisdom III.91
  meeting West III.102–20
  teachings II.146
Eastern approach II.221
Eastern deities III.55
Eastern expressions II.227
Eastern philosophy II.149, II.160–1
Eastern Religions and Western Thought (Radhakrishnan) I.216–17
Eastern sages III.155
Eastern sources II.221
Eastern traditions *II.147*
Eastern wisdom I.lxi, II.166
easy problem of consciousness *q.v.* I.146–7
Eccles, Sir John I.35, I.39, I.77, I.338, III.304, III.313
ecclesiastical languages II.5
Eckhart, Meister III.33, III.35, III.51
ecliptic (astronomy) III.23
ecological crisis II.126
ecology III.222, III.248
economics III.323–34
ecstasy (genuine or artificially aroused) III.194, III.199, III.200
ectogenesis III.336
ectoplasm I.68, I.119
Eddas II.71
Eddington, Sir Arthur I.xlv, I.36–7, I.38, I.265, I.317, I.332, III.263
Eddy, Mary Baker I.288
Edelman, Gerald I.8–9, I.352
Edison, Thomas I.234, II.223
education I.214–15, II.73, II.184, III.1, III.273
effects I.303, I.304, I.326, III.50, III.77
  of causes II.78
  and Ideas III.107
  of spiritual experience III.200
efflorescence (human attributes) III.199, III.210
Efron, Robert I.350
Egg III.247
  see also Auric Envelope
Eglinton, William II.57
Ego II.20, II.25, II.39, II.42, II.45–7
  see also Higher Ego
ego I.49, I.50, I.301, II.133, III.35, III.311
  and Steiner II.184
  and third current III.151
  see also Personal ego
Egoic centres II.46, II.47
Ego Mind II.164
egotism III.112
Egypt (Mystery centre) II.3
Egyptian *Book of the Dead* I.175
Egyptian bull I.267
Egyptian Gnosticism III.25–6
Egyptian gods and goddesses III.24, *III.27*
Egyptian Mysteries/Mystery Schools I.213, I.264–7, I.280
Egyptian Pyramid III.65
Egyptians I.199, I.260, III.18
Egyptian sphinx III.49
Egyptian system II.172, *II.173*
Egyptian teachings II.172
Egyptology III.25
eidolon II.81
Eighth limb III.191
  see also Samādhi
Eighth Sphere (consciousness *q.v.*) II.85–6
  see also Avītchi
Einstein, Albert I.lvii, I.lxxxiv, I.35, I.67, I.123, I.318, I.319, I.323, II.14, II.219, II.224, III.274, III.282–3, III.326
  on affective brain III.43
  brain of I.134, *I.135*
  on cosmic ether II.210–11
  on Deunov I.219, III.188
  on distinction between real Truth and relative truth III.119
  on energy and matter I.95
  on ether III.180
  on fairy tales III.49
  on fame III.313

on God's thoughts III.109–10
on his achievements II.213
on invariant speed of light II.209
and limitations of quantification II.135
on love I.234
on mathematics III.349
and Miller II.208
on Newton III.205–6
on science III.264
and *Secret Doctrine* I.xlvii
on *The Soul of the Universe* I.81
and spooky action at a distance I.108–10, I.111, I.112
and Theory of Relativity I.133, I.332, I.333, II.207, III.353
and transmissive function I.172
and ubercausalität I.44, I.335
Einsteinian mass-energy II.6
On the Einstein Podolsky Rosen Paradox (Bell) I.336
elderly man suddenly expired, spectral energy of II.83
Elder Souls I.274
Eldredge, Niles I.350
Eleatic school of philosophy III.73
electrical circuitry (computers *q.v.*) II.130
see also metaphor circuitry
electrical field, heart III.42
electrical metaphor II.202
electricity II.38, III.114, III.173–4
electro-chemical interactions III.136, III.162
electromagnetism II.28, III.40, III.42, III.44, III.174, III.377
electron (quantum physics *q.v.*) I.95
electronic computer/device II.113–14
electroscope III.201
Elegischer Gesang (Beethoven) II.99
ELEMENT III.289–91
Elementals I.245, I.276
elementals III.198, III.247
elementary particles III.83
Element–Principles III.59, III.154, III.158, III.168
Elements III.76, III.157–9, III.160, III.238
elements I.278, II.6, III.11, III.13, III.57
Element–Substances III.154, III.158–9, III.168
Elephanta Caves I.215–16, *I.216*
Eleusinian Mysteries I.180, I.213, I.263, III.38
elimination
consciousness II.119
subjectivity II.117
see also computationalist argumentation
eliminative materialism I.30
Eliot, T. S. II.54, III.xviii
Elizabeth I, Queen III.46
Ellis, George I.336
Ellison, Arthur I.lxxxiv, I.102, I.336, II.8, II.91, II.223, II.224
flower-bowl experiment I.68, I.319
and lucid dreams I.91
out-of-body experience I.90, II.56
Ellora caves I.216, *I.216*
Elōhīm III.46, III.131
Elsaesser, Evelyn II.95
Elysium II.70
emanation III.60, III.61, *III.103*, III.134, III.142, *III.143*, III.148
from Ātma III.63
and evolution III.224
and Lower mind II.88
pure III.217
emanational descent III.102, III.121, III.122, III.126, *III.128*, III.155, *III.157*
emanational emergence III.88, III.141
emanational manifestation III.141–2
emanational unfoldment II.30
emanationist cosmology III.122
embodiment II.115
see also computationalist argumentation
embryo I.71, I.73, I.75
Emerald Tablet I.228, I.248, *I.249*, I.264
emergence
of consciousness II.131
definition III.237
emanational III.88, III.141
emergentism I.30, III.137, III.237, III.291, III.295, III.305, III.306
Emerson, Ralph Waldo I.57, I.239, I.286, I.287, I.288–9, I.291–9, I.302, III.271
emissary II.123, III.130, III.186, III.188, III.275
Emotional body II.153
emotional nature III.253
emotional responses, subtlety and capacity II.121–2
emotional rollercoaster II.119
Emotional Soul II.164
emotional support structure III.197
emotions II.120, II.121, III.13, III.42, III.192, III.254
Empedocles II.177

The Emperor's New Mind: Concerning computers, minds and the laws of physics (Penrose) III.164
Empire State Building (Helen Keller's 'view' of) II.120
empirical evidence I.67
empirical falsification I.31
empirical observation III.309
empirical sciences I.31
empiricism I.33, II.125
empowerment III.274
encumbrances of possessions II.97
see also transitions, unnecessary difficulties during
endless duration II.76
endless opportunities II.48
endocrine system III.192
Ends and Means (Huxley) I.xviii
The End of Science (Horgan) I.353
end purpose, unified entity towards II.11
the Enduring III.118
enduring spiritual entity I.297
enemy of reason (science *q.v.*) I.320–2
energetic body III.113
see also Prāṇa; prāṇa
energetic causation I.47
energetic pattern, very low-grade II.83
see also suicide
energizing man II.34, II.195
energy III.24, III.97, III.109, III.192
energy–consciousness III.147
energy counter-part of Physical body *q.v.* II.83
see also Etheric double
energy fields II.83, II.165, II.166
energy healing III.78
energy quanta I.95, I.332
energy-substance II.6
enforced death II.93
English language (limitations of) II.3, II.4–5, II.6, II.227
enigma of genius *q.v.* to mainstream psychology *q.v.* II.71
enjoyment III.111
see also Sāṁkhya philosophy
enlightened knowledge II.41, II.171
enlightened science I.8, I.132, III.48–9, III.264, III.265
enlightened scientists/psychologists II.65, III.115, III.163–4, III.328
enlightenment II.202, II.203, III.5, III.198, III.255–6, III.326–7
ennobling thoughts II.107
enquiry, holistic approach to I.166–7
ensoulment/ensouled (with the Monad *q.v.*) II.86, II.108
Entangled Life (Sheldrake) III.223
Entangled Minds (Radin) I.111–12
entanglement (quantum physics *q.v.*) I.109, I.111
see also quantum theory
entelechy I.70–1, I.72, I.346, I.348, III.220
enterprise III.119
entertainment, frivolous II.xv
entities II.xviii, II.18, II.195, III.86, III.93, III.163, III.198, III.355
entrenched attitudes II.219, II.222
entropy I.44, I.45
enveloping atmosphere III.179
environment II.90, III.219
environmental disasters III.187
environmental science I.23
ephemeral authority III.244
epigenetics I.105, III.192
epiphenomenon I.16, I.55, I.236, II.xvi, II.119, II.138, III.368
and consciousness III.120, III.137, III.351, III.369
epistemology I.25, I.54–5, I.202, I.235
epochs/eras II.188, III.18, III.187, III.188
EPR paradox I.110
equations III.150, III.151, III.208, III.220
The Equilibrium Law III.90–1
erasure (computers *q.v.* and mind *q.v.*) II.128
Erkelens, Herbert van III.357
errors (of thought *q.v.*) II.xvii, II.3, II.115, II.137, III.109, III.306
Ertz, Susan II.76
escape routes III.211
escapism III.118, III.321
the esoteric, definition I.187–92
The Esoteric [E. S.] Instructions of H. P. Blavatsky III.72, III.78, III.121
E. S. Instruction No. I III.122–6
esoteric allegory (Tabernacle of Moses *q.v.*) III.252
esoteric and spiritual instruction III.235
Esoteric Buddhism II.167–8, *II.169*
Esoteric Buddhism (Sinnett) II.149
esoteric cosmogony *I.253*
esoteric cosmologies III.238
esoteric dimension III.36, III.48, III.295
esoteric doctrine I.187, I.236, II.35

esoteric enumeration III.78
esoteric evidence II.110
esoteric fossils II.224
esoteric import II.174
esoteric insights II.69
esotericism I.80, I.187–92, I.201–2, II.xvi, II.199, III.95, III.115
 and Brahmins II.80
 chief centres of I.213
 and the composition of man II.1
 crucial insight of science has strong bearing on III.163
 definition I.182, I.204
 and Doctrine of the Heart I.193
 and Emerson I.298
 and evolution III.122
 and figurative language III.3
 and Wallace III.316–17
 and Water Element I.276
 Western schools of II.174–88
esotericist I.165, I.187, I.201, I.202, I.245
esoteric kernel (degeneration of) III.19
 see also animal sacrifice
esoteric key II.4, III.142
esoteric knowledge III.10
esoteric literature II.28, III.4
esoteric meaning/significance II.85, III.37, III.47, III.66
esoteric perspective II.133
esoteric philosophers III.34
esoteric philosophy I.187, I.197, III.121, III.271, III.284, III.286, III.287, *III.292*
esoteric powers I.202
esoteric precepts II.153
esoteric principles II.222
esoteric psychologist III.31
esoteric reasons III.192
esoteric science I.4, I.195, I.197, I.247, II.209, III.83, III.110
 definition I.204
Esoteric Section, Scientific and Medical Network I.141
Esoteric Section, Theosophical Society I.283, II.151, III.121, III.181
esoteric societies III.294
esoteric symbolism III.60
esoteric systems II.188, II.189, III.5
esoteric taxonomy II.65, II.196
esoteric teachings II.147, II.175, III.284
esoteric terminology II.4
esoteric truths II.86, III.16
esoteric wisdom III.13
Esoteric Writings (Subba Row) II.168
ESP of Quarks and Superstrings (Phillips) I.341
ESP Wars East and West (May) I.92
Essence I.153, I.296
essence II.222, III.372
essential character III.218
essential nature II.xvii, III.94, III.342
established theories II.209, III.230
the establishment I.219, I.220, II.131
establishment science II.213, III.xviii, III.72, III.216, III.232, III.316, III.318
 see also mainstream science
establishment scientists III.230, III.295
the Eternal III.110, III.118
Eternal and Ageless Wisdom III.253
eternal cyclicity *III.27*, III.29
eternal damnation II.78
Eternal Duration III.141
Eternal Ego II.177
eternal man II.175
eternal Monad II.162
eternal principle III.173
eternal truth II.191
eternal verities II.91, II.175, III.283
Eternal Wisdom I.xxxix, I.107–8, I.282, I.291, III.108, III.118, III.253, III.274
 is universal III.154–5
eternal youth, secret of III.110
Eternity III.172–3
eternity II.76, II.77, II.99, II.101, III.142
ether II.36, II.164, II.207, II.209, II.213, III.178–9, III.180
'Ether and the Theory of Relativity' (Einstein) II.210–11
ether-drift II.208, II.213
the ethereal (gross material body, aspect of) III.115
ethereal body II.28
ethereal counterpart III.97
ethereal substance III.183
Etheric body II.153
etheric body II.150, II.183, II.184
etheric counterparts III.197–8
Etheric double II.18, II.19, II.28–9, II.54, II.83
 and Besant System II.154
 and Jinarâjadâsa System II.160
 and post-classical Theosophy II.153
 and Sāṁkhya Sūtras III.114
etheric template II.83
ethics II.116, III.36, III.324, III.338

Ettinger, Robert III.335
etymology II.16
eugenics III.336
Euler, Leonhard I.207, III.206, III.364
Europe (Mystery centre) II.3
European alchemy I.280
European culture II.183
Eurythmy II.182
evangelists II.220
Evans, Warren F. I.288
Everett, Hugh, III I.335
ever-living teachings II.218
ever-Present II.53
everyday consciousness III.362, III.363, III.365, III.371
everyday language III.42–3
evidence I.319, III.59, III.264, III.267
  about auras III.203
  about consciousness beyond the material brain III.243
  after-death communications II.94–6
  of Ancient (Ageless) Wisdom III.64
  anomalous I.115, III.230, III.232
  for the antiquity of man III.233
  complex has evolved from the simple III.291
  on creative poles of the spine III.185
  for earthbound afterlife II.82
  on evolution III.228
  extraordinary I.103–15, I.142, I.321
  on fossils III.324
  on hand-washing (Semmelweis, Ignaz) III.318
  on matter and consciousness III.276, III.307
  for the multiverse III.240
  photographic (apparitional phenomena) II.83–4
  and preconceptions and prejudice I.319
  for pseudoscience III.30
  psychic communication II.92–4
  refusal to examine I.321
  research III.329
  scientific and esoteric II.110
  transitional state between life and afterlife II.91–2
evil I.268, II.25, II.85, II.106, II.109, III.119, III.294, III.322–3
  and Angra-Mainyush I.267, II.174
  and Blavatsky II.203
  Garden of Eden I.269
  parable of the two wolves II.26
  Strange Case of Dr Jekyll and Mr Hyde II.89
Evil One I.268
Evil Thought II.174
evil twin II.174, II.267
evolution I.55, I.56–8, I.240–4, I.345–57, II.162, III.64, III.93, III.121–2, III.245, III.257, III.285
  and allegory of Deucalion and Pyrrha III.9
  and aura II.154
  biological III.245
  and Blavatsky II.134
  and the brain II.xvi, II.129
  and Causal Body III.175
  of consciousness III.263, III.304, III.327
  Darwinian I.346, III.219–20
  definition III.218
  and dying for the sake of life III.341
  and Emerson I.297
  and four lower planes of kosmos III.92
  and Hardy I.52–3
  and Huxley III.336
  and immortality III.340
  and involution III.182–3
  and kingdoms of nature III.220–7
  limitless and never-ending III.216, III.217
  of man II.223, III.227–42
  of matter III.225
  and māyā II.74, III.120–1
  and moral sense III.245
  and Mystery Teachings II.xvii
  and neural transducers (consciousness) III.166
    see also James, William
  originally begun from above III.65
  and other kingdoms of nature III.224
  and Physical body II.29
  pressure of III.242
  scientific preconceptions and prejudics on III.244
  selfishness in III.244–5
    see also The Selfish Gene
  solar system II.222
  and the Source III.255
  from the spiritual perspective II.205
  and Stanzas III.74
  theory III.314
  transitions III.304
  and Trine I.304
  of the vehicles III.173
  and vitalist and organismic theories I.70
evolutionary biology I.52, II.109
evolutionary chain III.98

evolutionary cycle III.183
evolutionary journey III.86
evolutionary movement II.219
evolutionary purpose II.110
evolutionary scientism ('theology' of) III.244
evolutionary spirituality III.40
evolutionary theory II.131
Evolution in Action (Huxley) I.349
Evolution in Four Dimensions: Genetic, epigenetic, behavioral, and symbolic variation in the history of life (Jablonska and Lamb) I.355
evolving consciousness III.295
evolving life III.47
evolving mind III.246
examination, school II.66
ex-carnation of a soul from Labyrinth *q.v.* III.8
exceptional scientists III.172
Exclusion Principle I.84
excommunication II.131
executioner (symbol in alchemy *q.v.*) III.14
exercises to develop psychic powers *q.v.* II.164
existence II.36, II.117, II.124–5
  earthly III.6
  of man III.219
  ordinary III.118
  separate III.161
  transitory nature of III.116
  the exoteric, definition I.187–90, I.192–3
exoteric equivalent III.78
exoteric form III.37
exotericism I.182, I.193–4
exoteric narrative III.47, III.251
exoteric religion II.85
exoteric rituals III.19
exoteric teachings III.284
exoteric theology II.80
Expanding Force in Newton's Cosmos (Castillejo) I.303
expectations I.67–8, I.69
experience I.xl, I.1, I.68, I.342, II.123, III.98, III.127
  childhood II.90
  and computers II.118
  conscious III.115
  from the dreary norm III.xx
  drug-induced III.200
  and Dweller on the Threshold III.198
  familiar II.79
  individual II.186
  inner life II.130
  internal III.163
  is state of being II.129
  life-transforming II.91, II.100
  of light III.203
  and neural correlate III.135, III.136
  past III.177
  personal I.2, I.122
  and *philosophia perennis* III.288
  profound III.xx
  and psycho-physical problem III.355
  of sensation III.137–9, III.154
  and the senses III.112, III.135, III.150
  of service to humanity II.153
  spiritual II.183
  subjective III.134
  and theory I.46, II.124
  transformative I.190, *I.191*, I.192
  and transmutation from neurology III.161–5
  veridical I.70–1
  where stored II.60
Experience and Essence (Walder) III.355
the experiential II.4
experiential aspect III.352
experiential doctrine II.164
experiential testing II.219
experimental evidence II.126
experimental method I.197
'Experimental Realization of Einstein-Podolsky-Rosen-Bohm Gedankenexperiment: A New Violation of Bell's Inequalities' (Aspect et al.) I.339
'Experimental Test of Bell's Inequalities Using Time-Varying Analyzers' (Aspect et al.) I.339
experimenter bias II.208
experimenter effect I.84
experiments III.xx, III.85, III.171, III.265, III.272, III.277, III.288
  converging II.36
  and neuroscience III.307
  vivisection III.317
experts, world's top on brain processes (consciousness *q.v.*) III.162
explanatory closure I.50
explicate and implicate order III.225
the explicated III.74
exponential advances in technology *q.v.* II.139
expression II.38, III.13, III.38, III.163, III.173, III.192
extended mind III.201, III.361, III.362
external aural perception III.135
external environment III.219

external God III.89
externalizing III.145
see also concretion
external light III.226
external pressures on human beings *q.v.* III.xvii
external stimulation on mind *q.v.* III.150
external stimulus to physical sense organ *q.v.* III.137, III.174
external world III.64, III.149, III.150, III.154, III.334
extinction of consciousness II.63, II.65
Extinction Rebellion I.150
extraordinary claims I.103, I.104, I.106, I.108–11, I.142, I.322
extraordinary evidence I.103–15, I.142, I.321
extraordinary powers II.58, III.194
extrasensory perception (ESP) observations I.98
Extra-Sensory Perception of Quarks (Phillips) I.339
extra-terrestrial life III.22–3
extremism II.222
extrinsic 'Creator God' III.240
Eye of Dangma III.182
Eye of Horus III.182, III.190
Eye of Śiva III.183
Eye of Wisdom III.79
eyes II.142, III.39, III.46, III.79, III.203, III.269, III.377
closing of I.207
mystery in III.201–3
new III.249
eyes of flesh/spirit I.194, II.57, III.xix, III.328
eyes of spirit II.57, III.328
Ezekiel's vision III.89

fables I.199, I.282, II.80, III.2
fabric
of our earthly existence, twin strands III.xx
of the universe III.145
face (anatomical symbolism of) III.46
of coin (illusion) III.117
see also māyā
facts III.280, III.281, III.282, III.288, III.312, III.313, III.321
denial of repeated observation of III.326
of unassailable experience III.323
faculties II.42, II.181, II.197, III.98, III.101, III.186, III.190
failure (schools of modern philosophy) III.119
faith II.135, III.105, III.313, III.317, III.319
Faivre, Antoine I.244
fall, and pride III.9
fallacy (Royal Society statements of) II.140
Fallen Angel III.237
fallen state III.236
fallopian tubes III.184
the false (eliminating) III.211
false personality II.42, II.46
falsifiability I.31, I.334
see also Popper
familiar experiences II.79
family breakdown (factors involved in) III.274
family man (simile) II.13
the famous (distinguished from the great) II.84
famous scientists I.77, III.269–70, III.313
see also under individual scientists
Fantappiè, Luigi I.44, I.335
Farthing, Geoffrey II.220
Farvashis II.53
Fate III.12, III.90
fate II.216, III.338
Father I.266
Father Mind III.26, *III.27*
Father–Mother III.35
Father of Metaphysics III.73
Fathers of Fountains III.26, III.27
fatigue, inner, of mind III.xviii
Fatima II.53
Faust (Goethe) III.145
favoured theories II.209, II.213
fear of death III.200
feelings II.19, II.117, II.119, II.128, II.183, III.134, III.313
and the heart III.43
from vibrations III.135
Feldman, Christina III.199
female number (meaning of) III.77
feminine soul II.73
Fenwick, Elizabeth I.14, I.100
Fenwick, Peter I.14, I.100, II.95
Festinger's syndrome I.119
Feynman, Richard I.336, II.224, III.205, III.356
Fichte, Johann Gottlieb I.302, III.265
Fidelio (Beethoven) III.15–16
Field, John III.149
fields II.5–6, III.144
of discourse II.127
of influence III.83
morphogenetic/morphic I.74, I.78–9
of organization I.73, I.81, I.82, III.174
Fields, Douglas III.307

the fiery (gross material body *q.v.*, aspect of) III.115
fifth Element III.46
The Fifth Miracle (Davies) I.354
Fifth Root-Race III.187
fig tree II.76
figurative language III.1–2, III.19
figures, three (Tarot cards *q.v.*) III.13
file draw effect I.86
see also cognitive bias; cognitive habits; statistics
filtering out of anomalous evidence II.221
filter media (simile) I.322
filter model of brain *q.v.* I.88, II.137–8
final thought of dying youth II.82
fine-structure constant III.355, III.356
fine tuning III.85, III.238, III.239, III.240, III.241
fingers (anatomical symbolism of) III.46–7
finished product of thought *q.v.* III.92
finite experiences II.46
fire of candidate's Divinity III.252
First Biblical Command III.202
first class of human beings *q.v.* III.334
first mental current III.149
first emanation of God III.226
first eye III.183
First Fundamental Proposition/axiom III.51, III.105, III.119
First Generation (Theosophical) literature II.148
First Logos III.174, *III.175*
first principles (physical constants derivation of) III.355
First Principles of Theosophy (Jinarâjadâsa) II.160
first sheath (Physical body *q.v.*) II.35
see also kośas; sthūla-śarīra
First stage II.93, II.97, II.98
The First Three Minutes: A modern view of the origin of the universe (Weinberg) I.337, III.268
fish (symbol of) III.10
five Cosmic Elements III.156–9
Five Element–Principles III.158
Five Elements III.160
Five Element–Substances III.158–9
five kośas II.150
five objects of the senses III.105, III.113, III.114, III.115
five Root-Causes III.113
five senses II.75, III.10
five streams III.10–11, III.112, III.158, III.254
Five Years of Theosophy (Mead) II.168
fixed stars III.23
fixed Zodiac III.23
flame III.58–9
see also Saptaparṇa
The Flamingo's Smile (Gould) I.57
flaws in computationalist master analogy II.128
flesh, born of (Christ *q.v.*) II.69
Florestan (*Fidelio q.v.*) III.15, III.16
flower (symbol of) III.39
flower-bowl experiment I.68–9, I.319
flowering of latent human faculties *q.v.* II.72
Fludd, Robert III.60
fluid dynamics III.365, III.366, III.368
'fluidic consciousness' III.369
fluid law III.278
focus, maintain III.6
focussed imagination III.120
foetus III.36
Fohat II.223, III.96, III.97, III.174
Fohatic (kosmic plane) III.96
folklore III.10, III.229
followers II.125
Fontana, David G. J. (afterlife transition) II.82
food (mind–sensation problem *q.v.*) III.163
fools
scientific attitude to III.279
glorification of in popular culture III.326
footprints (antediluvian) III.232
Forbidden Archeology – The Hidden History of the Human Race (Cremo and Thompson) I.137, I.138, I.352, III.229–30
Forces II.44, II.204, III.171, III.175–6
forces II.37, II.79, *III.27*, III.172, III.265
active principle II.7
archetypal III.5
commutation of II.231
involution and evolution III.225
and matter III.350
psycho-energetic vortices of III.191
spiritual centres of III.50, III.181
force-side III.155, III.159
Ford, Henry I.304–5
forest (symbol of) III.7, III.9
form, rather than principles II.158
formal education II.73
formation of mental images III.141
formative causation I.47, I.73, I.74, I.345, I.351, II.132, III.177
form-building II.7, II.181
formless planes of Unmanifest Worlds *q.v.* III.91

Formless spiritual realm III.226
forms II.160, III.86, III.116, III.120, III.174, III.368
  in appropriate bodies III.248
  death of III.221
  five III.115
  materialization of III.65, III.122
  and matter III.179, III.220
  and mind III.146–7
  and nervous ether III.178
  new III.88
  outer III.246
  physical III.219
  prototypal III.130
  renewal of III.3
  and spirit III.36
  suitable III.173
  united with life III.38
form-side of evolution *q.v.* (emanational descent *q.v.*) *III.175*, III.225
formula (mathematical simile for methodology of occult science *q.v.*) III.71, III.73–4, III.77
fossilised esotericists II.224
fossilized teachings II.219
fossils I.251, III.229, III.234, III.324
the Foundation III.26
foundation II.43, II.200, II.204
of form III.64
The Foundations of Newton's Alchemy (Dobbs) I.231
fountainhead
  of consciousness III.40, III.120
  of vital principle ('nervous ether') III.178
fountain pen (contrasting use of) III.147
Fount of Being II.20
four (number) III.77
four basic stages III.92
four beasts (*Revelation* 4:6) III.108
Four Elements III.46, III.76
Four Ideas III.107, III.109
four lower planes III.86, III.92–4
four-part rule for applying Hermetic Axiom *q.v.* I.248
four-quadrant grid (Wilber's transpersonal psychology *q.v.*) II.186
four secondary colours (simile for planes of kosmos *q.v.*) III.86
four secondary entities (simile for human constitution *q.v.*) II.18
four secondary principles of human constitution *q.v.* II.18
four states of being III.26
fourth dimension III.249
Fourth Root Race III.183, III.187
Fourth stage II.97, *II.98*
The Fourth Way (Ouspensky) II.181
Fourth Way classification II.181, *II.182*
Fourth Way School II.178
Fourth Way teaching II.165, *II.180*, II.181
Fox, Emmet I.300
fractal I.246, II.14, III.95
fraction, of the spiritual nature II.78
fractional conscious selves III.237
fractional incarnation of man *q.v.* III.127
framework II.188, II.189
framing (our questions, manner of) III.280
Francis of Assisi, Saint III.202
Fraternitas Rosicruciana Antiqua I.278
Fraternity of the Rosy III.60
fraud I.49, I.102
Frauenliebe und -leben (Schumann) II.101
Fravasham II.9
Frawley, David I.285
free choice III.352
Freedman, Stuart I.111
freedom III.16, III.271, III.334
freedom of enquiry II.224
freedom of expression III.164
freedom of thought II.189, II.224–5
Freemasonry I.273, III.14, III.190, III.341
Freemasons I.209
free will II.119, III.12
Freud, Sigmund I.146
Friedmann, Alexander I.333
friend (Death, in *Death and the Maiden q.v.*) II.100
frontal lobe II.119
fulcrum (human constitution *q.v.*) II.160
full spectrum healing II.165
functional dependence I.168–9, I.170, I.172–3
functionalism I.29, II.117, II.118
functionalist theorists I.39
functioning, of consciousness III.175
functioning principles II.160
functions II.7, *II.13*, II.34–5, II.123, III.83, III.161
  corresponding III.167
  and purpose II.11
  sense organs III.161
  and vāhana II.37
Fundamental and Molecular Mechanisms of Mutagenesis (Lieber) I.354

fundamental areas (simile of human nature *q.v.*) II.12
fundamental dualism III.156
fundamental elements II.12
fundamentalism I.50, II.220, II.223, III.312, III.319
fundamentalist creationists III.217
fundamentalist mindset II.218
fundamentalists II.8, II.133, III.239–40
fundamental law III.223
fundamental mechanism III.168
fundamental physical constants III.238–9
fundamental propositions III.287–8, *III.292*
fundamental substance III.277
fundamental unity II.6
funeral ceremonies and prayers II.88
fungi (*Entangled Life*) III.223
 see also Wood Wide Web
FUTURE III.117
 see also Māyā
the future III.264, III.328
On the Future (Rees) III.337–8
Future Circular Collider (FCC) III.310

Gaia theory/hypothesis/principle I.57–8, I.237, I.349–50
Galen of Pergamon III.317
Galilei, Galileo I.32, I.41, I.51, I.218, I.220, II.131
 letter to Kepler I.7, I.132, I.142
 and Monteverdi III.327
Galileo Commission I.142–3, III.331–2
Galileo Commission Report I.343, III.328, III.329, III.330, III.331
Galton, Sir Francis III.337
gametes III.248
Gamow, George I.335
Gandhi, Mahatma I.219, II.xv, II.153, II.165, III.265
Ganges, river I.280
Ganzfeld studies I.14
Garden of Eden III.38
The Garden of Universal Knowledge and Wisdom I.166, *I.167*
garments II.29, II.102, II.196, III.145, III.296
 see also vestures
the gaseous (gross material body *q.v.*, aspect of) III.115
Gates, Bill II.116
gateway to higher consciousness *q.v.* III.192
 see also cākra
Gāthās I.268
gaze (rays from eyes *q.v.*) III.377
Gébelin, Antoine Court de III.13
Gebser, Jean II.186, *II.187*
Geddes, Sir (later Lord) Auckland I.171–2
Geddes, Sir Patrick III.278
geek's pipe dream (computationalists *q.v.*) II.116
Gefter, Amanda I.342
Gelernter, David II.112, II.126, II.138
Geller, Uri I.119
Gell-Mann, Murray I.99
gene frequencies I.56
the generalist II.124
generalized term II.10, II.11
general principles II.218, III.140
general relativity theory *see* relativity theory
'General Scholium' II.77, III.37, III.105–6
general theory of relativity *see* relativity theory
generation of man II.177
generative organ III.185
generative system I.179, III.38, III.39
generic terms I.152, II.38
genes I.9, I.11, I.56, I.72, I.350
 or environment II.90
 and fields of organization I.73
 and talent I.10
 and transformers and transducers I.78
Genesis II.73, III.102
 1:4 III.356
 2:7 II.16, II.30
genesis
 of germinal/germ cells *q.v.* III.247
  see also Weismann
 of cosmos and man III.285
genetic code I.74–5
genetic determinism II.110
genetic material II.178
genetic predisposition II.90
genetics I.8, I.75, I.345, I.347, III.223, III.279, III.336
Genetics and the Origin of Species (Dobzhansky) I.348
genie I.81
genitalia III.185
 see also pineal gland
genius I.9, I.219, II.71, II.88, II.100, III.165, III.256
 and Antaḥkaraṇa II.90
 and Beethoven II.99
 and genes I.10
 and inner life experience II.130

genius (continued)
and intuition III.189
and madness III.336
mathematical III.171, III.208
and Newton I.11
and spiritual nature III.129
and yogi II.202
geographical regions II.6
see also lokas; tala
geological disasters III.187
geology (theories in) I.108
see also prehistoric continents
geometry III.14
see also chess
Gerhart, John I.355
German idealist philosophy II.182
German section, Theosophical Society II.183
Germany and Austria, Theosophical Esoteric Society for II.183
germinal/germ cells *q.v.* III. 247, III.248
germ plasm III.247–8
germs II.79
gestation II.68
gestures (meaning and significance of) III.42–3, III.72
ghost III.351
The Ghost in the Machine (Koestler) II.14
Gibran, Kahlil II.26, II.64, II.79, II.99, II.109, III.55, III.326
Gifford Lectures I.53, II.197
gift, from the gods III.73
Gītā, Bhagavad II.225
Gitanjali (Tagore) I.1
glands III.171, III.172, III.182, III.191–2
Glazewski, Andrew I.82
Gleiser, Marcelo I.132
global outlook III.265–6
Globes III.88–9
globes III.63, III.93, *III.93*
glory of God III.268
glowing fireballs (astronomy) III.268, III.269
glue (simile for union of thought *q.v.* and desire *q.v.*) II.201, II.202
Glynn, Ian I.173
gnosis II.164, III.10
Gnostic Christianity I.199
Gnosticism I.188, II.164, III.25–6
Gnostic Order II.183
Gnostics I.209
Goal III.102
goal II.221, III.194
God I.lxxv, I.184, II.16, II.174, III.15, III.295
and bottom-up approach I.55
and the Chaldeans III.65
and Darwinism I.56, III.245
and Dawkins III.311
definition III.51
everlastingly involved in the universe III.142
external III.89
face of II.xv
first emanation of III.226
glory of III.268
and Grand MAN III.34
ineffability of I.293
and intelligent design III.239
kingdom of II.69
and Moses III.251
and New Thought I.289
and objective universe III.36
omnipresence of I.320
pervading principle of three worlds III.22
and Russell I.307
and science II.229
Son of III.35, III.115
and Strömberg I.80
substance of III.105
and Tabernacle III.252
and top-down approach I.54
God-as-designer III.295
God-delusion III.311
Godel, Kurt III.352
Godhead III.35
God-like state II.198
God–Men III.205
God of the gaps III.312
God of Wisdom I.247
gods II.77, II.216, III.6, III.24, *III.27*, III.159
God-spark III.108
God the Father III.117
Godwin, Joscelyn I.208, III.341
Goethe, Johann Wolfgang von I.41–3, I.208, I.209, III.145, III.199
Goethean science I.40, I.42–3, I.57, I.165, II.182, III.172
Goetheanum II.182
gold III.15, III.147
Gold, Thomas I.335
golden egg II.39
Golden Rule II.67–8
golden thread I.303, I.327
The Golden Verses of Pythagoras II.63
golden womb II.39

Goldfried, Marvin I.342
good I.267, I.268, I.269, II.25, II.26, II.89, II.203
and Spento-Mainyush II.174
good man II.81–2
Goodman, Dan III.307
Goodrick-Clarke, Nicholas I.179–80, I.181, I.244, III.122
good science II.221
good Theosophy II.221
Good Thought II.172
good twin II.172
Goodwin, Brian I.43–4, I.72, I.243, I.346, I.352, I.355
Gordon, John I.187, I.194, II.219
Gospel III.102
Gospel of John III.102
Goswami, Amit I.346, I.352, I.353, I.354, I.355, III.228
Gottwald, Franz-Theo I.353
Gould, Stephen Jay I.57, I.164, I.350
Gouy, Louis Georges I.117–18
governance of nations III.14
Governors III.26, *III.27*
GPS (Global Positioning System) fitted to Amazon personnel I.4
Grace III.199
graded 'step down' (electrical simile) II.38
graduated scale III.288
Grand Man III.34
Grand Man III.63–4
grand unification III.357
Grand Unified Theory III.308
grave (Al-Haqqani on destination of body *q.v.*) II.96
gravitation I.305–6, III.108
gravitational radiation III.85
gravitational waves III.85, III.262
gravity I.250, III.78, III.278
Graziano, Michael I.356–7, III.314–15
the great (distinguished from the famous) II.84
great adjuster III.90
Great Beings III.189
Great Breath III.144
greater Consciousness II.135
greater life III.223
Greater Mysteries I.180, I.270, I.271, I.283–4
Great Hermetic Axiom I.239
great Illusion III.117, III.118
Great Pyramid I.285, III.33, III.50, III.129
Great Serpent Mound I.274, *I.274*
Great Spirit I.278
great thought *III.27*
great universe II.205
Great White Brotherhood I.211, I.280, I.281
great wisdom traditions III.227
Greece (Mystery centre) II.3
Greek Centaur III.49
Greek language II.3, II.5
Greek Mysteries I.262–3
Greek mythology III.9, III.25
Greek system II.175, *II.179*
Greek teachings II.175–8, *II.179*
Green, Jim I.104
The Green Snake and the Beautiful Lily (Goethe) III.199
Gregory/Mayo syndrome I.120
'Greta effect' I.150
grief, effect of II.82
Griffiths, Bede II.221
Grinberg, Jacobo III.191
gross bodies II.210, III.179
gross constitution III.18, III.252
Gross Element–Principles of matter III.159
Gross Elements III.158–9
gross material III.237
gross matter II.2, III.115
ground breaking theories II.209
group consciousness I.149–51
group memory I.78–9
group mind I.52, I.149
group soul II.110
Group theory I.274
Grove, Sir William I.50, I.316, I.327
growth (evolution *q.v.*) III.224
On Growth and Form (D'Arcy Wentworth Thompson) I.74, I.348
guardian angel III.12
Guardian of the Threshold III.198
Guénon, René I.41, I.208–9
guidance of Spiritual Ego *q.v.* III.293
guiding law in Nature *q.v.* III.72
see also analogy
gulf in human traits *q.v.* II.9
gullibility (avoiding predisposition to) III.313
Guṇas III.113
Gunton, Richard III.241
Gupta Vidyā I.xxxix, III.88, *III.90*, III.91
Gurdjieff, George II.178, II.180, III.117
Gurney, Edmund II.56
Gurwitsch, Alexander I.71
Guterres, António III.187

Guth, Alan I.338, I.340
Guthrie, Kenneth S. I.279

habitat of lost souls *q.v.* II.85
habitual patterns to maintain status quo II.133
Hades II.65
Haeckel, Ernst I.346–7, III.184, III.229
HAL 9000 (sentient computer) II.138, II.139
Haldane, J. B. S. I.348, III.336
Haliburton, Thomas Chandler III.286
Hall, Manly P. I.lii, I.lxxxi, I.179, I.181, II.221, III.18, III.22
on adepts II.57, II.59
on black arts III.272
on blinds I.206
and Book of Thoth III.25
on death II.102
on Divine Nature III.127, III.129
on exoteric and esoteric I.194
on Guthrie I.279
'The Human Body in Symbolism' III.44
on immortality III.130
Invisible Records of Thought and Action III.234
on lotus and rose III.60
on man III.52
on misuse of symbolism III.16–17
on the Mysteries I.178, I.205, I.214, I.274
and *philosophia perennis* II.219
on Pythagoras I.182–3
on Qabbalah I.188
on Saptaparṇa III.56
The Secret Teaching of All Ages III.5
and the Supreme Mystery II.51
on symbolism III.1, III.19, III.67
on unwritten teachings III.4
on white and black magic I.200
on the zodiac III.28–9
al-Ḥallāj, Manṣūr I.218, III.33, III.34, III.35, III.51
'Hallelujah Chorus' III.268
hallucinations II.56, III.115, III.315
hallucinogenic drugs III.197
haloes III.202
Hamblin, Henry Thomas I.289
Hameroff, Stuart I.97–8, I.148, III.163
Hamilton, Craig III.40
Hamlet (Shakespeare) II.xv, II.63
Hammerklavier Sonata (Beethoven) II.122
Handbook of Psychotherapy Integration (Goldfried, Pachankis and Bell) I.342
Hand of Grace (spiritual experiences *q.v.*) II.56
Hands of Light: A Guide to Healing Through the Human Energy Field (Brennan) II.165, II.166
hand-washing (COVID-19 *q.v.*) III.318
Hansel, C. E. M. I.120
haplous III.202
see also Light III.201–2
happiness I.xlii, II.26, II.124, III.186, III.320, III.322
al-Haqqani, Nazim (known as Shaykh Nazim) II.34, II.58, II.96
hara II.165
hard lesson from nature *q.v.* III.110
hard problem of consciousness *q.v.* I.28, I.147, III.40, III.163
Hardy, Alister I.52–3, I.350
Hardy, Godfrey Harold III.206, III.207, III.208, III.278–9
harm from premature psychic arousal III.194
Harman, Willis I.54, I.144–5, I.340, I.354
harmony II.146, II.188, II.189, *II.190*, III.101, III.102, III.188
Harmony: A new way of looking at our world (Charles, Prince of Wales) III.273
a harmony of philosophers (Leibniz *q.v.*) II.188
Harry Oldfield's Invisible Universe (Solomon and Solomon) II.84
Harry Potter books III.325
Harry Potter and the Prisoner of Azkaban (Rowling) II.85
Hartmann, Franz I.220–1, I.294
Harvey, William III.317–18
hauntings II.82
Hawaiians III.18
Hawking, Stephen I.xlviii–xlix, I.84, I.336, I.343, III.219, III.228, III.312
on AI II.112, II.116, III.339–40
A Brief History of Time III.109
and the multiverse III.85
head III.46, III.112, III.252, III.254
back of III.184
of a tape/video recorder II.59, III.95
transplant III.272, III.339
two III.264
see also Janus
headless bodies (upshot of physical sciences *q.v.*) III.262
healings I.171
health II.60, III.127, III.180, III.265, III.283, III.320
healthy scepticism I.317

hearing II.120–1, II.142, III.xix
Heart II.32, III.111, III.113
heart I.xlvii–xlviii, II.45, II.229, III.41–3, III.87, III.227, III.317
 and brain III.40, III.41, III.42
 desires of III.114
 disease III.41
 impressions of II.60
 left side of the body III.44
 and meditation III.203
 and Mysteries I.179, I.214
 primacy of III.33
 sacred correspondence with the sun III.44
 seat of consciousness III.254
 and secret doctrine III.46
 source of life III.38
 and spiritual nature III.39
 and Sūtra 6 III.112
 transplant III.41
 unprepared III.199
HeartMath Institute Research Center III.40, III.41–2
heaven II.6, II.63, II.90
Heaven and Hell (Swedenborg) I.167
heavenly being II.96
Heavenly Man I.264, III.123, III.155
heavenly things (John *q.v.*, Chapter 3) II.69, II.70
Heaven of orthodox Christianity II.70
heavens (astronomy and astrology *q.v.*) III.22
Hebrew language II.3, II.5, III.45
Hebrew theology I.193–4
Heifetz, Jascha II.137
Heindel, Max II.164, III.198
Heine, Heinrich II.56
Heisenberg, Werner I.42, I.172, I.320, I.335–6, I.337, II.74, III.351
 dying intuitions III.165
 on reductionism I.53–4
 and uncertainty principle I.109, I.333
hell II.6, II.63, II.78, II.84–6
Helmholtz, Hermann von I.116
hemispheres, of the brain II.23, II.123
Hempel, Carl I.31
Hempel's Dilemma I.31
Herder, Gottfried von I.287
hereditary transmission III.247–8
heredity I.101, I.137
heresy II.131
heretical views III.313
heretics II.132
Heretics Society III.336
The Heritage of Copernicus: Theories 'pleasing to the mind' (Miller) I.350
Hermes III.224
Hermes Trismegistus I.247, I.264, III.82
Floor Mosaic in the Cathedral of Siena *I.247*
Hermetica I.247
Hermetic Anthropos III.129
Hermetic Axiom I.lxxv, I.83, I.228, I.244, I.246–54, II.76, II.205, III.34, III.70–1, III.122
 and aura electricities III.114
 and Bembine Table of Isis III.22
 and Cosmos III.28, *III.28*, III.88
 Fourth Principle I.239
 and law of analogy III.83
 and man I.lii
 and Newton I.231, III.81, III.90
 and *philosophia perennis* I.xlix, III.287, *III.292*
 and Root Races III.375
 and unfolding of consciousness III.101
 what applies to the universe, applies to man III.173
Hermeticism I.197, I.244, I.248, II.73
Hermetic life III.11
Hermetic Order of the Golden Dawn I.188, I.286, III.172
Hermetic philosophy II.125
Hermetic relationship II.151
Hermetic Wisdom III.73
The Hermit (Tarot cards *q.v.*) III.11–12, *III.12*
Hershkovitz, Israel III.233–4
Hertog, Thomas I.343, III.85
Herz-Sommer, Alice II.55
Ḥesed III.63
Heston, Charlton III.230
heterogeneous wisdom-streams II.189
Heydon, John II.57
Hiawatha I.272–3
The Hidden History of the Human Race (Cremo) III.229–30
hidden influences III.325
hidden laws of Nature III.243
The Hidden Power (Inglis) I.119–20
hidden purposes in nature *q.v.* III.326–7
hidden variables theory I.80, III.281
Hierarchies II.113
 of conscious and animate Beings III.72
 of whole and parts II.14
hieroglyphics III.25
Hieronymus, Thomas Galen II.166
hierophants I.210

Higgins, Frank C. I.188
Higgins, Godfrey I.206, I.284
Higgs, Peter III.310
Higgs boson III.310
high altitude lack of oxygen (scientific explanation of sensed presence *q.v.*) II.55
high creativity III.255
Higher Beings III.99
higher centres *II.180*, II.181
Higher Consciousness I.148
higher consciousness II.65
higher dimensions II.53, II.154, III.93, III.249, III.250
Higher Ego II.41, II.46, II.47, II.52, II.53, II.106
  and Antaḥkaraṇa II.48, II.87, II.88
  and Devachan II.70, II.71, II.78
  divine light II.216
  loses all influence over its lower selves II.84–5
  and natural separation from personal elements II.68
  and Personal ego II.89, II.97
  and rebirth II.79
  and shell II.81
  and spiritual aroma II.68
  tablets of memory II.73
higher entity III.237
higher internal vision III.250
higher life II.81, III.224
Higher Manas II.41, II.68, II.97, II.150
  and Antaḥkaraṇa II.48, II.87
  and classical Theosophical literature II.149, II.150
  and Lower manas II.99
  and Saptaparṇa III.58
Higher Mind II.23, II.41, *II.42*, II.59–60, II.123, III.6, III.321
  and intuition III.189
  qualities II.107
  and Upper Triplicity I.148
higher nature II.90
higher orders of existence II.4–5
higher planes II.53, III.95
Higher Power III.342
higher power II.56
higher principle II.38, III.16
Higher Self I.175, II.17, II.162, II.220, II.227, III.xxi, III.204, III.211, III.242
  and Joad II.199
  and Radiant Light II.203
higher states III.171
Higher Thought I.288, I.291
Higher Thought Centre I.288
Higher Triad II.106, III.66
Higher Worlds II.164
higher worlds III.199
Highest Cause III.36
highest, Divine Consciousness *q.v.*, to lowest level of descent *q.v.* III.154
highest principle III.256–7
highest spiritual faculty III.189
highest teachings III.17
high initiates III.193
high intellect III.271
Hildegard of Bingen III.311
Hiley, Basil I.337
Hill, Napoleon I.305, II.26
Hilton, Steve I.4, I.53
Himalayan Brotherhood I.280
Hinduism II.53, III.173
Hindu philosophy III.102
Hipparchus III.23
hippocampal structure I.162
Hippocratic Oath III.316
hippy fraternity III.196
Hiraṇyagarbha II.39, III.125
His thoughts (Einstein *q.v.* on God *q.v.*) III.110
historical evidence (unity of *philosophia perennis q.v.*) III.59
historical labyrinth (Crete) III.7, *III.8*
historical transfer of knowledge III.59
history
  of ideas II.123
  of science III.317
The History and Theory of Vitalism (Driesch) I.348
History of the Reign of Henry the Seventh (Bacon) III.60
Hitler II.131, II.132
  see also Maddox
hit-men, science *q.v.* I.120
Hobbes, Thomas I.51
Hod III.63
Hodgson, Marshall I.xviii
Hodgson Report I.212
  see also Blavatsky, H. P. I.219, II.134
Ḥokhmāh III.63
holiness II.65
holism I.161, I.345, III.265
holistic approach I.43, I.254, *I.255*, I.345–6, II.135, II.204, III.250, III.285–6
  and analytical approach I.166–7

holistic biology III.278
holistic complement to reductionism *q.v.* I.75
holistic psychology II.186
holobionts III.222
hologram I.76, I.246, I.341, II.14, III.95
holographic field II.197
holographic universe III.358
holons II.14
  see also Koestler
Holy Bible III.17
  see also Bible
Holy Ghost III.111
holy kiss II.73
  see also Zohar
Holy of Holies III.252
Holy Qur'an I.192, III.52
The Holy Science (Śrī Swami Yukteswar Giri *q.v.*) III.102, III.104–20, III.126
Holy Spirit III.303
holy war (true meaning of) I.296
  see also jihad
Homayouni, Dr Massoud III.226
Home (spiritual meaning of) II.99
  see also Elegischer Gesang (Beethoven)
home (simile for human constitution *q.v.*) III.252–5
'Home, Sweet Home' (universal appeal of) III.275
hominids III.232, III.236
homunculi II.231
Hoomi, Mahatma Koot II.107
Horgan, John I.8, I.353
horizontal arm (primary differentiation) III.145
  see also Consciousness–Matter relationship
horizontal differentiation III.144
hormones, reproductive III.182
horoscopes III.30
hosts III.131, III.223
House of the Mysteries III.13
houses, domestic II.202, *II.203*
the 'how' (brain *q.v.*, hemispheres of *q.v.*) II.123
see also McGilchrist
How Consciousness Became the Universe (Chopra et al.) III.164
How the Leopard Got Its Spots (Goodwin) I.352
'How to Think Like a Scientist' (Shermer) I.12
Hoyle, Fred I.107, I.335, I.340
H.P.B.'s Diagram of Meditation III.121
Hubble, Edwin I.334
hubris (scientific) III.306, III.312
hubristic materialist III.243
human ancestry III.243
human animal II.216
human antiquity III.229–35
human artefacts III.229, III.230–1
human beings I.2, I.3, I.5, II.xviii, III.182, III.235, III.236, III.288
  complex creatures III.xvii
  and Deucalion and Pyrrha III.9
  divine instrument III.172
  and emanation III.134
  life-principle II.231
  and solar consciousness III.223
  and violence III.243
human biology III.336
human birth I.252, *I.253*, III.83
human body I.2, I.99, I.209, I.244, III.33–4, III.35–6, III.44–7, III.295–6
  correspondences to evolution III.222
  and cross (symbol of) I.206
    see also Rosicrucian Order; Higgins, Godfrey; Waite
  and drugs III.197–9
  and human form I.241
  occult centres of consciousness in I.279
  a projection of the divine and a channel for It III.120
  and Sephirothic Tree III.60–1
  and sodium chloride I.2
  symbol III.37
  and Tabernacle III.252
  temple, in form of I.179
'The Human Body in Symbolism' (Hall) III.44
human brain *see* brain III.357
human capacity II.181
human carnivores III.42
human conception III.271
human condition II.100, II.135, III.33, III.34
human consciousness *see* consciousness II.115
human constitution *see* constitution of man
human culture II.124
human development III.187
Human Devolution (Cremo) III.235
human DNA I.241
  see also DNA
Human Ego II.46, II.70, II.176, II.216
human energy fields II.84, II.165, II.166
human entity II.14, II.29, II.196
human evolution I.25, II.xvii, II.162
  see also evolution
human form, distinguished from human state or condition I.241

human gestation III.355–6
human head transplant III.272
human heart *see* heart
Human Immortality: Two supposed objections to the doctrine (James, William) I.168, I.169, II.xvi
human incarnation II.22
human intelligence *see* intelligence
human intervention II.129
humanitarian ideals II.153
humanity II.130, II.153, III.92, III.121, III.221, III.236
  and karmic burdens II.164
  and Ladder of Life III.235
  and objective physical plane III.97
  paradigm III.61
  phase state of consciousness III.221
  quests for knowledge III.118
  whole of III.248
humankind *see* human beings; man II.197
Human Kingdom III.130
human larynx III.252
human life *see* life
humanlike intelligence III.231
humanlike species III.236
human–machine boundaries, blurred II.139
human mind *see* mind
Human Monad II.22
human nature *see* nature II.222
humanness II.116
humanoid jogger *II.139*
human operator II.129
human origins III.324–5
human physical senses *see* senses
Human Principles III.74–5, *III.75*
human principles III.70, III.76, *III.76*, *III.79*, III.80, III.98, *III.99*
  and correspondences II.151
  critical aspects III.121
  see also constitution of man; Principles of Man
human programmers II.114, II.121, II.129, II.130
human psyche III.3, III.5
human qualities II.141, III.325
human regeneration III.15, III.51, III.190
human sacrifice III.18
human senses *see* senses II.204
human skeletons III.232
human society, moral sense in III.244
Human Soul I.99, II.19, II.38, II.45, II.110, II.176
  and Taimni System II.162
  and transformer (simile) II.202
human soul I.223, I.239, I.264, I.293, I.334
human spine III.80
  see also Veena
Human Spirit II.164
human stage III.98
human state III.33
human suffering III.43
'Human Territory' *II.21*
human traits II.88–90
human vision III.377
human voice II.230
Hume, Allan Octavian II.107, II.108, III.130
Hume, David I.287
humility II.128, II.166, II.221, II.223, II.224, III.243, III.281
Hunahpu I.275
hunger, spiritual II.xv
Hurwic, Anna (and Curie, Pierre *q.v.*) I.117
Hüttenbrenner, Anselm (and Beethoven *q.v.*) II.99
Huxley, Aldous I.xxxviii–xxxix, I.52, III.195, III.337
Huxley, Julian I.52, I.349, III.336
Huxley, Thomas Henry III.337
Huygens, Christiaan II.207
hybrid discipline III.43
  see also neurocardiology
hydrogen I.241
  see also DNA
hydrogen atom I.98
  see also occult chemistry; *Occult Chemistry*
hylomorphism II.127
hylozoic principle I.238
Hypatia I.217, I.218
hyperbola curve III.359
hyperbolic function III.359
hypnotism III.201
hypocrites, reprimanded by Jesus I.290

'I' II.45, II.73, II.74, II.184, III.221
'I am,' cognition of II.45
IBM
  Project Debater II.114
  supercomputer Deep Blue II.113
icons I.190–1, I.192, I.193, III.4
I Corinthians (on human constitution *q.v.*) II.32
idealism III.352
Ideal Numbers III.371
ideals III.38

Ideas III.35, III.151, III.152, III.368
in Divine Mind III.107, III.108
Four III.107, III.109
ideas II.6, II.123, III.37, III.107, III.126, III.185, III.265
in consciousness III.116, III.120
of gross matter III.115
illusory III.112
innovative III.222
as intellectual playthings III.262
and meaning III.152
original III.92
and symbols III.1
Ideation III.120
ideation III.92, III.146
ideative realm III.123
identification of illusory appearances with the Real *q.v.* III.108
identifying the mechanism with informing principle *q.v.* II.127
see also Walshe
identity, and God III.35
identity theorists I.39
ideology I.9, I.13, I.53, I.67, I.141, I.143, II.133
Christian I.208
Darwinian I.115
racial I.292
idiocy I.221
idiom II.3
idiot (tale about) III.279
see also scepticism
idolatry III.16, III.37
Ignorance III.111
ignorance I.221, III.11, III.49, III.109, III.321, III.326
ignoring, what distinguishes man from a computer II.117
'I – I' II.198
Iliad III.47
Iliffe, Rob III.284–5
ill health (Ramanujan, Srinivasa *q.v.*) III.210
Illuminati I.211
illumination III.7, III.196, III.199
Illusion III.117
Illusion Body II.52
illusions II.54, III.xx, III.xxi, III.117–18, III.147, III.148, III.196
and the real III.197
world of III.56
illusive form II.54
illusory appearance II.74
illusory body II.54
illusory idea III.112
illusory power III.140
illusory spell III.119
images III.16, III.37, III.38, III.51, III.80, III.141–2, III.148
correct III.247
of God III.106
mental III.167
mental sensuous III.154
multiple III.253
imagination II.42, II.70, III.49, III.117, III.120, III.312
imagining II.118, III.135
immanence I.327
immaterial element II.127
immaterialism I.34
immaterial wave-structures I.80–1
immersion of self *q.v.* III.191
see also Samādhi
Immortal body III.338
Immortal Dweller III.342
immortal entity II.97
immortal heretic III.180
immortal Individuality III.254
immortal individuality I.148
Immortalist Society III.335
immortality II.73, II.76–7, II.205, III.200, III.312, III.332, III.335–43
and Hall III.129
and László II.197
of the soul III.130
and transmission (scientific ignorance of) I.173
see also James, William
Immortal Man I.265
immortal man II.160, II.196, II.200, II.201, III.59
immortal portion, of body III.247
see also Weismann
immortal principle I.324, II.175, III.341
Immortal Self I.265
immortal soul I.270, II.102, II.197, III.67, III.338
immutability II.76
impact, after-death communications II.94
impaired memory II.59
impelling force II.24
Imperial College III.196, III.306–7
imperishable Ego II.176
impermanence I.33, I.263, II.28, II.29

impersonal Ego II.89
impersonal thoughts II.107
implements, from antiquity III.233
the implicate III.74
implicate order I.251, II.132, III.225, III.295
implicit memory I.101
imposters III.326, III.334
Inca Empire I.273, I.276
incarnation II.25, II.48, II.76, II.79, II.224, III.75, III.127
  and Antaḥkaraṇa II.216
  and devachanee II.73
  innumerable II.72
  present II.89
  and psychological orbits III.8
  and Steiner II.183
Incas I.273, I.276–7, I.280, I.281, III.18
The Incas (OAS) I.277
incorrect assumptions II.209
indefiniteness, insecurity of III.280
independence III.334
independent organizing principle III.177
independent thought II.224
India (Mystery centre) II.3
Indian classical music III.80
Indian classifications II.168–71
Indian metaphysics II.35
Indian Mysteries I.269–72, I.280
Indian occultism II.172
Indian Shadow Land (of American Indians *q.v.*) I.274
Indian systems II.167–71, *II.173*
individual II.12, III.95
individual–collective axis (Wilber, Ken *q.v.*) II.186
individual ideation III.146, III.151, III.152, *III.153*
Individuality II.16, II.17, II.18, II.23, II.38, II.45, II.46, II.177
  and Ātma II.227
  comprises II.64
  and Cube unfolded III.66
  derivation of II.105–6
  immortal III.254
  and personality II.200
  real II.52
  and Taimni System II.162
  and Vedantic classification II.170
individuality I.99, I.109, I.148, I.151
individualization II.110
individual mental worlds III.148
individual mind III.97, III.134, III.149, III.150, III.151, III.153, III.167
individual path, liberty to pursue II.189
individual self III.161
individual soul III.303
individual units of consciousness III.236–7
individual water droplets (simile for units of consciousness *q.v.*) III.237
  see also devolution
individuation I.151, III.256
indivisibility (essential meaning of) II.105
Indo-Caucasians I.286
indriyas III.145–6, III.160, III.161
induced light experience III.203
  see also auras; meditation
induction (scientific method *q.v.*) I.31
inductive method I.229, I.235
industrial accidents III.266–7
indwelling Boundless Life III.86
indwelling consciousness III.295
indwelling power III.9
inert matter III.146
Infeld, Leopold I.xliii, I.230
inference, unwarranted (brain states *q.v.*) II.119
  see also computationalist argumentation
inferior part, twofold constitution of God *q.v.* and man *q.v.* III.38
inferior principle II.34
inferior universe I.279
Inferno II.84, II.86, *II.87*
infimum (mathematics *q.v.*) III.358
the Infinite I.184
Infinite in All Directions (Dyson) I.340
Infinite Intelligence I.289
infinitely small/large as polarity of time II.76
infinity, and infinite II.77, III.142
The Inflationary Universe: The quest for a new theory of cosmic origins (Guth) I.340
influence II.84, II.89
information
  carrier of III.42
  from human brain to a machine III.272
  process III.307
information processor II.129
informing principle II.126, II.127
Inglis, Brian I.119–20
ingrained habits III.xvii
inherent intelligence I.136
inheritance I.75, I.78, III.248
initiant I.210
initiate, middle centre of III.38

Initiates III.92
initiates I.210, I.219, II.75, III.6, III.37, III.193, III.304
initiatic teachings II.175
initiation I.179, I.180, I.222–3, II.69
innate faculties III.57
innate potency III.217
innate potentiality III.219, III.220, III.375
innate purpose III.295
inner chamber III.253, *III.254*
inner clarity III.363
inner deterioration III.194, III.197
  see also psychedelic drugs
inner doors to the internal, subjective world of human body *q.v.* II.60
  see also Psychic and Noetic Action
inner ear II.120–1
Inner Ego II.46, II.87, II.106
inner founders, Theosophical movement *q.v.* III.130
Inner Group, Esoteric Section III.121
Inner Group Instructions, Theosophical Society *q.v.* I.283
Inner Group Teachings III.181
Inner Group Teachings of H. P. Blavatsky (Blavatsky) I.209
inner illumination III.199
inner life I.304–5, II.13, II.130, III.xix, III.321
The Inner Life (Leadbeater) II.156
Inner man II.2, II.37, II.136
inner meaning II.4, III.189, III.303
innermost self II.32
inner motive III.334
inner nature III.253, III.328, III.334
inner person II.12
inner planes III.86
inner poverty I.5
  see also technology
inner sight III.189
inner significance III.276
inner spiritual eye III.186
inner structure III.121
inner subjective state II.136
inner voices II.55, III.xvii
inner worlds III.xix, III.245
innovative ideas III.222
inorganic intelligences III.338
insentient aggregate III.174
insights III.11, III.263
instinct I.74, I.75, I.78, II.109
instinctual soul II.177, II.178
institutionalised religion II.125
institutionalized science III.48
  see also establishment science
instructions II.113, II.114, II.195
instrumentality III.153, III.154, III.167, III.182, III.188
instruments II.89, II.228, III.161, III.306
  indriyas III.160
  of mind III.172
  musical II.121, II.230
  and users II.126, II.127, II.137, II.138
insulting retorts II.133
integral outlook II.30
integral psychology II.185–6
Integral Psychology (Wilber) II.186
Integrated Consciousness III.148, III.167
integration II.29, III.225, III.371
Integrative Physiological and Behavioral Science (Goswami and Todd) I.353
intellect II.1, II.22, III.105, III.227, III.256, III.275
  borrowed light III.254
  and cunning III.294
  jñāna III.250
  misuse III.276
  no guarantee of elevated spirituality III.271
  pure II.41
  and reason III.189
  and scepticism III.280
  and science III.313
the Intellectual (man *q.v.*, nature of) II.39
intellectual development II.220
intellectual honesty III.267
intellectualist higher centre III.38
intellectualists III.242
intellectual materialism III.30
intellectual model III.92
intellectual myopia (Plato, allegory of the cave *q.v.*) III.377
  see also tunnel vision
intellectual power III.39
Intellectual Soul II.164
intellectual stature II.89
intellectual world III.26
intelligence I.132, I.134–6, II.84, III.118, III.231, III.241–2, III.326
  and evolution III.182
  and human body III.52
  inheres in every atom of matter I.243, I.244
  and intuition III.250
  ordinary III.171

intelligence (continued)
  outside mainstream science III.172
  range of III.236
  traditional definitions of III.223
  and transhumanism III.338
intelligence-bearing agent II.210
Intelligence Came First (Smith) II.224
Intelligence principle II.160
Intelligences I.285, III.99, III.176, III.327, III.342
intelligent being II.23
intelligent design III.238–42
intelligent designer III.236
intelligentsia I.149
Intelligible Triad II.205, III.36
intentionality, dimension of II.165
interchange of energy III.192
  see also cākras
interconnectedness
  of life III.223
  non-local III.307
  of things in the world II.126
interconnection III.57, III.264
interdependence III.57, III.264
interdisciplinary science of consciousness III.331
interfaces II.79, II.160, III.140, III.161, III.165–6
interferometry work (optical physics) II.208
interior–exterior axis II.186
intermediary part (human nature *q.v.*) II.37–8
  see also soul
intermediary sphere (God *q.v.* and man *q.v.*) III.38
intermediary stage (evolution *q.v.*) III.340
intermediate cycle between incarnation *q.v.* II.73
  see also Devachan
intermediate stages III.199
intermediate mental vehicle (evolution *q.v.*) II.110
intermingling elements in man *q.v.* II.107
internal bias III.xxi
internal cleansing III.199
internal condition III.187
internal experience III.163
internal faculties II.xviii
internal instrument II.86
internal landscapes II.146
internal light III.226
internal platforms (simile for souls) II.204
internal pressures III.xvii
internal subjective experiences III.131
internal thought III.72
International New Thought Alliance I.289
International Society for the Study of Subtle Energies and Energy Medicine II.83
internet radicalization III.272
The Interpretation of Nature and the Psyche (Jung and Pauli) I.335
interrelated problems III.140
interrelated questions III.164
inter-species transitions (evolution *q.v.*) III.245
inter-subjective validation (Wilber, Ken *q.v.*) III.11
Inti I.276
  see also South America; Mysteries
Intimations of Immortality (Wordsworth) I.152–3
Introduction to Science (Thomson) I.332–3, III.278
introspection I.2, I.30
Intuition I.42
intuition I.153, I.184, I.285, I.297, III.3, III.186, III.189, III.205, III.209, III.243
  and Bergson I.172
  definition III.205
  from Divine Ego III.255
  and mystics I.186, I.201
  of Pauli III.355
  and Ramanujan III.207
Intuition Principle II.18, II.19, II.20, II.22
intuitive mind (Buddhi) III.13
'On the Intuitive Understanding of Non-Locality as Implied by Quantum Theory' (Bohm and Hiley) I.337
invariant speed of light II.209
inverted triangle (simile for terrestrial man) III.123
Investigation of the phenomenology and impact of perceived spontaneous and direct After-Death Communications (ADCs) II.94–6
the invisible I.304
invisible body of man III.179
invisible forces III.116
Invisible Higher Power III.xxi
invisible powers III.37
Invisible Records of Thought and Action (Hall) III.234
invisible region III.97
invisible universe II.142
invisible world of spirit III.64

involution I.346, III.9, III.93, III.161, III.217, III.225
definition I.242–3, III.182–3, III.218–19
and Goswami I.354
and Śrī Aurobindo I.348
involutionary cycle III.183
ion channels (brain *q.v.*) III.351
Iron Age III.9
Irrational, meaning III.129
irrational man III.236
irrational soul II.176, II.177
irrational Spiritual Soul III.129
Irwin, Richard III.357
Isis I.180, I.266–7, I.280, III.26, III.190
Isis Unveiled (Blavatsky) I.liii, I.236, I.247, II.107, II.148–9
Islam I.192
isolation, life of (Ramanujan *q.v.* and Newton *q.v.*) III.208
Iśvara III.173, III.370

Jablonska, Eva I.355
Jack the Ripper II.89, II.215
Jahn, Robert I.85, I.116, I.317, I.318, I.319
Jainism III.102
James, Gospel of I.264
James, William I.xviii, I.lxxxii, I.88, I.167, I.174, I.175, II.xvi, II.110, II.137, III.165, III.195, III.255
on the brain I.161, I.162
and functional dependence I.168–9, I.170, I.172–3
Some Problems of Philosophy I.317
on Troward I.300
Janus III.4, III.264–8, III.293
Jeans, Sir James I.xliv–xlv, I.265, I.317, *III.27*, III.263
on bottled-up waves I.37, I.334, III.156
Jesus I.290, II.80
Jewish mysticism I.193–4
see also Qabbalah
jigsaw puzzle (missing pieces in science provided by occult science *q.v.*) II.90
jihad (true meaning of) I.296
Jinarâjadâsa, Curuppumullage II.7, II.153, II.158–60
Jinarâjadâsa System II.158–60
Jīva (kosmos *q.v.*, the macrocosm *q.v.*) III.96
jīva (human constitution *q.v.*, the microcosm *q.v.*) II.27
Jivaic III.96
jīvanmukta III.186
see also Third Eye
Jīvanmukti III.303
jñāna II.171, III.227
Jñāna Yoga I.165, I.283
Jñānendriyas III.113, III.160
Joad, C. E. M. II.195, II.198–9
Jobst, Dr Kim III.273
John, Gospel of
14:2 II.60
14:12 III.257
Johnson, Samuel I.287, III.311
Jones, William III.364
Josephson, Brian I.244, I.322, I.339, I.351, II.132–3
on agents as sources of physics I.243, I.342, III.72, III.159
journey (after-death communications *q.v.*) II.95
joy II.90, II.120, II.231
Judaism III.4, III.17
Judge, William Quan II.156, II.219, III.1, III.211
The Judgement (Tarot cards *q.v.*) III.11, *III.12*, III.13
judiciary astrology III.30
Jung, Carl I.45, I.71, I.91, I.335, III.275, III.352
on alchemy I.245
on cākras III.192
on death III.341
and ‘homesickness’ of the soul II.9
on individuation I.151
on rebirth I.103
on *The Tibetan Book of the Dead* II.97
and uroboros III.3
on world-views I.xix
Jungian terms III.256
junk DNA I.106
Jupiter (Greek Mysteries *q.v.*) I.263
justice II.78
see also karma
Just Six Numbers (Rees) III.238–9

Kabbalah *see* Qabbalah
Kabiri III.303
Kaṭhaka Upaniṣad III.132, III.169
Kāla III.107
Kalahaṃsā III.84
kaleidoscopic mirage III.255
see also Māyā; māyā
Kali Yuga II.125, III.187
Kalkin/Kalki I.272
Kalms, Lord III.324

Kāma II.23, II.24, II.25, II.26, II.43, II.46
and Archetypal III.96
and classical Theosophical literature II.150
and Lower manas II.68
and Manas II.123, II.176
and passion and urgency II.109
and Saptaparṇa III.58
kāma III.13, III.186
Kāma-loka II.25, II.65–8, II.215
Kāma-manas II.23, II.25, II.41–2, II.123
and Archetypal III.96
and Besant System II.155
and classical Theosophical literature II.149
and Esoteric Buddhism II.168
and pawns (chess) III.14
and Rāmāyaṇa III.9
and Sūtra 6 (*The Holy Science*) III.112
Kāma-prāṇa III.96
Kāma–Prāṇa–Sthūla-śarīra II.42, II.43
Kāma principle II.41
Kāma-rūpa II.24–5, II.28, II.47, II.52, II.59, II.170, III.77
and Antaḥkaraṇa II.88
and classical Theosophical literature II.149, II.150, II.151
and Esoteric Buddhism II.168
and psychic corpse II.81–2
kamic proclivities II.47
Kamionkowski, Marc III.262
Kant, Immanuel I.34
Kapila I.217, I.270
Kāraṇopādhi II.52, II.170
Kardec, Allan II.107
karma I.301, II.68, II.78, II.106, II.136, III.326
and Antaḥkaraṇa II.215
burdens of humanity II.164
four types III.127
and personality II.216
psycho-physical III.337
residues III.247
Karma, Law of/karmic law I.99, I.240, I.295, II.79, II.203, III.89, III.90
Karmendriyas III.113–14, III.160
Karmic Body II.47, II.51, II.52–3
Kasparov, Gary II.113, II.114
Kaufman, Steven I.355
Keats, John II.102, II.134–5
Keller, Helen I.5, II.120–1, *II.121*, II.230–1
Kelvin, Lord I.123, I.331
Kennedy, John F. III.131
Kepler, Johannes I.7, I.51, I.132, I.142, III.30, III.264
Kesey, Ken III.196
Kether III.61, III.63, III.64
Keynes, Lord I.234, III.205
keys III.16, III.36, III.269
and death III.341
esoteric III.142
to evolution III.224
to highest and divinest consciousness III.184
mystic III.17
to Old and the New Testaments III.60
philosophic III.17
to the riddle of life III.38
to the secret of death II.64
universal III.5
to wisdom II.205, III.xx, III.19
The Key to Theosophy (Blavatsky) I.236, II.150
on Higher Self II.227
Al-Khalili, Jim I.17
Kim, Jaegwon I.27, I.30–1, I.32
king (chess *q.v.*) III.13
kingdom of God II.69
Kingdoms of Nature I.286, III.97
kingdoms of nature I.241, III.218, III.220–7, III.245
King's Chamber, Great Pyramid I.309, III.50, III.129
King's College Library (Cambridge) I.228
Kingsley, Peter I.181, III.73
Kircher, Athanasius III.25, III.26
Kirschner, Marc I.355
kiss (esoteric significance of) II.73, III.66
knights (chess *q.v.*) III.13
Knoche, Grace I.271
Knossos, Crete III.7–8
the knower and the known, inseparability of III.331
knowing II.22, III.xx–xxi
Knowing By Heart: Cellular memory in heart transplants III.41
knowledge I.23, I.202, II.218, III.118, III.282, III.296
about everything III.281
absolute III.119
of consciousness I.16
detailed III.285
direct II.41
driven by desire II.171
enlightened II.41
gained only by wider outlook III.377

and good and evil I.269
and The Hermit (Tarot cards) III.11
historical transfer of III.59
is power III.210
meaning of science I.181
and Newton I.11
and opinion I.33
politics of I.140
scientific III.309
sea of III.xviii
testable III.30
three divisions II.171
widen the gates of III.171
Knowledge, Divine I.183, III.364–5
Knowledge and the Sacred (Nasr) III.118
knowledge argument I.31
knowledge filtration I.115–19, I.134, II.36, II.207–13, III.229, III.232
Knowledge of the Higher Worlds (Steiner) III.198
knowledge suppression mechanisms I.116–17
Koestler, Arthur II.14
Koricancha (South America, Mysteries *q.v.*) I.276
kośas II.35, II.42, II.43, II.52, II.150, II.168
Kosmic Ādi III.88
kosmic hierarchy III.238
Kosmic Intellect III.26
kosmic life III.84–5
Kosmic Physical plane III.88
Kosmos III.84–8, *III.89*
kosmos III.82, III.84, III.92, III.99, III.121, III.238, III.240
Kovak, John III.262
Kṛṣṇa/Krishna I.270, I.272, II.2
see also Avatars
Krishna, Arvind II.114
Krishnamurti, Jiddu I.lxxxii, I.19, I.166, II.155, II.156, II.220, III.282
on bee II.222, III.302
on death III.340
and negative thinking III.280
on Truth I.lvii, I.lxxxiii–lxxxiv
Kriya II.202
kriyamāṇa (karma *q.v.*) III.127
kriyāśakti/kriyashakti I.105, II.156
Krumm-Heller, Heinrich Arnold I.278
Kumāras I.215, I.286
Kuṇḍalinī I.262, III.174–5, III.190
Kūrma I.271
Kurzweil, Ray I.lxii, II.115–16, II.139
Kutastha Caitanya III.111
LaBerge, Stephen I.91
laboratory conditions II.56
labyrinth (symbolic meaning of) III.5, III.7–8
Ladd, George Trumbull I.243
Ladder of Life III.130, III.223, III.235
Laetoli footprints III.232
la Ferriere, Serge Raynaud de I.277
Laithwaite, Eric I.149, I.319
Lakoff, George II.129–30
Lamarckian inheritance I.52, I.75
Lamassu III.49
Lamb, Marion I.355
lamp (symbolic meaning of) III.11
human constitution (simile) III.253, *III.254*
see also Divine Ego
landscapes *see* evolution
language II.1, II.3, II.4–5, II.130, II.131, II.220, III.1–2
everyday III.42–3
of the Mysteries II.205, III.xx
The Language of the Prophets (Newton) I.230–1
Lanka, Battle of III.9
see also Rāma; Sīta
Lao Tzu/Lao-Tze I.250, II.172
Laplace, Pierre Simon I.xlv
Large Hadron Collider (LHC) III.310
largest organisms III.223
large truths III.17
larynx III.252
see also Tabernacle of Moses
Lashley, Karl I.76, I.161, I.349
László, Ervin I.71, I.153, I.342, II.197
latent powers II.45, II.59, III.48, III.171, III.181, III.190–210
Later-generation Theosophists II.44
Latin language II.3, II.5
Latin philology III.25
Laughter Clubs I.150–1
Laver of Purification III.252
see also Tabernacle of Moses
Law, synonym for Karma III.89
Law Courts II.90
see also crimes; criminality; criminals; karma
The Law of Success (Hill) I.305, II.26
laws/Laws
of Affinity and Transference II.79
of analogy II.126, III.70, III.80, III.83
of correspondences III.122
of Karma I.99, I.240, I.295, II.79, II.203, III.89, III.90
of Manu I.271

laws/Laws (continued)
of Nature I.xlviii, I.180, I.203–4, I.266, II.198, III.243
of nature III.241
of Retribution II.78
septenary III.99
Layard, Sir Austen Henry III.64
layers in human energy field (subtle bodies *q.v.*) II.3, II.166
Lazar, Sara I.163
Leadbeater, Charles Webster I.98, I.105, II.7, II.153, II.156, II.158
Leadbeater System II.156, II.158
League of Nations I.272
Leakey, Louis III.233
Leakey, Mary III.232
learned societies I.361–2
Learning from Leonardo (Capra) II.125
Leary, Timothy III.195–6
leaves (metaphysical symbolism of, human constitution *q.v.*) III.57
left brain I.164, I.165, II.124, II.133, II.135
left eye III.79
left half of body III.44–5
Left-Hand Path I.200, I.202, I.275, III.45, III.333
leftovers (Cosmic Elements *q.v.*) III.160
see also bhūtas
left temporo-parietal junction II.55
legendary scientists III.281
see also celebrity scientists
legends II.80, III.5, III.9, III.10
Leggett, Peter I.lxxxiv, I.18, II.127, II.223
Lehrs, Ernst I.43
Leibniz, Gottfried I.xxxviii, I.79, I.251, II.146, II.188, II.189, III.149
Leibniz–Mill argument III.352
Lemaître, Georges I.333, I.334
Lemuria III.229
Leonore (*Fidelio q.v.*) III.15, III.16
Le Plongeon, Augustus I.278–9
lesser lives III.222, III.223
Lesser Mysteries I.180, I.270, I.271, I.283–4
lethargy (post-mortem) II.79
see also post-mortem states
levels
of being III.192
of consciousness III.xix–xx, III.78, III.249, III.256
of descent III.154, III.167
of existence III.219
kosmic planes III.98
lives III.225
lowest III.154
of meaning of symbols III.3, III.65
mix-up of II.3
and numberless Universes III.240
three II.8–9
and transducers III.136
Levi, Eliphas III.25
Lewis, C. S. II.221
Lewis, David I.29
liberal arts I.215
liberals (human beings *q.v.*, class of) III.334
liberty
to pursue one's individual path II.189
of thought and of expression II.225
lid-sitters, science *q.v.* I.120
Lieber, Michael I.354
life III.77, III.221
all III.221
Blavatsky definition of III.xvi
classroom of II.75
conditions for III.241
conscious and sapient III.240, III.241
cyclic periods of waking and sleeping III.234
higher III.224
meaning of III.332
metaphysical and spiritual dimensions III.188
more than just chemistry III.177
NASA definition of III.xvi
and numberless Universes III.240
origins III.262
unity and interconnectedness of III.223
worth living III.263
life-altering feature I.151
life-atoms II.30
life body II.183, II.184
life-breath II.154
life currents III.179
The Life Divine (Aurobindo) I.348
life-force II.27, II.83, III.113, III.202
life forms, new III.222, III.279
life-giving II.7, II.181
lifeless physical matter III.22
Life of Isaac Newton (Brewster) III.279
Life principle II.18, II.19, II.27, II.73, II.154
life-principles II.231, III.55
life processes III.174
life purpose II.165
life review II.67, II.88

life sciences I.331, I.345–57
life side, body III.174
  see also Prāṇa; prāṇa
Life Spirit II.164
life spiritual III.252
life-support II.86
lifetime II.69, III.41, III.127
life-transforming experiences II.91, II.100
life waves III.201, III.376, III.377–8
Light III.13, III.111, III.201–2, III.253, *III.254*
light I.37, I.170, *I.171*, II.36, II.195, III.40, III.165
  clouds II.42
  experiences III.203
  external and internal III.226
  and Lord of Light II.73
  and Lower manas II.215
  of Manasic reason II.109
  and Newton III.205–6
  reflected III.256
  right half of body III.44–5
  speed of II.209
  wave theory II.207
light beam (simile for single source of wisdom) II.189
light-bearing substance II.210
Light Changes: Experiences in the presence of transforming light (Puhle) III.203
Light Emerging (Brennan) II.165, II.166
Light of Asia (Arnold) III.372
Lighthall, W. D. III.336
limbic system II.119
limbo state (post-mortem) II.78
limbs (stages in yogic practice) III.191
liminal condition III.187
limitations
  Darwinian theory III.122
  of diagrammatic representations III.93
  of the expression of the spirit-side III.225
  reductionist field, molecular biology III.177
  theories II.122, II.128
  of words II.36
limited expression III.155
The Limits of Natural Selection as Applied to Man (Wallace) III.237–8
Linde, Andrei I.341–2
linear consciousness III.249
linear time III.234
linear understanding III.250
Liṅga-śarīra II.28–9, II.54, II.59, III.13, III.58
  and Besant System II.154–5
  and classical Theosophical literature II.149, II.150
  and Model body III.96
  and post-classical Theosophy II.153
  and Sūtras III.114
Linnean Society III.222
Lipton, Bruce I.355
  the liquid (gross material body *q.v.*, aspect of) III.115
Liquor Vitæ III.179
listening, and hearing III.xix
Lister, Sir Joseph II.131
Liszt, Franz II.71, II.101, III.216–17
literalism II.77, II.124, III.79
literature II.63, II.135, II.148–51, III.55, III.83
litmus tests of Truth *q.v.* I.233
liver (role in occult physiology *q.v.*) II.60
lives
  causative link between III.247
  distorting II.124
  lesser III.222, III.223
  myriads of III.131
living being II.125
Living in a Mindful Universe (Alexander) III.162
living message, dogma and dead ritual III.185
Living Nature I.244–5
living organism III.174, III.177
living power, Theosophy *q.v.* II.8
The Living Stream (Hardy) I.53
living tissue III.177
local causality I.110
Locale I I.90
  see also out-of-body experience
Locale II I.90
  see also out-of-body experience
Locale III I.90
  see also out-of-body experience
locales, corresponding II.25
local politics III.18
Locke, John I.32, I.144, I.152
Lodge, Sir Oliver I.306, II.223
loftier standpoint III.275
lofty ideas III.152
logic II.120, III.51, III.73, III.118, III.271, III.333
Logic, Laws and Life: Some philosophical complications (Efron) I.350
logical positivism I.23
  see also Vienna School; positivism
The Logic of Scientific Discovery (Popper) I.334
Logos III.152, III.173, III.174

logos II.2, II.162, II.176–7, II.177
LOGOS, unmanifested I.242
lokas II.6, II.25
London Paddington North Pole depot III.366–7, *III.367*
London taxi drivers I.161–2
loneliness III.274, III.275
looking, and seeing III.xix
Lorber, John I.134, I.135
Lord God II.16
Lord Kṛṣṇa (Krishna) I.270, I.272, II.2
Lord of Light II.73
Lord's illusory power III.140
Lorenz, Edward I.lx
Lorimer, David I.23, I.55, II.95, III.188, III.308
lost continents III.229
Lost Key of Masonry III.190
lost souls II.85
lotus flower III.55, III.72, *III.73*
lotus plant III.219
love I.44, I.45, I.234, II.125
  between Ariadne and Theseus III.6
  and Darwin III.244
  and desire II.26, III.185
  of God III.227
  between the Spiritual Soul and the Human Soul III.16
  undying III.15
  universal III.245
  unrequited II.79, III.42
  of wisdom I.xxxix
Love, Universal III.111, III.113
Lovell, Sir Bernard I.lxxxi
Lovelock, James I.58, I.137, I.349–50
The Lovers (Tarot cards *q.v.*) III.11, III.12, *III.12*
loving bond III.66
loving intelligence II.56
lower centres *II.180*, II.181, III.38
Lower Consciousness I.147–8
Lower ego II.45, II.46, II.47, II.88
lower entity III.237
Lower manas II.23, II.24, II.41–2, II.48, II.97, III.112
  and Antaḥkaraṇa II.87, II.216
  and Besant System II.155
  and light II.215
  and Saptaparṇa III.58
  struggle with Higher Manas II.68, II.99
  and upādhi II.37
lower mental aspect II.155
Lower mind I.147–8, II.23, II.41–2, II.53, II.59, II.123, III.48, III.166
  atmospheric haze/partly open door (simile) III.254
  and classical Theosophical literature II.149
  and Esoteric Buddhism II.168
  qualities II.107
lower moving centre (Fourth Way teaching *q.v.*) II.178
lower nature I.308, II.90, III.15
Lower Perishable Quaternary II.23–4
lower planes III.87, III.166, III.248
lower pole (human beings *q.v.*) II.185, III.123
lower principle II.38
lower psychic faculties III.194
Lower Quaternary I.148, II.18, II.106, II.177
  and *The Chemical Marriage* III.14
  and Cube unfolded III.66
  and Pavri System II.160
  and physical nature III.76
  and Plato II.175
Lower self I.175, II.17, II.73, II.89, II.106, II.199
lower self (Steiner *q.v.*) III.199
lower sentient consciousness II.65
Lower Triad II.19, II.23, II.27, II.65, II.73, II.99
lower vehicles III.166
lowest level III.154
Loye, David Elliot III.244, III.245
LSD III.196
lucid dreaming I.87, I.90–1, II.53, II.56
Lucifer I.274
ludicrous associations (symbolism) III.17–18
lumbering robots II.53, II.118, II.124, II.141
luminaries II.135, II.219, II.220, III.205
luminiferous ether II.207
Luminous Egg III.125
luminous light III.202
Luminous Self II.53
luminous sphere III.179
Lunar Chain III.377
lunar Races I.270
lunar vehicles (subtle bodies *q.v.*) II.165
  see also Aun Weor, Samael
lunatics II.108
Lytton, Edward Bulwer II.53

machine II.114, II.117, II.123, II.178, II.196, III.338
  action of I.43
  the brain II.xvi
  and da Vinci II.125

distinction with the mechanic II.126
metaphor of I.51
machine language II.129
see also flaws in computationalist master analogy
machine paradigm I.4, I.56, I.163, II.117, II.126, III.314–15
machinization of human beings *q.v.* II.116
Maclaurin, Colin I.250
Macrocosm I.lii, III.34, III.36, III.61, III.63, III.123, *III.124*
macrocosm I.256, II.124, II.125, II.126, II.151, II.196, II.205
definition I.246–7
Macrocosmic MAN III.36
Macroprosophus I.lii, III.34
macro-scale, Root Races III.187
Maddox, Sir John I.49, II.131–2, III.176
madness, and genius III.336
Madonna (visitation of) II.53
Mae-Wan Ho I.352
Magi III.205
magic I.199, I.200–1, I.202, I.275, I.282, II.131
magnetic affinity II.81
see also Kāma-rūpa; spooks
magnetic field III.42, III.113
magnetic sphere III.125
see also auras; Hiraṇayagarbha; Luminous Egg
magnetism (human heart *q.v.*) III.40
Maguire, Eleanor I.162
Mahābhārata I.191, I.270, III.235
Mahābhūtas III.157, III.158–9
Mahākala III.141, III.142
Mahākāśa III.141, III.142
Mahāmāyā III.117
Maharshi, Ramana I.99, I.217, II.90, II.220, III.118, III.188, III.253
and eyes III.201
on the heart II.32
and Thought Producer I.166
on the Vedas II.16
Mahat III.96, III.97, III.112
Mahatic III.96
mahātmā III.186
Mahatma KH II.57
The Mahatma Letters to A. P. Sinnett II.57, II.149
mahātmān I.211
Mahātmās I.212, II.90
Maheśa I.45, III.168, III.173, III.174, III.244
Mahler, Gustav III.332
maidens (Tarot cards *q.v.*) III.12
Maier, Michael III.60
main centres (Fourth Way teaching *q.v.*) II.178
mainstream biology II.xvi
mainstream cosmology III.92
mainstream culture III.196
mainstream dictum II.131
mainstream evolutionary biology III.317
mainstream natural science III.285
mainstream neuroscience II.44–5, II.112, III.306, III.307
mainstream psychology II.71
mainstream reaction, to new ideas I.322
mainstream science II.8, II.84, II.135, II.136, III.51, III.77, III.115, III.264
deficiencies in paradigm III.xvii
intelligences and forces outside of III.172
on origin of anatomically modern humans III.233–4
mainstream scientists II.126
'The Making of the Rose Diamond' II.59
Malade Imaginaire (Moliere) I.196
malaise in contemporary Western society II.186
male energy (human body *q.v.*) II.27
male number (meaning of) III.77
Malkuth III.63, III.64
Mama Killa (South America, Mysteries *q.v.*) I.276
Mammon (worship of) I.290
Man II.1
Man I.297, II.1, II.196, III.22, III.35
see also Principles of Man
man II.1, II.2, II.175
analogies III.74
and animals II.108–9
antiquity of III.229–35
archetype of III.60–1
average III.256
brain quality III.256
common noun I.297
composite nature of I.296
composition of II.2–14, II.34, II.155, II.205
condition of III.236
destiny III.326
and Divine Perfection II.196
and Divinity III.34
existence of III.219
formed physically out of dust of the Earth III.131
generation of II.177
in God's image III.106
growth and refinement of is limitless III.242

man (continued)
  and Human Ego II.70
  indissoluble relationship and connection with Cosmos and Nature III.255
  infinitesimal unit in the structure of the universe III.47
  Inner II.2, II.37, II.136
  inner nature III.253
  and inverted triangle III.123
  invisible body of III.179
  miniature universe III.82
  modes and aspects II.19
  nature of III.63
  and Newton II.125
  ordinary III.255
  origins of III.227–42
  physically-embodied III.202
  of polygenetic origin I.240
  and principles II.5, III.75–7
  and problems III.283
  scientific definition III.xvii
  self-realized immortal being III.341
  soul of II.25
  and Spiritual Soul II.22
  splendour of III.257
  stage in the evolution of consciousness I.241–2
  sublimation of III.192
  and the universe III.52
  unregenerate III.304
  see also constitution of man
Man, God and the Universe (Taimni) II.161–2
Man, the Unknown (Carrel) I.348, III.177
management, of desires II.26
Manas II.43, II.46, II.52, II.176, III.97, III.112
  and Auric Body III.125
  and classical Theosophical literature II.149, II.150
  and Cube unfolded III.66
  dual function II.107
  and Ego II.47
  and The Hermit (Tarot cards) III.12
  and Jñānendriyas III.113
  and Kāma II.123
  and Mahatic III.96
  meaning of II.22–3
  and Saptaparṇa III.58
  and Steiner II.185
manas III.189
Manasic principle II.109
manasic propensities II.47
Manas-kāma II.42, *II.42*
Manas-Manas II.41, *II.42*
mandragora II.231, III.56
Manifest III.146, *III.146*
manifestation II.137, II.142, III.64, III.141–2, III.362
  of CONSCIOUSNESS III.370
  of consciousness III.120, III.369
  of Divine Consciousness III.202
  and endocrine system III.192
  and involution and evolution III.225
  manvantara and pralaya II.77
  objective III.75
  and personality II.106
  of Ultimate Reality III.144, III.173
  and universe III.118
manifested Deity III.173
manifested event III.142
manifested universe III.147
manifesting stars III.172–3
Manifesto for a Post-Materialist Science I.141, I.342
Manifest outer planes III.87
Manifest Worlds III.61, III.63, III.86, III.92
manifest worlds III.226
manipulative characteristics (human traits *q.v.*) II.89
  see also soulless beings
mankind II.1, II.223, III.106, III.187, III.217, III.248, III.257
manmade III.109
  see also Ideas in Divine Mind
manmade disasters III.187–8
Manomaya-kośa II.168, II.170
Man or Matter (Lehrs) I.43
mansions, many (John, Gospel of *q.v.*) II.60
Manson, Neil III.240
Manu I.271, III.10
Manus I.270
manvantara II.76–7, III.234
see also Day of Brahmā
MAN: Whence, How and Whither (Leadbeater) I.105
The Man Who Knew Infinity II.71
Many-Worlds interpretation of quantum mechanics I.xlvi
map, occult anatomy III.254, III.254
'map' and the 'territory' II.196, III.3, III.150, III.230, III.232
'Mapping the brain's metaphor circuitry' (Lakoff) II.129–30

al-Maqtul, Sohravardi III.35
Māra I.268
Margulis, Lynn I.58, III.222
The Marriage of Sense and Soul (Wilber) III.11
Mars (water discoveried on) I.104, I.105, III.8,
for future humanity III.321
Marsh, Henry I.17
martyrs (utterances of) III.35
masculine spirit II.73–4
Masefield, John I.2, I.3, III.xvii
mask II.106, II.119, III.30, III.294
Masnavi III.221
Masonry I.210, III.14, III.190, III.341
mass attacks by scientists *q.v.* II.133
masses III.2
see also parables
Master II.123, III.xvii
master analogy theory of computationalists *q.v.* II.113, II.126–30
The Master and His Emissary – The Divided Brain and the Making of the Western World (McGilchrist) II.122
master gland III.182
Master-inspired literature II.219
master Intelligence III.176
masters I.211, I.212, II.106, III.192, III.193, III.275
material II.36, III.94, III.161
material ambitions II.71
material body III.36, III.109
material changes III.174
material constitution III.13
material development III.104
material elements III.129
material form III.235
materialism I.16, I.17, I.22, I.26–32, I.35–8, II.117, III.275, III.304–26
and bad science II.221
brutal III.261
and causal closure I.24, I.26
cul-de-sac of hypotheses III.136
and death II.65
definition I.xliii–xliv, I.13
and drugs III.196
historical basis and genesis I.51–4, I.134
Human Soul imprisoned in III.16
ideologies III.293
modified I.39, I.40
paradigm I.25, I.45–50
and person's awareness III.xviii
philosophical and metaphysical basis I.24
preconceptions III.328
promissory III.270, III.277
radically altered verdicts on theories III.23
re-named physicalism I.23
research evidence incompatible with III.329
and science of qualities I.44
sole arbiter of truth II.133
solutions III.274
on transmutation from neurology to experience III.162
two deathblows to I.93–5
unbridled III.48
the materialist, faith of I.16
materialistic arguments II.55, II.138
materialistic bunker III.270
materialistic culture II.74
materialistic dogma II.74
materialistic fortress III.48
materialistic paradigm I.320, II.131–2, II.186, III.180, III.265
materialistic perspective/lens III.30, III.122
materialistic philosophy II.141
materialistic science III.30, III.271
see also materialism
materialistic scientists III.61
materialistic terms II.128
materialistic theories II.130–1, II.134
see also materialism
materialistic world-view I.4, I.343
materialist lower centre III.38
materialist mind-set III.241–2
materialist philosophy III.265
materialists II.133
materializations II.82, II.83, III.65, III.122
material life I.305
material mechanism III.167
material organism III.316
material organs II.142
material particles III.83
material plane III.87
material potencies III.225
material principles II.23
material properties II.126
material qualities II.215
materials, of the Physical body III.97
material side, body III.174
material world/realm I.80, II.39, III.149
The Mathematical Connection Between Religion and Science (Phillips) III.61, III.250, III.357
The Mathematical Foundation of Quantum Mechanics (von Neumann) I.334

mathematical map III.143
'A Mathematical Solution of the Psychophysical Problem' (Walder and Bilimoria) III.355
Mathematical Structures of the Universe (Carr) III.241
mathematics II.115, II.196, III.86, III.166–7, III.206 7, III.349–72
  equations III.151
  evidence III.240
  geniuses III.171, III.189
  and parabola (simile) III.150–1
  Pythagorean III.25
  and science III.150
The Mathnawi [Masnavi] of Jalaluddin Rumi II.xiv
matrix II.150
Matsya I.271, III.10
MATTER III.218
Matter I.280, I.295, *III.27*, III.145, III.156, III.218, III.224
matter II.7, III.115, III.217, III.227, III.334, III.350–2, *III.350*
  analogies III.74
  and Chandogya Upaniṣad III.147
  circumference III.4
  complete separation with spirit II.125
  complex forms of III.240
  and consciousness I.139, I.149, I.155, III.72, III.140, III.146, III.237, III.276, III.307
  definition III.218
  forms III.115, III.220
  inanimate III.287
  lifeless physical III.22
  as a machine III.269
  and mathematics III.349
  mental in essence III.289
  and mind III.140, III.235, III.308
  and nervous ether III.179
  and number four III.77
  passive and negative principle II.11
  primacy of III.310
  and promissory materialism III.277
  and Self-realized master III.104
  seven states of III.77–9,
  as shadow III.333
  and spirit III.225
  and universe III.86
  wave nature of III.163
as matter and not in matter (involution *q.v.* of consciousness *q.v.*) III.161, III.168, III.226, III.330
Matter-side III.158
matter-side III.155
Maturana, Humberto I.58, I.351
Mawlânâ (Jalāl ad-Dīn Mohammad Rūmī) II.48
Maxwell, James Clerk II.207
Maxwell, Nicholas III.273
May, Edwin I.92
Māyā III.106, III.156
māyā I.35, I.37, II.74, III.115, III.117–21, *III.143*, III.265
  and Leonore III.16
  and Schrödinger III.290
Maya people I.273, I.276
Māyāvi-rūpa I.211, II.24–5, II.47, II.52, II.54–9, II.65, III.188
  and classical Theosophical literature II.150, II.151
  and post-classical Theosophy II.153
Mayer, Jean-François II.164
Mayo/Gregory syndrome I.120
Mayr, Ernst I.348–9
Mazdean philosophy II.53
maze III.7
  see also labyrinth; meander
McChrystal, Stanley I.lx
McClintock, Barbara I.233–4
McCraty, Rollin III.41–2
McDermott, Drew II.116
McDougall, William I.75
McGilchrist, Iain I.186, I.343, II.122–4, II.135, III.276, III.288, III.322
McKenna, Terence I.46
McMoneagle, Joe I.93
Mead, G. R. S. II.168, III.78, III.121
meander III.7
  see also maze; labyrinth
meaning (words *q.v.* and viewpoint *q.v.*) III.2, III.104, III.237, III.293, III.296, III.308
  common III.286
  of the comos III.271
  distinctions of III.84
  and ideas III.152
  inner II.4, III.303
  of life III.332
  multiple levels of III.5
  shades of III.70
'Meaning in Evolution' (Goodwin) I.355
the measurable I.38, II.112, II.117, II.118
the measure of (man *q.v.*) III.106
measurements, cosmos III.37
measures of time III.141

the mechanic, distinction with the machine II.126
mechanically repetitive, rule-based activity II.141
mechanical universe III.142–3, III.291
mechanical world-view III.270
mechanism I.43, II.xvi, II.119, II.125, III.137
  complexity of III.164
  for Divine Mind to act on individual minds III.153, III.167
  identifying with informing principle II.127
  and mortal animal body II.xvii
  of sense perception III.154
  and vitalism III.309
  and Weinberg III.270
mechanistic grid of natural selection III.40
mechanistic ideology III.180
mechanistic outlook I.4
mechanistic paradigm I.40, I.331, II.xvi, III.48, III.140, III.196, III.270, III.307
mechanistic philosophy of life III.334
mechanistic theories II.55, III.246
mechanistic transformation III.248
Medawar, Sir Peter II.176
Medawar's syndrome I.120
Medical Royal Colleges, Academy of II.xiv
media (influence of) I.55, III.xvii
mediæval philosophers III.14
mediæval superstition I.181–2
mediation I.245, I.326
medical research III.196–7
medical science I.261, II.135, III.34, III.189, III.192, III.282
medical technology III.320
medicine I.49, II.xvii, II.184, III.41–3
meditation I.163, I.234–5, II.132, III.106, III.142, III.253, III.254
  and Dhāraṇā III.191
  H.P.B.'s Diagram of III.121
  and neuroscience III.266
  and Yogananda III.203–4
medium (nervous ether) III.178, III.179
mediums (practitioners) I.91–2, I.320, II.63, II.74, II.150
megalomania III.293
Mehta, Phiroz I.37–8, I.268, I.284, II.20, II.174, II.220, III.238
Mein Kampf II.131
Meister, William J. III.231–2
melatonin III.182
members, of the body III.33
memes II.115
memory I.70–1, I.75–6, I.81, I.243, II.42, II.138, II.202
  and Astral Light III.95
  categories I.163–4
  collective I.352
  exists even at the cellular level II.60
  group I.78–9
  of heart and brain III.40
  impaired II.59
  implicit I.101–2
  in man III.82
  nature of I.152–4
  panoramic II.67
  universal III.234
memory banks I.76, I.78
memory glue II.202
memory in nature I.74
memory traces I.76
Mendel, Gregor I.347
Mendeleev, Dmitri I.133
Mendelian genetics I.75
Mensa Isiaca III.24–5, *III.25*
the Mental II.39
mental aspects II.168
mental attunement III.153
Mental Body II.153, II.154, II.164, II.165
mental characteristics III.247
mental chatter III.107
mental co-ordinates III.148–9
mental discipline III.203
mental events I.83
mental examination III.149
mental faculties II.22
mental forces III.56
mental functions II.123, II.186
mental health I.lix, I.4, III.197, III.275, III.336–7
mental hygiene I.300
mental illness III.274–5
mental images III.141, III.149, III.152, III.167
mental in essence III.289
mentalism II.138
mentality II.220
mental level III.192
mental life III.192, III.324
mental models II.8
mental nature III.110
mental object III.120
mental perceptions II.60
Mental phenomena III.146
mental plane II.110, III.245–6

mental powers III.245
mental realm III.351
mental relations III.151
mental science of truth III.358
mental sciences II.47, II.85
mental sensation III.137
mental sensitivity III.208
mental sensuous images III.154
mental silence III.142
mental spaces III.141
mental states II.118, III.362–3
mental subject III.151
mental vehicle II.110
mental verities III.38
mental world III.148, III.149, III.166–7, III.371
merit, of incarnation II.76
Merzenich, Michael I.162–3
mescaline III.195
messages II.82, III.227, III.261
Messenger III.303
messenger (role of idol) III.16
  see also idolatry; symbolism
Messiah (Handel) III.268
meta-analysis I.86
meta-biology III.248
metabolism III.223
metallic spheres (prehistoric antiquity of) III.230–1, III.231
metaphor circuitry II.130
  see also electrical circuitry
metaphorical thought II.129–30
metaphors I.282, II.3, II.6, II.88, II.89, III.1–2, III.47–8
Metaphysic (Aristotle) I.202
the metaphysical II.1
metaphysical foundations I.320
metaphysical rationale II.196
metaphysical terms II.4, II.227
metaphysical thought II.77
metaphysical truths II.174
metaphysician III.31
metaphysics I.45, I.72, I.235, II.117, II.154, III.188, III.271, III.277
  and Blavatsky II.136
  definition I.182, I.202–3, I.204
  Indian II.35
  and origins and purpose III.262
  and physics III.49, III.110, III.172, III.265
  principles III.19
  relationships III.38
  of a science of consciousness III.77
  underpinnings III.162
meta-Spirit II.2
Metcalfe, Samuel III.180
metempsychosis II.79, II.80
method III.15, III.102
Method of Composition I.229
methodologies II.59, II.94, II.126
Michelson, Albert I.104
Michelson-Morley experiment I.104, II.207, II.208–9, III.180
microbes (Venusian clouds) I.107
Microcosm I.liii, III.34, III.36, III.61, III.63, III.123, *III.124*, III.179
microcosm I.246–7, I.256, II.124, II.125, II.151, II.196, II.205
  law of II.126
Microcosmic man III.36
Microprosophus I.liii, III.34
micro-psi vision I.235
micro-scale, human development III.187
microscopes, limitations of I.261, II.100
microtubules III.163
middle centre III.38
Middle Duad II.19, II.23, II.24, II.42, II.68, II.73
Middle East (Mystery centre) II.3
middle emotional centre II.178
Middle Path III.104
middle principle II.178
Midgley, Mary I.123, II.124
migraines III.311
  see also Hildegard of Bingen
Miller, Dayton II.207–8
Miller, Francis Trevelyan I.306
Miller, Jeanine I.lxxxiii, II.227–8
Miller, Stanley I.349, I.350
Millikan, Robert II.208
Mills, Joy III.130
Milne, Edward I.334
MIND I.242, I.243
Mind II.164, III.263, III.269, III.365, III.369
  and Bembine Table of Isis III.27
  dual, or twin-nature of II.174
  and fundamental reality I.316
  Lower I.147–8, III.48, III.166
  nature of III.310
  Supreme I.264, I.265
  universal III.263
  and uroboros III.4
  see also Divine Mind; Higher Mind; Universal Mind

mind
affects matter I.83
and body I.39
and brain I.xlvi, I.11, I.16, I.18, I.32, I.55, I.76, I.149, II.119, III.36
and Brunton II.1, II.136–7
and Chandogya Upaniṣad III.147
and computers II.128, II.129
conjunction of subjective and objective aspects III.161
and consciousness I.139, I.148, I.154, III.140
and cultural issues II.122
and desire III.58
distinguished from thought I.301
emergent property III.305, III.308
evolving III.246
executioner (symbol of) III.14
see also CHiram Abiff
extended III.201, III.361, III.362
and eyes III.201
filters reality III.195
and form III.146
and Great Pyramid III.50
health of III.283
indeterminate effects III.352
inner fatigue of III.xviii
intractable problem of III.237
in its essential nature III.164
junction of the subjective and objective aspects of III.168
and luminaries II.135
materialistic model III.275
and matter III.140, III.235, III.238, III.350
and mechanistic paradigm II.xvi
and mental images III.141–2, III.149
on modern physics III.164
modern Western III.204
modifications of III.147
non-material II.126
non-physical, non-local functioning of I.82
ordinary III.117
and panpsychism I.9
and physical world III.151
primacy of I.3, I.97, I.316
pure II.41
quality of III.51
reduced to a physical machine II.117
scientific basis of I.25, I.38–45
and senses III.137
and Sherrington II.197
and space–time III.353
and state and condition III.34
subconscious III.357, III.362
theories of II.91
and universal memory III.234
unprepared III.199
and upādhi II.37
and world image III.167
see also Lower mind; *individual mind*
'Mind, Matter, and Quantum Mechanics' (Stapp) I.337
mind-altering drugs I.262
Mind and Brain (Eccles) I.77
Mind and Cosmos: Why the materialist neo-Darwinian conception of nature is almost certainly false (Nagel) I.137, I.150, I.356, II.130–1
Mind at Large III.195
Mind-centric explanation, cosmogony I.305
mind closure I.50
see also causal closure; explanatory closure
mindfulness I.xlii, II.109
Mind-in-itself *II.42*
mind maps I.165–6
mind of God III.269
The Mind of God (Davies) III.109
Mind of the Solar Logos III.151
mind over matter I.85
Mind Principle II.18, II.20, II.22–3, II.42, II.46, II.47
and Besant System II.155
and classical Theosophical literature II.149, II.151
and Desire principle II.202
double nature of II.174, III.112
and The Hermit (Tarot cards) III.12
higher aspect II.19
'join' the immortal and mortal parts of man II.200, II.201
and The Lovers (Tarot cards) III.12
and Mahat III.97
and Saptaparṇa III.58
and Subject–Object relationship III.146
'vertically divided' double nature of Mind Principle II.123
see also McGilchrist; *The Master and His Emissary*
mind–sensation problem III.134, III.135–6
mindsets II.129, II.218, III.264, III.276
mind-stuff I.36
mineral kingdom III.246
miniature universe III.34, III.47, III.82

minimum-consensus model III.330
Minkoff, Eli I.355
minor cākras III.192
Minotaur III.2, III.5, III.6, III.7, III.9, III.49
miracles I.46, II.72, III.188, III.189, III.190
miraculous ability (saints *q.v.* and adepts *q.v.*) II.58
mirages III.196
see also psychic planes
mirror II.73, II.174, III.77, III.80, III.83, III.148
dusty (simile for human mind *q.v.*) III.253, *III.254*
mirror image III.123
see also Heavenly Man
misconceptions II.105, III.44–5
misinterpretation III.90
see also 'General Scholium'
misnomer III.165
see also neural correlate of consciousness
misperception III.276
see also confusing terminology
missing gaps, knowledge III.246
missing links, evolution I.138, III.229, III.245
'missing ships' phenomenon I.68
mistakes III.264, III.294, III.334
The Mistress of Vision (Thompson) I.252
misunderstandings III.90, III.246, III.278
misuse of powers III.210
Mitchell, Edgar III.151
Mithra I.267
Mithraism I.222–3, I.267–9
Mithras I.267
mob consciousness I.149
Model body II.28–9, III.96
model-body III.8, III.13
models II.150, III.3, III.96
mode of vibration III.250
modern civilization III.243
modern cosmology III.238
modern developmental biology III.177
modern esoteric scholarship II.219
Modern Man in Search of a Soul (Jung) III.275
modern physics II.6, III.108, III.164
modern psychology *II.187*
modern sages II.220
modern science II.7, III.39, III.44, III.77
anthropocentric outlook III.235
and astrology III.29–31
and Chandogya Upaniṣad III.147
and occult science III.277
progressive aspect III.223
and Theosophy II.222, II.223
three pillars of III.265
modern scientific paradigm I.22
modern shoe III.231
see also Laetoli footprints
modern Theosophy II.175
modes of consciousness II.196, III.87
modes of existence II.14
modes of motion III.163
Modes of Thought (Whitehead) I.334
modifications of mind III.147
modified materialism I.39, I.40
Modular Prosthetic Limbs III.267
molecular biology I.8, I.135, I.345, II.132, III.176, III.177, III.309
and developmental biology I.75
and epigenetics I.105, I.115
and Turing I.73
molecules III.177, III.178
the Monad *I.253*, II.41, II.86, II.110, II.176, III.254
and Individuality II.106
and the Pilgrim III.173
and Taimni System II.162
monad III.175
Monadic Essence II.39, II.41
Monads III.75, III.151, III.152, III.224
monism III.156
Monk, Marilyn I.135
monkeys III.228, III.236, III.272, III.273
monotheism II.218
Monroe, Robert I.90
Montero, Barbara I.27
Monteverdi, Claudio III.327
Moon I.280, III.8, III.256
moon II.177, II.178
moonlight III.255–6
moral actions I.294, III.271
moral being II.23
Moralia, Volume XII II.177
morality III.321
moral precept III.193
moral sense II.109, III.244, III.245
moral support III.200
More, Henry I.293
Morgan, Thomas Hunt I.347
morphic resonance I.74–9, I.351, I.353, I.359, III.177
morphogenesis I.69–70, I.71–2, I.73–9, I.346, II.6, III.174
morphogenetic attractors I.72

morphogenetic/morphic fields I.40, I.74, I.78–9, I.353, I.359
Morris, Simon Conway III.176, III.324
mortal and corruptible man II.175
mortal animal body II.xvii
mortal body I.324, II.175
mortal clothing II.32
mortal coil II.79, II.99
mortal counterpart II.28
mortal Ego II.25
mortal elements II.27
mortal Individuality II.17
mortal man II.97, II.160, II.196, II.200, II.201, III.59
mortal personality I.148, II.23–4, II.162, III.13
mortal residue II.99
see also kāma-rūpa; reincarnation
Mortal vesture II.47, II.51
mortal vestures III.75
Moses III.4, III.251
Mother (Isis *q.v.*, symbolism of) I.266
mother II.82, II.88
motion III.72, III.178
motives II.78, III.95, III.119, III.185, III.191, III.334
motoric, Indriyas III.160
motorium III.114
motor-metabolic system II.184
motor principle II.24
mountaineers II.55
mouth
silence, symbol of I.207,
anatomical symbolism of III.46
movable Zodiac (astronomy) III.23
movement III.256, III.267
moving centre II.178, II.181
Mozart, Leopold I.10
Mozart, Wolfgang Amadeus I.10, I.218, II.71, II.100, II.219, III.5, III.209
on death III.341
MRI scans (physical body *q.v.*, investigation of) I.261, II.118
M-theory II.7, III.250
Muhammad I.218
Mukhopadhyay, Asok K. III.43
Muldoon, Sylvan I.90
Müller, Max I.lxxx, I.300
multi-cursal labyrinth III.7
see also maze; labyrinth; meander
multi-dimensionality III.140
multifaceted organic entity III.287
multilingual project (after-death communications *q.v.*) II.94
multiple images III.253
multiplicity I.306
see also Russell, Walter Bowman
multiverse III.85–6, III.240, III.242
mummies III.13
mummification III.336
mummy case I.266, III.13
mundane tree III.65
murdered ten year old girl III.41, III.375
murderous agencies (symbol of) III.14
see also Rosicrucian Brotherhood; CHiram Abiff
muscles III.179
see also 'General Scholium'
Museo Egizio III.24
music I.11, II.128, II.135, II.188, III.134, III.135, III.209, III.327
common high purpose III.149
and genius I.9, I.10
and Helen Keller II.230–1
Indian III.80
and Schubert III.165
musical instruments II.43, III.80
musical note (simile) III.86
see also planes of Kosmos
music drama III.5
musicians I.162, II.219
Musk, Elon II.116, III.272, III.273
mutations I.3, I.56, I.72
mutual correlations, and unitary consciousness III.168
Myalba II.100
Myers, Frederick W. H. II.91
myriad forms III.86
myriads of lives III.131
Mysteries I.178, I.179–81, I.204–10, I.213–15, I.262–82, III.283
on apes III.236
concealed in allegories and myths III.51
and form III.36
House of III.13
and idolatry III.37
initiation into III.129
language of II.205, III.xx
and Moses III.4
and universe inside man III.319
The Mysteries of the Mind (Penfield) I.76
mysterious powers II.59
The Mysterious Universe (Jeans) I.37, I.334

mystery
of the breath, the heart, and the eye III.203
of Consciousness III.342
of consciousness II.45, II.140, III.40, III.175
in the eyes III.201
of life II.100, III.137
of man III.50
and zodiac III.24, III.30
MYSTERY, protective veil of I.212
Mystery Schools I.180, I.207, I.213–23, I.261, III.121, III.199, III.304
Mystery Teachings I.xxxix, I.179–80, I.181, I.210, I.283–5, II.204, III.283
on anatomy and physiology (subtle bodies) II.2–3
and blinds I.205
definition I.203–4
and Freemasonry III.341
Greeks II.175
and human evolution II.xvii
Indian II.167–71
on lost continents III.229
not all man's spiritual nature incarnates in matter in one lifetime III.127
resolve scientific conundrums III.xvii–xviii
and secrecy I.207
and symbols III.3
and the Three Selves II.51
Mystery traditions I.lxxxi, II.2, II.3, III.52
the mystical II.1
mystical bird III.84
mystical experience II.198
mystical poet III.xix
mystical scientist I.234
mystical state II.198
mystical tradition I.281
mystic Christianity II.164
mysticism I.xl, I.160, I.201–2, I.204, II.132, III.165, III.329
definition I.182, I.184–7
and Grand Unified Theory III.308
Jewish I.193–4
and scientists III.277
and Steiner II.182
and Theosophy II.149–50
mystic keys III.17
mystic meditation III.206
mystics I.201, I.234, II.198, III.33, III.44, III.264
of Islam III.201
and science III.266
My Stroke of Insight (Taylor) II.122
Mythical Tree III.55, III.64–5, *III.65*
Myth of Er I.89
mythological beasts III.49
mythological creatures III.47
mythology I.276, I.278, I.282, III.5, III.9, III.47–9, III.286
myths I.191, I.193, I.282, III.25, III.51, III.183, III.281
My View of the World (Schrödinger) II.80

Nadine, the android receptionist II.140, *II.140*
Nagel, Thomas I.48, I.115, I.220, I.319, III.228
Mind and Cosmos I.150, I.356, II.130–1
nails, three (constitution of man *q.v.*) I.206
see also subtle bodies
Namagiri Thayar of Namakkal III.208
see also Ramanujan
Nanyang Technological University II.140
Narasiṃha I.271
Narlikar, Jayant I.340
narratives (philosophia perennis *q.v.*) III.284
narrow-minded attitude (danger of specialization) III.285
NASA Science Newsletter II.xvii
Nasr, Seyyed Hossein II.58, III.101, III.118–19, III.131
National Science Foundation III.30
nations, governance of III.14
natural body II.32
natural death II.93
naturalism I.23
naturalists II.231
Natural Philosophy III.106
natural science I.23, I.24, I.25, I.54–5, I.69, III.285
natural selection I.9, I.10, I.52, I.56, I.58, I.137, III.317
and the brain II.xvi
and deception I.12
and Goodwin I.44
mechanistic grid of III.40
natural separation II.68
natural world II.134
Nature
discoveries of III.279
Divine I.327, III.127, III.129
guiding law in III.72
innermost recesses of I.xlix
laboratory of II.85
Laws of I.xlviii, I.180, I.203–4, I.266, II.198, III.243

Living I.244–5
and Mind Principle III.97
and occult science I.195
planetary I.286
and Prakṛiti III.156
and Purāṇas I.270
and recycling II.86
secrets I.199–200
and theosophy I.183–4
unity of with Cosmos and Man III.22, III.255
universal memory III.209
nature I.326, II.1, II.5, *II.40*, II.204, III.245
absolute III.352–3, III.365
of after-death communications II.94
allegory of III.55
and Altar of Burnt Offerings III.252
and American Indians I.273
analogies III.74
and ancient records III.50
and animals III.24
archetypal forces in III.5
of the black arts III.272
compound III.66, III.284
of consciousness II.224, III.329
and constitution II.10–14, II.34
and correspondences III.18, III.95
divine III.11, III.252, III.257
dual II.38, II.123
and Emerson I.294
emotional III.253
essential III.94, III.342
and eyes III.201
final laws of III.269
first eye III.183
and Goethe I.42
habits of I.78
higher II.90
inner III.253, III.328, III.334
as kaleidoscopic mirage III.255
kingdoms of I.241, III.218, III.220–7, III.245
laws of III.241
lower II.90, III.15
and manmade disasters III.188
and *Man or Matter* I.43
physical III.183
and physical body III.110
planes of III.64
primordial I.270
principles III.75–7
processes, of III.74
quintuple II.39
septenary II.39–43
subtler realms of III.250
transpersonal III.10
triple II.38–9
true and inner III.49
vital and alive II.125
see also spiritual nature
Nature and the Greeks (Schrödinger) I.335
'The Nature of Consciousness' (Walker) I.336
The Nature of the Physical World (Eddington) I.36–7, I.332, I.333
Nature Spirits of matter III.131
nature versus nurture II.90
Navier–Stokes equations III.365–6, III.370
Naydler, Jeremy I.43
Nazis I.200, II.85
propaganda poster II.134
see also Thunberg
Neanderthals I.241
The Near Death Experience II.74
near-death experiences (NDEs) I.15, I.17, I.49, I.87–9, I.152, I.171, III.162
and master analogy theory II.128
and neural correlate III.306
veridical experience I.70–1
near-death states II.91–6
Nebuchadnezzar's dream III.63
necromantic practices II.81
negative capability II.135
negative characteristic II.5
negative pole III.333
negative principle (abstract meaning of) II.11, II.34
negative statement III.279, III.280
negative thinking III.280
negentropy I.44
neo-Darwinian synthetic theory I.56
neo-Darwinism II.131, III.222, III.228
neo-Darwinist reductionism I.44
neo-Darwinists I.58, II.110, II.133, II.222
neo-Gnostic II.164
neonatal amnesia I.101
nerve fluid III.179
nerve properties III.114
nerves ('General Scholium' *q.v.*) III.179
see also nerve fluid; nervous ether
nerve/sense system II.184
nervous breakdown I.282
nervous ether III.163
nervous/nerve impulses III.137

nervous system II.184, III.41, III.163, *III.193*, III.195
nested hierarchy II.14
see also holons; Koestler
nether regions/worlds II.6, II.85
networker II.189
see also Leibniz
Netzah III.63
Neumann, Erich III.3
Neumann, John von I.334, II.115
neural correlate of consciousness III.112–13, III.120, III.135, III.136–7, III.146, III.165–6, III.306
and neuroscience III.174
and Sperry I.83
Neuralink III.272
neural mechanism III.135
neural networks III.162
neural pathways II.90
neural transducers III.136, III.166, III.171
Neurath, Otto I.23
neuroanatomic connections III.41
neuroanatomy III.44, *III.45*
neurobiologists II.135
neurobiology I.xlvi, I.8, III.136, III.237
neurocardiology II.44, III.33, III.41–3, III.42
neurogenesis I.101
neuroimaging experiments III.115
neurological imperative III.305–8
neurology II.120, II.121–2, II.123, III.43, III.120, III.161–5, III.311
neuronal events III.136
neuron assemblies II.xvi
neurons I.8, I.11, II.118, II.119, III.40, III.314, III.366, III.368
and Alexander III.162
Basic and Clinical Neurocardiology III.41
and Hamilton III.40
neuroplasticity I.77, I.105, I.161–3
neuroscience I.xlvi, I.7–8, I.10, I.102, II.112, III.266, III.305–8
bottom-up approach to consciousness III.146
and the brain I.105, II.181
debt of gratitude to I.261
and divided theories of consciousness III.351
evidence III.203
and hard problem of consciousness II.xvi
mainstream II.44–5
and neural correlate III.174
and Novella and Shermer I.11–12
and prosthetic devices III.267–8
and Schrödinger Mind–Sensation Problem III.134, III.135–6, III.165–6
on transmutation from neurology to experience III.161
neuroscientists II.44, II.122
neurosurgery III.162
neurotransmitters II.118
neutralizing attributes III.113
neutron I.98
New Age I.160, I.291, II.162, III.294
New Ager II.222
New Concept of the Universe (Russell) I.305
'A New Consciousness for Global Peace' (Taormina) I.341
A New Continent of Thought (Ross) I.160
new discoveries (clash with orthodox *q.v.*) III.230
new era III.196
see also Leary
new evidence (science *q.v.*) III.264
new eyes (consciousness levels *q.v.*) III.249
new forms (Cosmos *q.v.*) III.88
New Ideas in Space and Time (Dirac) I.133
new individual III.247
see also germ plasma; Weismann
new life forms III.222, III.279
new man (reincarnation *q.v.*) II.80
New Metaphysical Foundations of Modern Science (Harman) I.340
new particles III.310
A New Science of Life (Sheldrake) I.49, I.71, I.351, I.356, II.131–2
New Scientist III.314
New Testament I.188, III.17, III.51, III.60, III.101, III.104–20, III.312
New Thought I.260, I.286, I.287–307, I.298, I.305, I.308
Newton, Isaac I.xxxix, I.10–11, I.51, I.123, I.156, I.218, I.244, I.264, II.101, II.219, II.224, III.71
on alchemy II.3, III.15
and astrology III.29, III.30
on the Bible III.284–5
and calculus I.79, III.149
and Castillejo I.302–3
The Chronology of Ancient Kingdoms Amended I.205–6
and consilience I.320
and diet III.208
on Divine Thought III.152–3
on Earth III.264

'General Scholium' II.77, III.36–7
and God of the gaps III.312
on gravity III.278
greatest mystical scientist I.234
and Hermetic philosophy II.125–6
holistic enquirer III.286
and intuition III.189, III.205–6
and Method of Composition I.229
mystic and occultist I.186, I.196–7
and omnipresence of God the Father I.155
Opticks I.34–5, III.89–90, III.327
parallels with Ramanujan III.207
on Plato III.68
and poetry II.135
and *Prima Materia* III.94
Principia I.334
and *prisca sapientia* I.117, III.118
research method I.230–2
and Russell I.305–6
on space and time III.142–3
and Spiritual Monad II.201
on substance of God III.105–6
on subtle spirit II.210, III.179, III.180
suffered nervous breakdown I.282
translation of Hermetic Axiom *I.249*, I.250, III.81
on unity I.237
and unknown sources II.71
Newton's Third Law of Motion III.90
new vistas III.180, III.249
new Worlds III.75
The New York American III.201
Nicaea III.23
Nicodemus II.69, III.xix
'A Night Inside the Great Pyramid' (Brunton) III.129
Night of Brahmā III.234
see also pralaya
nihilism I.192
nihilistic paradigm III.264
Ninth Symphony (Beethoven) II.230–1
Nirvāna II.167
nitrogen I.241
Noah's Ark III.10
nocebo reaction I.84
nocturnal birds (symbol of) I.200
Nocturne (music *q.v.*) III.149
noetic activity I.323, II.198, II.199
No Free Lunch: Why specified complexity cannot be purchased without intelligence (Dembski) I.355
nomenclature II.4, II.155
non-causal correlations I.96, I.109
non-drug based cures I.49
Nondual II.188
non-dualistic philosophical thought I.271
non-existence II.36, III.120
non-functioning II.120
non-instrumental action III.164–5
non-instrumental perception III.164–5
non-local interconnectedness III.307
non-locality I.75, I.96, I.111, I.213, I.252, I.338, I.339
and Einstein I.110
and entanglement I.109
non-material mind II.126
the non-physical I.13, I.27, I.75
non-physical counterpart II.121
non-physical planes III.94
non-reductive physicalism I.29–32, I.47, III.237
Non-Reductive Physicalism and the Mind Problem I.32
non-visible worlds III.92
normal senses III.187
North America
colonization of I.273
Indian folklore I.272–3
Mysteries I.273–4, I.278
North Pole of the spine III.185
nostrils (anatomical symbolism of) III.46
not-Self III.14
noumenal archetypes III.166–7
noumenon/noumena I.36, I.174, I.243, I.303, I.304, II.136, III.262
image of God II.77
and Nous II.2, II.177
and phenomena III.353, III.368
and principles II.6
Nous I.326, II.2, II.39, II.97, II.170, II.175–6
and Anaxagoras II.177
and The Lovers (Tarot cards) III.12
and Plato III.109, III.112
and Pythagoras II.176
nous II.41, II.198
Nous autokrates II.176
Novella, Steven I.11–12, I.13–14
the Now III.264
nuclear arsenal III.322
nucleic acids I.137
nucleosynthesis in stars III.75
nucleus III.187, III.224
number crunching (computers *q.v.*) II.115

numberless Universes III.240
see also multiverse; anthropic principle
numbers III.46, III.66, III.67, III.77, *III.79*, III.238–9, III.371
Numerical Analysis III.360
Nut II.2

obedience, upward links of in evolution *q.v.* III.226
obesity (deeper meaning of) II.99
Object III.145
the objective I.138, II.4
objective aspects
emanational descent III.155, III.156
mind III.161
unitary consciousness III.168
objective entity II.199
objective forms III.263
objective function III.154
objective manifestations III.75
objective perspective II.186
objective phenomena III.30, III.145
objective phenomenal universe III.156
objective physical plane III.39, III.86, III.97–8, *III.97*
objective physical sense organs III.127
objective Reality III.145
objective reality II.74, III.253, III.270
objective realms II.4
objective universe III.36, III.161
objective world III.97
objectivity III.44
objects II.126, III.265
of reality III.349
of the senses III.105, III.113, III.114
of worship III.37
oblivion II.73, II.79
observational inaccuracy II.208
observations I.46, II.117, II.118, III.278–9, III.309
pure III.363
of the universe III.240–1
observer I.43, III.291
observer effect I.98
obsessions III.198
obstruction III.166
Occam's chainsaw I.14
see also Occam's razor
Occam's razor (misuse of) I.13, I.14
Occident (sacred books of) III.304
occult, two different uses I.195–6
occult anatomy II.1, II.16, II.34, III.55, III.254
occult catechism III.221, III.227
occult chemistry I.98–9
Occult Chemistry (Leadbeater and Besant) I.339, II.156
Occult Cosmogony III.88–98
occult cosmology *see* cosmology
occult doctrines I.236–44, II.2, II.134, II.146, III.92–3
and modern science II.223
septenary classification II.175, II.196
Zarathuśtrian and Egyptian II.172
occult engineering processes (composition of man *q.v.*) II.200–3
occult faculties III.188
occult fundamentals II.160
Occult Hierarchy I.284
occultism I.xlix, I.194–201, I.202, I.204, I.235–54, II.149, III.276
definition I.182, I.197
discerns a life in every atom III.131
and figurative language III.3
and Galileo Commission Report III.329
and Hermetic Axiom III.70
is true exact science III.243
and The Lovers (Tarot cards) III.12
and *philosophia perennis* III.287, *III.292*
practical III.121
occultists I.202, I.207, I.210, I.212, I.251, *II.108*, III.41
definition I.195, I.201
on sun and the heart III.44
occult literature *see* literature
occult metaphysics II.162
occult method I.230–3, I.235
occult neuroanatomy III.44, *III.45*
occult philosophy I.236, III.159, III.173
occult physiology II.34, II.48, III.39
occult powers I.201, I.202, I.209, III.48, III.210
occult schools of the East II.167–74
occult science I.lxxv, I.lxxvi, I.88, I.230–3, I.235–54, II.xviii, II.1–14, II.204, II.209, III.271
can account alone for the mysterious powers of adepts II.59
can explain aberrant behaviour or genius II.90
compared with physical sciences III.181
definition I.xxxix, I.195, I.197–8, I.204
and evolution III.245–8
hidden purposes III.327
and human senses III.101

and initiate I.210
and mainstream natural science III.285
and modern science III.277
and neuroscience III.166–8
and prāṇa III.162–3
a Royal Science III.283
and Schrödinger Mind–Sensation Problem III.134, III.136, III.165, III.172
on sensation III.137
and Spiritual particles III.83
and symbolism III.19
occult structural engineering (human constitution *q.v.*) II.202–3
occult symbols III.26
occult taxonomy III.28
occult teaching II.147, II.174, II.175, II.176, II.181, III.248
occult writers II.164
see also Besant; Blavatsky
oceanic crust III.222
Odinic Mysteries of Scandinavia I.213
Œdipus Agyptiacus (Kircher) III.25
offence, and punishment II.66
Ōlāms III.63, III.92
Ōlām Asīah III.63
Ōlām Atzīlūth III.63
Ōlām Berīāh III.63
Ōlām Yetzīrah III.63
Olbers, Heinrich Wilhelm I.331–2
Olbers' paradox I.331–2
Olcott, Henry Steel III.287
old, growing (spiritual implications of) III.110
older material (cosmogony *q.v.*) III.88
Older Wheels (Occult Cosmogony *q.v.*) III.88
oldest evolutionary ancestor (scientific hypothesis) III.325
oldest human artefacts III.230–1
Oldfield, Harry II.83, II.84
old man II.80
see also karma; Christos; Parent; parent
Old Testament I.188, III.17, III.60, III.251, III.312
Olivares, David Ferriz de I.277
olive branch of promissory materialism III.270
Omega Point I.45
omnipresence of consciousness I.155–6
Omnipresent Holy Spirit III.111
Omniscience I.xlvii
omniscience II.218, II.221, II.223
Omniscient Love III.111
the One II.73, II.174
ONE BEING I.237
one big question III.263
one-eyed giants III.183
one fundamental law III.223
one Goal III.102
one infinitesimal cell III.247
One Life III.99
One Life III.93
one lifetime III.127
one light III.253
one method III.102
oneness III.266
One-Only-One II.2
ONE REALITY III.155, III.172
One Reality III.225
One Self II.227
ONE THING I.237
one-track idealism II.218
one-track purist approach II.204
One unchanging cause I.306
one voice II.188, III.286
onion skins (human constitution *q.v.*, simile for) II.10
online group consciousness I.150–1
Ono, Ken III.207
ontology I.25, I.54–5, I.202, I.235
open dialogue II.189
see also Leibniz; networker; a harmony of philosophers
open-ended questioning I.50
open eye III.39, III.186
Opening Heaven's Door (Pearson) II.55
opera (Beethoven's *Fidelio q.v.*) III.15–16
operational centres (human constitution *q.v.*) II.181
Operative Masonry III.190
opinions I.33, II.117, III.282, III.377
Oppenheimer, Robert III.281
opportunities for wisdom *q.v.* and spiritual fulfilment II.48, II.71
opposite forces III.225
opposites in evolution *q.v.* and involution *q.v.* II.218
Opticks (Newton) I.34–5
oral teachings I.193, III.17
orchestrated universe III.239
order, and chance III.239
orderliness, of creation III.84
Order of Melchizedek I.280
Order of the Essenes I.280
Order Out of Chaos: Man's new dialogue with nature (Prigogine and Stengers) I.229, I.339

orders of space in manifestation III.141
ordinary existence III.118
ordinary individual III.185
ordinary intelligence III.171
ordinary man III.255
ordinary mind III.117
ordinary people III.325
organic Being III.82
organicism I.70, I.71–82, I.346
organic life III.291
organic molecules I.107, III.76–7
organic selection I.52
organic understanding III.250
organic unity II.34, III.80, III.285
organisms III.76–7, III.223, III.265
organizing fields I.73, I.79–82, III.174
organs II.130, II.199
 of action III.113, III.224
 of consciousness III.39
 eyes III.201
 of Protogonos III.63
 of psychic plane III.185
  see also pituitary body; pineal gland
 of sense III.113, III.153
 see also sense organs
Orient (sacred books of) III.304
Oriental terms II.4
 see also Sanskrit
Origen Adamantius I.189
origin III.10, III.55, III.65, III.285
 of life and the universe III.262
 of man III.227–42, III.243, III.248
original design III.60
original idea III.92, III.262
original light III.254
The Original Russell–Einstein Manifesto *I.19*
original state III.235
original teachings II.155
original theology III.90
Originant Element III.158
Originating Source III.58, III.59
'The Origin of Mutants' (Cairns, Overbaugh and Miller) I.351
The Origin of Species (Darwin) I.56, I.58, I.346, III.219
Origins: A skeptic's guide to the creation of life on earth (Shapiro) I.351
Origins of Gravy II.138
 see also computationalist argumentation
The Origins of Persian Gnosis (Homayouni) III.226
Ormuzd I.267, III.13
Orphic Mysteries I.180, I.213
orthodox biology II.xvii
orthodox Brahmanical eschatology II.80
orthodox Christianity II.80, III.323
orthodox religions I.132, III.xviii, III.295, III.303
orthodox science I.35, I.45, I.132, III.287
oscillation III.112
O'Shea, Michael II.xvi
Osiris I.266–7, I.280
Osiris-Horus I.266
Osiris-Lunus I.266
Osiris-Ptah I.266
Osiris-Typhon I.266
Osmond, Humphry III.195
Osteen, Joel I.290
ouroboros III.3–4
Ouspensky, P. D. II.181
outer form III.244, III.246, III.295, III.296
outer man II.2
outer person II.12
outer shell III.85
outer voices (human state *q.v.*) III.xvii
outer world III.xix, III.178
outlook III.137, III.200
out-of-body experience (OBE) I.70–1, I.87, I.89–90, I.309, II.55, II.56
outsmarting, computers II.115
outward appearances/behaviour I.297, II.xvii, II.xviii, III.295
outward circumstances II.13
outward movement III.256
Overman III.129
Over Mind III.363
Overself II.30, III.129
Over-Soul I.291, I.292, I.293–4, I.296, I.297, III.129
'The Over-Soul' (Emerson) III.271
overtones III.86, III.88
overweight (spritual simile for) II.97
Ovid III.2
oviform II.51
owls (symbol of) I.200
own Substance III.145
own universe III.85
own will (left brain *q.v.* hemispheres *q.v.*) II.123
 see also McGilchrist
oxygen I.241, II.55

Paabo, Svante I.355

Pachamama (South America, Mysteries *q.v.*)
    I.276, I.280
Pachankis, John   I.342
Padma   III.55
pagans   III.36
pain   II.120, II.231, III.187
palæontology   III.216, III.234
Pali   II.3
Palladino, Eusapia   I.117
Pañca (Pancha) Tattva   III.113
Pañca-vaktram   III.168
panoramic memory   II.67
panpsychism   I.9, III.289
pansophy   III.60
panspermia   I.106–7
pantheons   III.36
Paper 1 (E. S. Instruction No. 1)   III.122–6
parables   II.26, III.1–2
parabolic shape   *III.150*
Parabrahman   III.105
Paracelsus   I.220, I.250, I.272, II.142, III.179,
    III.284
paradigmatic realm   III.123
Paradigm Explorer   II.197–8
Paradigm of Humanity   III.61
paradigm of mind   III.40
paradigm police (establishment scientists *q.v.*)
    I.49–50
Paradiso   II.71, *II.72*
Paragranum (Paracelsus)   III.179
parallel grooves in prehistoric metallic spheres *q.v.*
    III.231
parallel universes (cosmology *q.v.*)   III.85, III.240
Paramātman   III.58
paranormal phenomena   I.13, I.83–93, II.132–3,
    III.250, III.329
paranormal research   I.68
Parapsychological Association   I.85
parapsychological library   I.361
parapsychology   I.13, I.83–4, II.132, III.323
Paraśurāma   I.272
Parent   II.79–80, II.88
parent   II.89, II.90, II.205
parental Intelligences   III.327
parent body   III.223
parent earth   III.36
parent plane   III.88
parents, features of (embryology)   III.247
Parisano, Emilio   III.317, III.318
Parmenides   III.73
part   III.93, III.95, III.237, III.238

Parti, Rajiv   I.15, I.88–9, II.91
participative consciousness   I.43
Participator   III.291
participator   I.43
Participatory Anthropic Principle   III.351
particle physics   I.99
particles   III.107, III.250, III.310
particle–wave duality   I.96–7
Particulars   III.72
PASSING (evolution *q.v.*)   III.117
passing reality (Russell, Bertrand *q.v.* on life *q.v.*)
    II.74
passion   II.24, II.26, II.78, II.109, III.9
Passions of the Soul (Descartes)   II.126
passive characteristic   II.5
passive consciousness   III.204
passive principle   I.266, II.11, II.34, II.137
PAST   III.117
    see also Māyā
the past   II.99, III.264, III.340
past experiences   III.177
past-life memories   I.101–2
Past Lives (Fenwick, P. and Fenwick, E.)   I.100
Patanjali   II.32, III.180–1, III.190–1
path of moral actions   III.271
Path of Return   II.125
Path of Spirit   III.334
Path of the Shadows   III.333, III.334
paths   II.205, II.215, III.332–5, III.340
pattern, Tree of Life   III.61
Paul, Apostle/Saint   I.264, II.175, II.178, *II.179*,
    III.269, III.294
Pauli, Wolfgang   I.lvii, I.45, I.84, I.335, III.349,
    III.352, III.355–6
Pauline teaching   II.149
Pavri, Pestanji Temulji   II.153, II.160
Pavri System   II.160, *II.161*
pawns (chess *q.v.*)   III.14
peace   III.322
PEAR (Princeton Engineering Anomalies
    Research)   I.85, I.116, I.317
pearls   III.125, III.342–3
pedagogic Egyptology   III.25
pedantry   II.94
Pedigree of Man (Haeckel)   III.229
peduncles   III.184
Peebles, James   I.336
peer pressure   I.140
peer review   I.23, I.37, II.209, II.213, III.293
Pelican   III.84
    see also Kosmos

Penberthy, Professor Kim II.95
Penfield, Wilder I.18, I.76, I.164, III.162
penitence II.89
Penrose, Roger I.97–8, I.352, II.142, III.151, III.163, III.209, III.365
  on electromagnetic aura III.44
  Shadows of the Mind III.164, III.352–3
  on the universe III.271
Penzias, Arno I.336
perceiver/perceived III.145
perception I.323, II.125, III.14, III.137, III.167, III.351, III.362
  direct II.22
  divine II.22
  and drugs III.195, III.197
  non-instrumental III.164–5
  of the physical world II.53
  and sensation III.134, III.154–5
  subjective III.161
perceptual order I.317
perennial intuition II.197
perennialism I.xxxix
perennial philosophy I.xxxix, II.164, II.188, III.284–8
  see also philosophia perennis
Perennial Philosophy (Huxley) I.xxxviii
Perennial Wisdom II.204, II.219
perennial wisdom III.277, III.337
Perfected Holy Ones II.174
perfection III.80
performance of real things III.3
  see also models
performer II.126, II.127, III.306
PERIODICITY I.237–8
  see also Three Fundamental Propositions/axioms
periodicity I.137, I.240, I.294, I.340, II.76, III.173
perisperm II.107
perispirit II.54, II.107
permanent Individuality II.105–6
permissive–transmissive theory I.171, I.172, I.173
perpetual puzzle III.146
  see also neural correlate of consciousness
Persian Empire II.172
Persian Mysteries I.267–9
Persian Mystery School I.213
personal consciousness II.73
personal details II.67
Personal ego II.46, II.47, II.48, II.56, II.176
  and Higher Ego II.84–5, II.89, II.97
  and Māyāvi-rūpa II.57
personal elements II.68
personal gnosis III.10
Personality II.171
personality I.99, I.148, II.16, II.17, II.18, II.38, II.177, III.254
  as actors II.106
  and brain damage II.119
  and child II.88
  false II.42, II.46
  and incarnation II.79–80
  and Individuality II.23, II.45, II.105, II.200
  is a composite II.106
  and The Judgement (Tarot cards) III.13
  and karma II.216
  powerful II.218
  and seven principles II.64–5
  terrestrial III.256
  traits II.119
  and Zohar II.73
personal level III.15–16
personal lives III.185
personal possessions II.99
personal reflection III.xxi
personal self II.59–60, II.90
personal testimonies II.92
personal thoughts II.88, II.107
personare (Latin: etymology of) II.106
personification *III.27*, III.47, III.51
perspectives II.124, II.186
'Perspectives: The Universe as Home for Man: Puzzles attached to consciousness, the quantum principle, and how the universe came into being suggest that the greatest discoveries are yet to come' (Wheeler) I.337
Peru I.276–7
Pervader III.174
  see also Trimūrti; logos; Viṣṇu (Vishnu)
petals (symbol of) III.58
Phaedo/Phaedrus (Plato) I.205, I.263
phantasizing mind I.92
Phantasms of the Living (Gurney) II.56
phantasy III.243
phases II.64, II.76, II.97
phase states III.221, III.235, III.326
phenomena II.2, II.6, II.8, II.177, III.353, III.366, III.368
  anomalous III.228
  and ether III.178

objective and physical III.30
subjective and objective III.145
unaccountable II.91
and visible world I.304
phenomenological experience III.203
phenomenology II.94, II.96
phenomenon of life III.237
The Phenomenon of Man (de Chardin) I.52, I.350
Philalethes, Eugenius II.57
philanthropy II.107, III.194, III.200, III.244–5
Phillips, Stephen I.99, I.120, I.235, I.339, I.341, II.223, III.61
philology III.25
Philo of Alexandria III.64–5
philosophers I.182–3, III.6, III.10, III.14, III.34, III.35
Philosopher's Stone I.206, III.14–15
philosophia I.183
Philosophia Naturalis Principia Mathematica (Newton) III.105–6
philosophia perennis I.xxxix, I.xl, I.xlii, I.xliv, I.xlvi, I.xlvii, I.lxxxiv, I.66, I.140, II.2, II.146, II.197, II.204, II.205, III.118, III.284–8, III.315
close interrelation of the diverse teachings of III.246–7
concentration of the complex in terms of the simple III.220
on Darwinism III.225
and evolution III.216, III.263
and experience I.xl
and harmony II.189, *II.190*, III.188
and Hermetic Axiom I.xlix
and immortality III.341–2
intellectual speculation on Deity is impossible III.271
and Lamarckian inheritance I.75
and the Mysteries III.283
and NDEs I.89
and neuroscientific hubris III.306
principal attributes III.261
and the quantum hybrid model I.98
and reminiscence I.152
and Schrödinger and Joad II.198
and scientists II.221
tenets of III.224
term coined by Leibniz I.xxxviii
and Theosophy I.lxxix–lxxx, I.184, II.162, II.164
and top-down approach III.146
and Trojan War (allegory) III.48
unity of III.59
universal solvent I.xlviii
and wisdom-Source III.101
see also esotericism; theology
philosophical Elements III.238
philosophical issues II.120, II.121–2
philosophical keys III.4, III.16, III.17
philosophical naïveté (neuroscience *q.v.*) III.306
philosophical precepts II.153
philosophical quicksand in computationalist argumentation *q.v.* II.126
philosophical weaknesses in brain-equals-computer *q.v.* analogy II.112
philosophy I.182–3, I.204, III.162, III.270–1, III.308, III.323
and the composition of man II.1
and Liszt III.216–17
and mathematics III.352–3
sources III.101
symbol III.67
The Philosophy of Freedom (Steiner) II.182
phoenixes II.69
phosphine I.107
see also Venus
phosphorus I.241
see also Comet 67P
photographs II.63, II.83–4, III.201, III.376
Phren II.176
the physical I.27, II.39, II.43, II.118
Physical (Animal) body II.17, II.19
physical and objective level II.8
physical and objective world III.148
physical aspect III.130
Physical body II.18, II.28, II.29–30, II.35, II.53–4, II.175
and Besant System II.154
and classical Theosophical literature II.151
and Divine Ego II.215
and Fourth Way teaching II.181
and hara II.165
and Jinarâjadâsa System II.160
and Lower ego II.47
and Prakritic plane III.97
and soul II.38
and Steiner II.183, II.184, II.185
and Sūtras III.114
and temple II.200
and transpersonal psychology II.188
physical body III.46–7, III.94, III.110
castles (chess) III.13
condensate III.116

physical body (continued)
connection of the monad with III.175
and drugs III.197–9
and Sūtras III.112
thoughts and emotions can affect III.192
physical brain *see* brain
physical causal closure I.49
physical chemistry III.180
physical chrysalis III.357–8
physical circumstances II.118
physical constants II.209, III.85, III.238–9, III.354–6
physical contact II.95
physical correspondences III.192
physical cosmology II.228, III.85
physical cosmos III.31
physical death II.63, II.65
physical domain III.137
physical entities III.93, III.163
physical events II.118
physical existence I.302, II.124–5
physical expression II.136
physical faculties III.183
physical field theory II.154
physical forms III.219
physical frame II.178
physical globes III.93
physical hereditary connection III.247
physical instruments II.xvii
physicalism I.23, I.24, I.28–32, I.46, I.47, III.289
physicality II.35, III.183, III.187
physical laws III.166, III.278
physical level III.98, III.192, III.219
physical life I.302, III.8, III.319
the physically observable II.117
physical man II.136, III.67, III.248, III.263
see also Physical body
physical matter III.92, III.114, III.163, III.227, III.307, III.349
physical means II.136
physical mechanisms II.125, III.250, III.269
physical medicine III.320
physical nature III.67, III.75–7, *III.76*, III.183, III.278
physical neurology III.163
physical organisms II.154, III.38
physical organs III.50, III.181
physical phenomena III.30
physical plane II.29, III.75, III.88, III.218, III.225, III.245
and Divine Ego III.254
and Sephīrāh III.64
physical plasm III.248
physical precipitation III.192
physical processes III.262
physical qualities II.210
physical realism, model of II.8
physical ritual III.18
physical sciences I.331–43, II.xvii, II.91, III.xxi, III.30, III.31
contrast with occult science III.283
and esoteric science III.110
phenomenal explosion in knowledge III.181
physical sensation II.204
physical senses *see* senses
physical sensory organs *see* sense organs
physical sight III.189, III.249
physical states III.137
physical substance III.94
physical substrate III.172
physical suffering III.273
physical system II.229
physical texture of the skin III.110
physical universe III.61, III.110, III.319
physical vehicle II.80, III.146, III.337
physical world III.85, III.87, III.109, III.166, III.353, III.369
and appearance of the mental world III.167
archetypally mental III.371
and mathematics III.151
physicochemical mechanism III.xvii
physics I.332–43, II.220
and agents I.243
classical I.22, I.95, I.96, I.109, I.133, I.318
and ether II.36
and field II.6
and higher dimensions III.250
and materialism I.36
and metaphysics I.203, III.49, III.77, III.110, III.172, III.265
Michelson-Morley experiment II.207
and the mind III.164
modern III.108
quantum II.126
on stars III.269
strictly defined boundaries of III.262
Physics and Philosophy: The revolution in modern science (Heisenberg) I.335–6
Physics of the Soul (Goswami) I.354
physiological connection III.184–5
physiological hypotheses III.165

physiological map III.287
physiology II.1, II.2, III.42, III.55, III.317
Piaget, Jean II.186, *II.187*
pianist (simile) II.127
piano (simile) II.127
Pike, Albert I.189
Pilgrim III.173
pilgrimage of life III.125
The Pillar of Judgement III.64
The Pillar of Mercy III.64
pillars III.64
see also Qabbalah
pineal gland III.172, III.181–2, III.184–6, *III.184*, III.190, III.197
pine cone III.190
see also pineal gland; Kuṇḍalinī
Pinkham, Mark Amaru I.277
Pio, Padre III.188–9
pioneering study of aura during meditation *q.v.* III.203
Pisachas II.81
Pi symbol III.364
pitch, discerning II.121
see also Keller
pituitary body III.181–2, III.197
pituitary gland III.172, III.185–6, III.190
Pivot-Point (human constitution *q.v.*) II.200–2
place (metaphysics *q.v.*) II.6
placebo effect I.84, III.351
In Place of the Self (Dunselman) III.197–8
plains of Cosmos (chess *q.v.*) III.13
Planck, Max I.xlv, I.lxi–lxii, I.104, I.133, I.218, I.320, I.323, III.315
and black-body problem I.332
on consciousness I.liii
discovers energy quanta I.95, I.332
on matter I.xlvii, I.35, III.350
Where is Science Going? I.334
Planck time III.354, III.356
planes II.2, II.6, II.7, II.161, *III.99*, III.246
action III.123
and causes II.78
corporeal III.122
and cosmos III.83
definition II.5
of existence II.153, III.74, III.77, III.221
and forms II.160
hierarchically lower II.37
higher II.53
of Kosmos III.86–8, III.91, *III.91*, III.92–4, III.95–8, III.98
lower III.166, III.248
of materiality III.225
mental II.110
of nature II.5, III.64
non-physical III.94
objective III.39
psychic III.185
and Saptaparṇa III.56
shell recycled back II.81
of spirituality III.225
and Taimni System II.162
terrestrial II.41, II.42
three III.22
and Vedantic classification II.168
see also physical plane
planet, life on II.134
planetary and solar schemes III.327
planetary cycle II.85
planetary disasters III.187–8
planetary influences III.8, III.30
Planetary manvantara II.77
Planetary Rounds III.240, III.377–8
Planetary Spirits I.285
planetary system II.154
Planet of Death II.85–6
Planets (Spirits of) I.265
see also The Vision
plant kingdom III.246
plant life II.184
plants II.231
plastic brain I.160–3
Plato I.154, I.156, I.215, I.251, I.252, I.270, I.303, III.15
allegory of the cave III.253, III.378
counsel of III.109
dialogues I.47
and Egyptian Mystery Schools I.217
and experience I.33
on Hermes I.247
man constituted of two parts II.175
and Parmenides III.73
Phaedo I.205
Phaedrus I.263–4
on psyche II.170
Republic I.37, I.89
and the soul II.177
and Supreme Deity III.48
and three principles I.324
on Universals III.72
Platonic archetype I.56, I.303
Platonic division II.175

Platonic forms I.72
Platonic mathematical world III.352
Platonic method I.230, I.235
Platonic solids III.55
Platonic standpoint III.286
Platonism I.288
Platonists III.96
The Plausibility of Life: Resolving Darwin's dilemma (Kirschner and Gerhart) I.355
playground III.144
  see also māyā; Space; Time
Plotinus I.183, III.261, III.328
plunder (ecological crisis *q.v.*) II.126
plurality of viewpoints II.189, II.190
Plutarch II.68, II.175, II.177–8, III.288
pneuma I.3
  see also spirit; Self
Podolsky, Boris I.110
Poe, Edgar Allan III.201
The Poet (Emerson) I.57
poetry I.2–3, II.63, II.135, III.327–8
poets III.189, III.327–8
Poimandres I.264
point (Theos) III.65
  see also God
point centre (consciousness *q.v.*) III.164
pointlessness of the universe III.268, III.269
  see also Weinberg
Point of Origination I.301
  see also Troward
Polanyi, Michael I.120
Polanyi's syndrome I.120
polar coordinates (mathematics *q.v.* and consciousness *q.v.*) III.363
polarities II.6, II.27, II.30, II.76, II.185, III.184–5, III.333
Pole, Wellesley Tudor II.82
poles III.111, III.114, III.123, III.185
politics II.209, III.18
politics of knowledge I.140
poltergeist II.82
Polycontrast Interference Photography (PIP) imaging system II.83
polygenetic origin (human evolution *q.v.*) I.240
polyonymous individuals I.211
polypi II.231, III.56
the ponderable I.38
  see also primary qualities; scientific materialism
pool (symbol of) III.10–11
the Pope II.131
Popol Vuh I.274–5, I.279
Popper, Sir Karl I.31, I.39, I.48, I.338, III.304, III.313, III.350
  and falsifiability I.334
  and promissory materialism I.35–6
popular books II.9, III.78
popular media III.xvii
Popular Science Review III.178
portal, to eternity II.99
positive characteristic II.5
positive pole III.333
positive principle (abstract meaning of) II.11, II.34
positive statement III.279
positivism III.308, III.309
  see also Vienna School; logical positivism
post-Blavatsky writers II.7
post-classical Theosophy II.151, II.153–62
posterior deities as attributes of the one God *q.v.* III.36
posthuman beings III.205, III.336
post-materialist paradigm I.56
post-mortem analogue II.78–9
post-mortem states II.2, II.24–5, II.48, II.65–8, II.78, II.97–9
  scientific corroboration for II.91–6
  suicide victims II.84
post-Mozart music II.219
postulate
  in science I.173
  about Unity (Emerson) I.294
potencies III.64, III.217
the potential (Aristotle *q.v.*) III.220
  see also Aristotelian philosophy
potentiality III.219, III.220, III.246, III.375
poverty I.5, II.xv, III.273
power II.129, II.130, III.9, III.64, III.319
  behind the eyes III.201
  of belief III.352
  of consciousness II.45
  of Ideas III.107
  invisible III.37
  and knowledge III.210
  latent I.180, III.190–210
  un*seen* III.51
powerful ideas III.107
powerful personalities II.218
power station (similes) II.41, II.195, II.202, *II.203*
practical occultism III.121
Prakṛiti II.174, III.155–6
prakṛiti I.270
Prakritic plane III.97

Pralaya III.88
pralaya II.76–7, III.234
see also Night of Brahmā
Prāṇa II.19, II.24, II.27, II.30, III.58, III.113, III.168
and Besant System II.154, II.155
and classical Theosophical literature II.149, II.150
and Esoteric Buddhism II.168
and Jivaic III.96
and knights (chess) III.13
and Pavri System II.160
from Viṣṇu (Vishnu) III.174
prāṇa III.162–3, III.176, III.179, III.180, III.246
Prāṇa–Liṅga-śarīra II.42
Prāṇa–Liṅga-śarīra–Sthūla-śarīra II.43
Prāṇayama III.180
prāṇāyāma II.202
Prāṇayama-kośa II.168, II.170
pranic reservoirs II.27
prārabdha (karma *q.v.*) III.127
Pratibha bhava III.164–5
prayer (efficacy of) II.93
see also Crookall
precepts III.220, III.261
precession (astronomy) III.23
precipitation III.192
see also cākras
precision over truth II.124
precognition I.86, I.92, I.122, I.141
preconceived theories III.244
preconceptions I.67–8, I.318, I.319, III.51, III.232, III.328, III.357
predictions (mathematics *q.v.*) III.356
predominance
of thoughts II.107
of Divine Forces in human being III.176
pre-existence II.79
see also reincarnation
pre-historical epochs III.184
prehistoric continents II.222–3
prejudice I.319, II.94, II.132, II.133, III.142, III.244
premature arousal of latent powers *q.v.* III.193
premature death II.75
premature destruction of Antaḥakaraṇa *q.v.* II.89
premonitions I.102, I.171
prenatal events II.97
prescience III.xix
presence, sensing II.94
The Presence of the Past (Sheldrake) I.71, I.138
Present III.117
see also Māyā
the present III.110, III.328
present incarnation II.89
present lifetime II.69
Preserver III.174
see also Trimūrti; logos; Viṣṇu (Vishnu)
preserver II.52
presumptions I.67–8
presuppositions I.13, I.91, I.115, I.141, III.140, III.162, III.308
about brain processes I.173, III.305, III.306
and Galileo Commission Report I.143
and proof III.309
Pribram, Karl I.76
price paid for scientific discoveries III.273–5
pride, and fall III.9
priest–hierophants I.215
Priest of Nature (Iliffe) III.284–5
Prigogine, Ilya I.229, I.339, I.351, III.269
primacy of Consciousness III.296
primacy of consciousness I.97, I.316, II.198, III.120, III.271, III.288, III.291
primacy of matter III.310
primacy of the heart III.33
primal Light III.202
Prima Materia III.94, *III.94*
primaries, three III.77
primary causes III.77
primary colours III.86
primary differentiation III.144, III.145
primary Element III.289
primary entities II.18
primary principles II.18
primary qualities I.24, I.32–3, I.34, I.35, I.38, I.54, II.xvi
primary vehicle II.52
prime of life II.81
primeval atom II.39
primeval spirits II.172
primitive shoe III.231
primordial gravitational waves III.85, III.262
primordial nature I.270
primordial point III.64
Primordial Reality III.370
primordial sense III.156
Primordial Thought III.92, III.263
primordial writing III.19
primum-mobile II.176
principal planes (Kosmos *q.v.*) III.86
Principia (Newton) I.231, I.334

PRINCIPLE III.105
see also First Fundamental Proposition/axiom
Principles II.154, III.159, III.168
principles II.6, II.7, II.11, II.19, II.161, III.154, III.296
analogous III.70
animating III.97
complementary II.74
definition II.5
of dying (evolution) III.221
emanational unfoldment of II.30
and Esoteric Buddhism and Tāraka Rāja-Yoga II.168
and Esoteric Science III.83
eternal III.173
of evolution III.221
first III.355
and form II.158
general II.16
higher and lower II.38
highest III.256–7
and human senses III.101
immortal III.341
immutable III.317
independent organizing III.177
of indeterminacy I.96
informing II.126, II.127
integration of the six II.29
intuition II.22
invisible III.37
man and nature III.75–7
of Space/Time III.141
specific application of II.16
stable II.74
subordinate creative III.238
and Theosophical literature II.2
underlying II.84
underlying sacrifice III.18
and vehicles III.140–1
Principles of Man II.5, II.19, II.20, *II.31*, II.146, II.196–7, II.220
and brain III.44, *III.45*
seven *II.49*, II.64–5
symbols III.11–12
and Theosophical literature II.149, II.150, II.151
prisca sapientia I.xxxix, I.117, III.90, III.118
Prisoners' Chorus (Beethoven's *Fidelio q.v.*) III.16
La Prisonniere (Proust) III.249
probabilities I.96, I.108–9, I.113–14, II.93
probation (initiation *q.v.*) III.50
problems III.135, III.136, III.140, III.283
Proceedings of the National Academy of Sciences U.S.A. I.339–40
Processes of Life: Essays in the philosophy of biology (Dupré) I.356
Proclus I.251, II.205, III.36
Producer (of entities *q.v.*) III.156
see also Prakṛiti
product II.119, II.137
productive function, brain *q.v.* I.168, I.169, I.175
see also James, William
product of one's times III.245
products, of time and space III.109
the profane (truth withheld from) III.276
profane philosophy III.118
prognosis, sombre III.310
programmable device II.114
see also computers
programmers II.129, II.140
programming II.118, II.121, II.122
programs II.114, II.115, II.128
progression, of creation III.104
progressive aspect, modern science III.223
Project Debater II.114
Project Happiness I.xlii
projection II.88, II.106, III.120
vehicle of II.54, II.56
Prolegomena (Kant) I.34
Promenade Concerts I.150
promise, to solve the 'insoluble' mystery of consciousness III.314
promissory materialism I.35–6, III.270, III.277, III.313–15, III.319
promotion, and death II.75
see also Devachan
proof
of perennial philosophy III.285
and presuppositions III.309
Proof of Heaven (Alexander) I.15, I.88
The Prophet (Gibran) II.64, II.109
Prophet for Our Times (Lorimer) III.188
prophetic relics III.17–18
prophetic visions III.311
Propositions/Axioms, Three Fundamental I.236–8, I.292–7
importance of III.287–8, *III.292*
The Prospect of Immortality (Ettinger) III.335
prosperity gospel church I.290
prosperity preachers III.323
prosperity theology I.290

prosperity thought III.272
prosthetic devices III.267–8
Protagoras II.112
Protogonos III.63
prototypal form III.130
Proust, Marcel III.249
proven facts (scientific dogma) III.312
proverbs (etymology of) III.2
providential designer III.240
Pryse, James Morgan I.274–5, I.279
Psalm 8:2 II.134
pseudo-materialist theories III.324
pseudo-occult phenomena I.200
pseudo-religious cult II.110
pseudoscience I.121–2, I.142, III.22, III.29–31, III.312, III.316
psi I.13–14, I.84–7, I.119, I.120–1, I.142, I.342, III.329
Psyche I.263, II.175, III.304
psyche I.3, I.324, II.73, II.133, II.170, II.177
psychedelic drugs I.169, II.45, III.xx, III.194, III.195–7, III.198, III.199
Psychedelic Research Group III.196
psychiatric problems III.274
psychiatry I.49, III.34
psychical body I.264, II.178
psychical research I.117–19, III.353
Psychic and Noetic Action (Blavatsky) II.59–60, II.198
psychic atmosphere, poisoning of II.81
psychic characteristics III.247
psychic communication II.92–4
psychic corpse II.81
psychic energies, unspent II.81
psychic faculties III.183, III.194
psychic happenings II.97
psychic investigations II.92
psychic manifestations II.83
psychic phenomena I.112
psychic planes II.81, III.185, III.246
psychic powers I.201, I.202, II.164
psychic realms II.39, II.64
psychic researches III.171
psychic studies II.93
psychic vesture II.80, II.99
psychic virus III.198
psychic visions III.185
psychic worlds II.39
psychism I.182, I.204, II.156
psycho-animal Lower self II.89
psycho-energetic vortices of force III.191
psychokinesis (PK) I.85, I.86, I.119, I.320
psychological baggage II.97, II.99
psychological jigsaw puzzle II.90
  see also Antaḥakaraṇa
psychological orbits III.8
  see also Cretan Labyrinth; Ptolemaic cosmology
psychological phenomena III.237
psychological studies II.92
psychologists II.65, III.115
psychology I.83–4, I.265, II.71, II.185–8, III.104, III.155
Psychology and Alchemy (Jung) I.245
psycho-mental degeneration II.85
psycho-physical body, new, karmically conditioned II.80
psycho-physical centres III.182
psycho-physical karma III.337
psycho-physical phenomena III.282
psycho-physical problem III.355
psychophysiology III.42
psychosomatic experiences I.169
psycho-spiritual connection III.184–5
psycho-spiritual life-support II.88
psychotherapy II.96
Ptolemaic cosmology III.7–8
publication bias I.86
pubs (England, names of) III.303
pulse, of life II.100
punishment II.78, II.100
  fits the offence II.66
Purāṇas I.270, I.327, II.6, III.17, III.65, III.74
Pure Consciousness II.20
pure Consciousness III.161, III.238, III.254
pure consciousness III.235
pure emanation III.217
pure intellect II.41
pure mathematics III.206
pure mind II.41
pure motives III.185
pure observation III.363
Purgatorio II.25, II.65–6, II.86
purgatory II.65–6
purification II.65
purified soul III.186
purifying, lower nature II.90
purist, and student II.224
purity I.213, II.88, III.95
purpose II.119, II.205, III.37, III.153, III.295, III.296, III.320
  and body II.29

purpose (continued)
of car (analogy) II.10–11
and cause I.137
common high III.149
of cosmos III.269
Darwinian theory III.220
hidden III.326–7
real II.48
universe III.293, III.311
and white dove of truth III.261
purposeful and comforting nature of sensed presence *q.v.* II.56
see also Māyāvi rūpa
purposeful energy III.263
purposeless universe (Weinberg, Steven *q.v.*) III.22
Puruṣa II.162, II.174, III.111, III.115, III.155, III.329
puruṣa I.270
Purucker, Gottfried de I.179, I.283, I.284, II.77, II.87, II.220
pyramid (shape, symbolism of) III.46
the Pyramids I.309, III.49–50, III.65
Pyrrha III.9
Pythagoras I.216, I.217, I.219, I.272, II.175, III.52, III.371
and cosmos III.84
on death II.63
on the Soul II.176
and the soul II.177
Pythagorean mathematics III.25
Pythagoreans III.67
Pythagorean School I.223
Pythagorean teachings III.66
Pythagorean Tetractys I.99

Qabbalah I.175, I.188, I.193–4, I.300, II.73, III.4, III.17, III.25, III.227
and Adam Kadmon I.265
and Sephirothic Tree III.60–4
Qabbalistic axiom/doctrine I.155, I.238, III.220
Qabbalistic cosmogony III.61
Qabbalistic proverb *III.292*, III.296
Qabbalistic Tree of Life I.99, II.165
Qabbalists III.47
qigong III.181
quadruped (evolution *q.v.*) III.237
see also Darwinian theory; *The Descent of Man in Relation to Sex*
qualia I.30, I.31, I.33, I.35, I.41, II.218
qualifications I.220–3, II.91, III.293
qualities II.107, II.135, III.98
quality II.105, II.136
mental life III.192
of mind III.51
of thought II.26
the quantifiable (science *q.v.*) I.32, I.38
see also primary qualities
quantifiable data III.137
quantification, limitations of II.135
quantitative paradigm I.331
quantitative results II.96
quantity over quality II.124, II.135
quantum action, indivisibility of I.95
'Quantum Concepts in Space and Time' (Aspect) I.339
quantum entanglement I.109
quantum experiments I.318
'A Quantum Explanation of Sheldrake's Morphic Resonance' (Goswami) I.353
quantum gravity III.163
quantum physics I.xliv, I.22, I.44, I.94, I.95–8, I.108–13
broken down philosophical implications of classical physics III.265
and *Consciousness and the Universe* III.164
discoveries have not penetrated the thinking of scientists II.126
and Exclusion Principle I.84
and Goswami III.228
and Planck I.xlv, I.104
and telepathy II.132
and Weinberg III.271
quantum processes III.163, III.164
quantum science I.43, I.80, I.134, II.xvi, II.74, III.147, III.308
quantum superposition III.369
quantum theory I.80, I.96, I.98, I.108–9, I.110, I.332, I.345–6
The Quantum Theory and Reality (d'Espagnat) I.338
quarks I.98, I.99
quasi-immortality II.76
quasi-occult treatise on life-force (Richardson *q.v.*) III.179
Quaternary (human constitution *q.v.*) III.66
queen (chess *q.v.*) III.13, III.14
queen bee (simile) III.137
quenchless spirit (Keller, Helen *q.v.* on Beethoven *q.v.*) II.120, II.231
questioning I.50, II.xv, II.119, III.263
Quiché I.274, I.275, I.280

quiddity III.158
see also Tattvas
Quimby, Phineas I.288
Quine, Willard Van Orman I.196
quintessential principle (Consciousness *q.v.*) III.289
quintuple functions (human nature *q.v.*) *II.13*
quintuple nature (human nature *q.v.*) II.39
Qur'an I.192, III.52

Ra III.190
see also pineal gland; pine cone
Rabbis (Hebrew) III.60
Rabi, Isidor I.337
races (evolution *q.v.*) II.222–3
see also Root Races; Rounds and Races
Racial Cataclysms III.376
Radhakrishnan, Sir Sarvepalli I.99, I.216–17, III.186
radiance of Consciousness III.253
Radiant Essence II.39
Radiant Light II.203
radiation I.37, I.305–6, II.53, III.108, III.201, III.203
radicalization III.272
Radin, Dean I.14, I.45, I.85–6, I.111–12
radionics II.166
radium I.95
Ragazzoni, Giuseppe III.232
rainbow (simile) III.86
The Rainbow and the Worm: The physics of organisms (Mae-Wan Ho) I.352
Rainbow Portrait (Queen Elizabeth I) III.46
Rainbow Snake II.87
see also Antaḥkaraṇa
raincloud (simile) III.237
see also devolution
raising consciousness III.248–55
Rājas III.113
Rāma I.272, III.9, III.16
Ramanujan, Srinivasa I.133, III.151, III.189, III.206–9, *III.207*, III.365, III.372
The Man Who Knew Infinity II.71
Rāmāyaṇa I.191, III.9, III.48, III.235, III.236, III.294
Randi, James I.120, III.326
random behaviour III.239
see also intelligent design
rants (scientists *q.v.* against religion *q.v.*) III.311
see also Dawkins, Richard
rapid eye movement (REM) II.75
ratiocination III.118
rational, meaning III.129
rational faculties III.34
rationalism I.33, II.125, III.73
rational soul II.176, II.177, III.129, III.236
Rāvana III.9
see also Rāmāyaṇa
raw material III.173
see also Third Logos
Ray II.216
see also Antaḥkaraṇa
rays III.39, III.201, III.377
reaction, to new ideas I.322
reaction–diffusion theory I.73
the Real III.108, III.111, III.117, III.118, III.197
real experience III.198
realism III.270, III.327
realities III.61
REALITY I.184, I.204, III.142, *III.145*, III.152, III.155, III.370
expression of III.173
Reality I.166, III.118, III.145, III.265
reality III.37, III.115, III.119, III.143, III.253, III.287
  and appearances III.106
  aspects of III.330
  of the basic substance III.147
  and Berkeley I.34
  deeper structures of III.331
  definition III.280
  fundamental I.316
  and illusion III.xx
  and internal and external stimuli I.147
  and matter I.13
  and metaphysics I.202, I.204
  nature of I.1
  objects of III.349
  and quantum physics I.22
  relativity of II.74
  and scientific materialism I.67
  and the senses III.137
realization II.82, III.126
real purpose (of life *q.v.*) II.48
Real Substance III.104, III.113
real substance III.105
real thing III.220
Real Truth III.119
reaping fruits where they were sown II.79
reason II.22, II.42, II.134, II.177, III.118, III.271, III.313
  definition III.189

reason (continued)
  and Gibran II.26
reasoning soul II.177
rebirth I.89, I.100, I.188, I.217, II.63, II.75, II.78
  and Jung I.103
  and Sixth Principle (occult doctrine) I.240
    see also karma
  spiritual II.69
receivers (photographic) III.201
  see also eyes, mystery in
receptiveness III.189
receptors III.154
Recherches sur la théorie des quanta (de Broglie) I.333
recollection I.152, I.153, I.154, II.101
reconciling characteristic III.285
recycling facilities in Nature *q.v.* II.86
Reddit (internet) II.116
redemption III.51
Rediscovering Darwin (Loye) III.244
reductionism I.9, I.17, I.43, I.53–4, I.111, III.275, III.276
  and biology I.69
  and causal closure I.32
  and molecular biology III.176, III.177
  neo-Darwinist I.44
reductionist paradigm I.331
reductive methodology III.83
reductive physicalism I.28, I.29
reductive psychology II.186
re-embodiment II.79
re-ensoulment II.86
Rees, Martin I.336, I.338, III.238–9, III.241, III.276, III.337–8
re-evolution, spiritual III.187
references, verifiable of Wisdom, Ancient (Ageless) *q.v.* III.64
refined substance III.242
  see also evolution
refined subtle medium III.178
refinement I.156, I.240, I.262, I.308, III.163, III.246
refining principle III.242
reflected lights III.256
reflection II.38, II.106, III.xxi, III.148, III.332
Reflections of the Father III.155
Reflections on an Ageless Wisdom (Mills) III.130
reflexive reference III.241
  see also anthropic principle
Reformation III.90
refraction II.197, III.152, III.165
refractive index, brain (simile) I.170
Regenerator III.175
  see also Trimūrti; logos; Kuṇḍalinī
regeneration I.70, I.71, I.280, I.369, III.3
regions of kosmos *q.v.* III.238
Reincarnating Ego II.42, II.73, II.79, II.80, II.106, II.150, II.162
reincarnation I.99–103, II.63, II.75, II.79, II.97–9, III.41, III.246
  definition II.78
  and Emerson I.297
  and László II.197
  and memory I.152
  Sixth Principle I.240
  and Stevenson II.91
  in St. John I.188
  and Vedas III.247
Reincarnation: The Phoenix Fire Mystery (Cranston) I.100
reinfleshment I.99
Reiss, Michael I.150
Relan, Jay III.43
relationships III.47, III.88, III.250, III.255
relative immortality II.76
relative terms II.78
relative truth III.106
relativity of reality II.74
relativity theory I.xliv, I.110, I.332, I.333, II.207, III.265, III.353
  and Dirac I.133
  and ether II.210
  and gravitational waves III.85
  and Strömberg I.80
  and thermal artefacts II.208
  on truth III.119
release, and death II.97
releasing/permissive function of brain *q.v.* I.168–9, I.170, III.165, III.166
  see also James, William
RELIGION III.323
  see also beliefs; belief systems; faith
religion I.lxi, I.lxxv, I.132, III.47, III.271, III.303, III.332, III.378
  and the composition of man II.1
  debates II.218
  dualistic II.172
  and Einstein III.313
  and Emerson I.295
  esoteric–exoteric contrast I.190–3
  exoteric II.85
  and extremism II.222

and Hardy I.53
institutionalised II.125
more fact-based than science III.323
and New Thought I.289
orthodox III.xviii, III.295
and psychic studies II.93
and Ramanujan III.208
and science I.150, III.270
sources III.101
and Theosophy II.149
training III.36
unity of I.217, III.102
and Dawkins II.144, III.311
and Weinberg III.270
religio perennis I.xxxix
religious art I.280, III.202
religious climate II.220
religious experience III.329
religious fundamentalism/religious fanaticism I.321, III.312, III.316, III.319
religious heretics II.132
remembrance I.152, I.153, III.195
reminiscence I.152, I.153–4, II.101
Rémond, Nicolas II.188
remorse II.90, II.109
remote dowsing I.92
remote viewing I.14, I.92–3
repentance II.90
repercussion II.150
see also Liṅga-śarīra; mediums
representation III.5, III.83, III.265
Representative Men (Emerson) I.293
representatives (material organs) II.142
see also Paracelsus
reproducibility (canon in science *q.v.*) I.13–14
reproductive hormones III.182
The Republic (Plato) I.37, I.89, III.377
Repulsion towards Matter *q.v.* (Puranic philosophy) III.112
see also Ahaṁkāra, III.103
res cogitans I.69
research II.91, III.171, III.306, III.329
on ADCs II.96
on brain damage II.119
grants II.133
method I.230–2
res extensa I.69
residual consciousness of post-mortem shell *q.v.* II.81
see also kāma-rūpa
residual energy (body of recently deceased) II.83
resistance III.137, III.262
resolution
Schrödinger Mind–Sensation Problem III.296
of scientific materialism III.172
resonance (analogy *q.v.*) III.95
see also kosmos
respect for science *q.v.* III.266
respectability (ethos of science *q.v.*) II.209
respiratory system (correlation with zodiac *q.v.*) III.28
responsibility II.184, III.12, III.47, III.121
rest (between incarnation *q.v.*) III.75
see also Devachan
The Restitution of Man (Aeschliman) I.xvii
The Restless Universe (Born) I.334
Rethinking Consciousness: A scientific theory of subjective experience (Graziano) I.356–7, III.314–15
retribution I.295, II.78
see also karma
retrieving mechanism (brain *q.v.*) III.95
see also transmissive function; transducers
retrocausality I.44
return cycle III.225
see also involutionary cycle
The Return of the Serpents of Wisdom (Pinkham) I.277
Reunification I.238
see also Propositions/Axioms; Three Fundamental
Revelation, Book of III.102
revelations III.37
see also constitution of man
reverence II.125, III.313
review, of former life II.70
Reviews of Modern Physics (Everett) I.335
revisionary physicalism I.29
revolution in education III.273
Rey, Georges I.30
Ṛg-Veda II.24, III.372
Rheingold, Howard I.91
rhythm (Keller, Helen *q.v.* on Beethoven *q.v.*) II.230
rhythmic (electromagnetic) field, heart III.42
see also heart; electromagnetism
rhythmic system (Steiner *q.v.* on human constitution *q.v.*) II.184
ribs (apostolic absurdities) III.17
Richardson, Sir Benjamin Ward I.347, III.180
Richet, Charles I.117, I.118, I.119

Riebe, et al. I.341
Riemann Integral III.358, III.361, III.362, III.363
Riess, et al. I.340
right brain hemisphere II.122, II.135
right-brain thinking I.165
right eye III.79
right half of body III.44–5
Right-Hand Path I.200, I.202, III.333
rigid distinctions I.33–8
rigour I.xlviii, I.50, I.67
Ring, Professor Kenneth II.95
Der Ring des Nibelungen (Wagner) II.71, III.325
Ring Pass-Not I.230, III.87
the ring with the *i* III.357
Rishis II.53, III.303
risks, artificial intelligence *q.v.* II.112
rituals I.180, I.191, I.192, I.193, III.18, III.19, III.303
Rivas, Titus I.87
RNA (Ribonucleic acid) I.137, I.241, I.356
Robertson, Howard Percy I.333
robes (vestures of consciousness *q.v.*) III.342
Robinson, Sir Robert II.71
roboticism II.117–18, III.xix
robots II.53, II.114, II.130, II.138–41, III.337–8
rocks (symbol of) III.9
Roe, Professor Chris A. II.95
Roll, Peter I.336
Romanticism I.287
roof apex (human constitution *q.v.*, simile for) II.200
  see also Ātma
root cause II.126
Root-Causes, five III.113
root matter I.270
Root Races III.187–8, III.236, III.375–6, III.377
roots III.55, III.64
Root Substance III.94
rose (symbol of) III.60
  see also Rosicrucian Rose; lotus flower; lotus plant
Rosen, Nathan I.110
Rosenkreutz, Christian III.60
Rosicrucian Brotherhood III.14–15
Rosicrucianism I.273, II.182, III.59–60
Rosicrucian literature II.57
Rosicrucian Order I.281, II.57, II.183
Rosicrucian philosophy II.164
Rosicrucian Rose III.55, III.60
Rosicrucians I.188, I.206, I.209, I.211, III.14, III.84
Confessio Fraternitatis I.208, I.212
The Rosie Cross Uncovered II.57
Rounds and Races II.222, III.377
Royal Institution of Great Britain I.16
Royal Mail's Nobel guru in telepathy row II.132
Royal Science III.24, III.283
Royal Society II.140, III.172
Rubinstein, Artur II.165
Rudra Śiva I.45, II.27
'Rules of Reasoning in Philosophy' I.231, I.250
Rūmi, Jalāl ad-Dīn Muhammad II.1, II.48, III.221
Rupert Sheldrake in der Diskussion. Das Wagnis einer neuen Wissenschaft des Lebens (Dürr and Gottwald) I.353
Russ, Charles III.377
Russell, Bertrand II.74, II.105
Russell, Walter Bowman I.237–8, I.268, I.286, I.305–7, II.72–3, III.108, III.224
Russell Cosmogony I.306
Russell–Einstein Manifesto I.19
The Russell Genero-Radiative Concept (Russell) I.305
Rutherford, Ernest I.95, I.98
Ryle, Gilbert I.51

Saadi of Shiraz III.325
Śabda-Brahmā III.156
Saccas, Ammonius I.183
Saccorhytus coronarius III.324–5
sacred affair (spiritual experience *q.v.*, hallmarks of) III.200
The Sacred Books of the East (Müller) I.lxxx
sacred fig tree II.76
sacred geometry I.99
sacred literature III.55
sacred matters (partial revelation of) III.125
sacred members, Protogonos *q.v.* III.63
  see also Qabbalah; Sephirothic Tree
Sacred Mysteries among the Mayas and the Quichés (Le Plongeon) I.278–9
sacred pine cone III.190
  see also pineal gland; Kuṇḍalinī
sacred purposes III.193
sacred sciences I.219, III.324
sacred scriptures III.271
sacred sound III.108
sacred thread III.6
sacred tongues II.5

sacred wisdom I.xxxix
see also philosophia perennis
sacrifice III.18, III.226
Ṣadrā, Mullā III.226
'The sad truth about the Action for Happiness movement' I.xlii–xliii
safety
awakening latent powers, method of III.190
science, methodology of III.267
Sagan, Carl I.103, III.75
sages III.108, III.256, III.277, III.284, III.286, III.332, III.342
calumny, heaped upon III.326
Sahtouris, Elisabet I.354
Saint Paul I.264, II.175, II.178, *II.179*, III.269, III.294
saints (exclamatory utterances of) III.35
Sakharov, Andrei I.336
Śakti III.144, III.243
salmon (symbol of) III.10
Samādhi I.151, III.181, III.191, III.204–5
Śambhala I.215, I.217, I.284, I.285–6
same consciousness in scientific theory and experiments III.288
same message (sages, truth from) III.188, III.227
same thing, revealing more (elevating consciousness) III.249
Sāṁkhya philosophy I.270, III.101, III.102, III.121, III.329
Samyama I.235, III.190–1
sañcita (karma *q.v.*) III.127
Sandberg, Anders III.337
Śankara I.217
Śankarācārya, Śrī I.271
Sanskrit I.205, II.3, II.4–5, II.6, II.227
sapient life III.240, III.241
Saptaparṇa III.56–8, *III.57*, III.59
Saraswati III.80
Sartre, Jean-Paul III.320
Sat III.104–5, III.111, III.112, III.144
Satan I.268, I.269, II.174
Sat–Chit III.145
Sattva III.111, III.113
Savulescu, Julian III.337
scales (science *q.v.*, hierarchy of) III.4
see also uroboros
scalpels (physical body *q.v.*, investigation of) I.261
scanned images II.84
see also human energy fields; Oldfield
scepticism I.50, I.103, I.210, I.287, I.288, I.317, II.94, III.279–80
and Harvey III.317
and Schrödinger III.261
Schaffranke, Dr Rolf I.133
Schelling, Friedrich I.288
schemata, constitution II.18
Schiller, Ferdinand Canning Scott I.167
Schiller, Friedrich von I.167, III.60
schisms II.220
see also Theosophical Society, divisions in
Schleiermacher, Friedrich Daniel Ernst I.287
Schneider, Susan I.32, I.47
scholarship distinguished from insight III.11
school examination II.66
see also Purgatorio; purgatory
Schopenhauer, Arthur III.265
Schrödinger, Erwin I.3, I.22–3, I.49, I.58–9, I.173, I.323, II.118, III.268, III.278, III.312
on colour I.35
on consciousness I.xlv, III.290
deeply versed in the philosophy of the Indians and the Greeks I.xlvi
on Eastern wisdom I.lxi, I.328
laments limitations of science I.65, II.127–8, II.229–30
on man's intrinsic divinity III.35
on materialism I.51
on mystics I.xl, III.33
My View of the World II.80
Nature and the Greeks I.335
and *philosophia perennis* II.198
on scepticism III.261, III.280
Science and Humanism I.335, III.322
and secondary qualities I.66
on sensation III.137
Tarner Lectures I.48
on Vedānta III.293
and wave mechanics I.97
Schrödinger Mind–Sensation Problem III.134, III.135–6
Schrödinger's cat (quantum physics *q.v.*) III.369
Schubert, Franz II.56, II.99, II.100, II.118, II.130, III.165, III.209
Schumacher College I.44
Schumann, Robert II.101
Schuon, Frithjof I.xxxix, I.194
Schweitzer, Dr Albert I.xxxvii, I.xxxviii, I.xxxix
Sciama, Dennis I.336
Science III.283, III.315

Science III.72, III.281, III.283
  meaning I.198
science
  anthropocentric outlook III.235
  and astrology III.29–31
  attitudes towards III.334
  blending interpretations with ancient sources III.183
  concept of time III.234
  conventional III.303
  crucial insight of on esotericism III.163
  debates II.218
  and electricity III.173–4
  and elementary particles III.83
  establishment II.213, III.xviii, III.72, III.216, III.232, III.316, III.318
  and evolution III.217
  and extremism II.222
  and higher level of consciousness III.250
  ignorance of III.172
  an industry III.322
  institutionalized III.48
  invention of calculus III.149
  is study of Truth I.254
  Janus faces of III.264–77
  and knowledge of physical man III.263
  limitations of II.128
  links with theosophy II.223
  and magic II.131
  meaning I.181, I.198
  and music III.134
  occult science's best ally III.39, III.223
  only considers evolution not involution III.183
  and *philosophia perennis* III.287, *III.292*
  physical III.xxi
  presuppositions of I.143
  progressive aspect III.223
  and religion I.150
  reproach on III.171
  revolutionary developments in I.79
  richer and better III.329
  and Schrödinger II.229–30
  and Science III.281
  and Spirit I.295
  and spirituality III.229
  teachings II.220
  and Theosophy II.149, II.222
  and truth III.119
  ultra-materialistic II.154
  what it does III.278
  will confirm what occult science affirms III.44
  see also mainstream science; modern science
Science (journal) III.314
Science and Humanism (Schrödinger) I.335, III.322
Science and Spiritual Practice (Sheldrake) III.265
Science and the Akashic Field: An integral theory of everything (László) I.342, II.197
Science and the Reenchantment of the Cosmos: The rise of an integral vision of reality (László) I.342
Science and Ultimate Reality: From quantum to cosmos (Linde) I.341–2
'The Science Delusion' (Sheldrake) I.50
Science of Agents III.72
  see also Josephson
science of consciousness I.100, I.141, I.316, I.320, III.43, III.136
science of natural theology I.53
science of qualities I.39, I.41, I.43–4, I.54, II.xvi, II.124, III.265
science of quantities I.41
scientia III.30
scientia sacra III.118
scientific age III.118
the scientifical II.1
Scientific and Medical Network I.lxxxiv, I.50, I.142, I.215, II.189
Esoteric Section of I.141
scientific attitude II.127
scientific community II.94, II.132
scientific corroboration II.91–6
scientific credibility III.245
scientific data III.229
scientific dictum II.63
scientific discoveries II.131, II.209
scientific endeavour III.119–20, III.219
scientific ethos I.317
scientific evidence II.110, III.183, III.203, III.227
scientific fundamentalism I.50
scientific hubris III.312
scientific investigations II.91
scientific knowledge I.318, III.309
scientific materialism I.16, I.51, I.67, I.163, II.222, III.30, III.266, III.296
  on chance and accident I.136
  and Galileo Commission I.142, I.143
  sole arbiter of truth II.133
  transhumanism and cryonics III.339

will explain everything III.277–8
see also scientism
scientific method I.43, I.50, I.113, I.142, I.229–30, I.233–4, I.235
scientific orthodoxy I.150, I.168
scientific outlook III.222
scientific paradigm II.96, III.xvii, III.180
scientific propositions II.131
scientific quest III.40
scientific sources II.113–14
scientific spirit III.282–3
scientific technology III.321
scientific thinking I.9, I.307
scientific training III.281–2, III.296
scientific understanding II.220
scientism I.lxi, I.13, I.51, I.122, I.132, I.321, II.125, II.132, III.312
and blind faith I.67
four key claims I.121
and Galileo Commission I.142
and quantum science II.74
versus the true spirit of Science III.317–19
and van der Post II.130
Scientism: Science, Ethics and Religion (Stenmark) I.121
The Scientist and the Saint: The Limits of Science and the Testimony of Sages (Chandra) III.142–3
scientists
drawn to the Theosophical Society II.223
enlightened II.65, III.115, III.163–4
exceptional III.172
famous contrasted with great I.77–8
revere past luminaries II.219
see also under individual scientists
scīre I.181
scriptures I.143, III.270
sea (simile) III.253
séances I.91, I.106, I.117–18, II.81, II.107
'Searching for the Impossible: Parapsychology's elusive quest' (Reber and Alcock) I.121
In Search of Secret Egypt (Brunton) III.129
'In Search of the Engram' (Lashley) I.349
seat of feelings III.43
secondary colours III.86
secondary differentiation III.144, III.145, III.148
secondary entities II.18
see also algebra; mathematics; primary principles
secondary phenomenon (life *q.v.*, scientific world-view on) III.287
secondary principles II.18
see also secondary entities
secondary qualities I.24, I.34, I.35, I.38, I.54, I.55, I.66
definition I.32, I.33
second brain III.40–1
second class of human beings *q.v.* III.334
second death II.68
see also Kāma-loka; Devachan
second mental current III.149
Second Fundamental Proposition III.86
Second Law of Thermodynamics III.239
Second Logos *III.175*
Second Object II.7, II.189, II.219
Second Race III.187
Second stage II.97, II.98
see also Kāma-loka; Devachan; butterfly; chrysalis
secrecy I.188, I.206, I.207–10, III.121
secret doctrine III.6, III.46, III.48
The Secret Doctrine (Blavatsky) I.xlvii, I.lxxxiii, I.15, I.236, I.283, I.335, II.150, II.166
on Absolute Motion III.144–5
and Crookes III.172
First Fundamental Proposition/axiom III.51, III.105, III.119
and Haeckel III.184
on MAHĀMĀYĀ III.117
'The Masks of Science' III.30
not the ultimate authority II.222
The Second Fundamental Proposition III.86
and Subba Row II.3
The Third Fundamental Proposition III.108
Three Fundamental Propositions/Axioms I.292
The Secret of Light (Russell, Walter Bowman) I.305, I.306
Secret Order (occult fraternity of) I.212
see also Mysteries; Mystery Schools
secret organizations III.11
secret passages (Great Pyramid *q.v.*) III.50
secret processes
human regeneration III.51
the Mysteries of III.129
secrets III.276–7, III.341, III.342
of death II.64
eternal youth III.110, III.335
The Secret Teachings of All Ages (Hall) I.310, III.5, III.221
sectarianism II.146, II.188, II.190

Secular Humanist movement III.336
security (science *q.v.*, methodology of) III.267
seed of the universe II.39
seed-pod III.58
see also lotus plant; Saptaparṇa
seeing II.120, III.xix, III.135, III.136
Seeing Myself (Blackmore) II.55
Sekhet-Aaru II.70
Selected Papers on Quantum Electrodynamics (Feynman) I.336
selection bias III.241
Self II.39, II.196, II.197, III.109, III.263
bio-physical body or divine light in man II.xv
and body III.110
and fractional incarnation III.127
'I am' II.45
and ignorance III.109
an illusion III.307
Lower I.175
and relation of not-Self III.146
and ultimate truth III.106
and white king (chess) III.14
see also Divine Self; Higher Self
self II.32, III.50, III.197, III.199, III.339
Lower II.17, II.73, II.89, II.106, II.199
The Self and Its Brain: An argument for interactionism (Popper and Eccles) I.35, I.338, III.313
self-awareness II.184
The Self-Aware Universe (Goswami) I.352
self-consciousness II.45, II.109, II.183, III.183
self-consistency I.xxxix, I.233, II.2, II.188, III.101, III.253, III.284
Self-Consistent Kosmos (Miller) II.227–8
self-development I.151
self-direction II.184
self-discipline III.194
Self-discovery I.xxxviii
The Self Does Not Die: Verified paranormal phenomena from near-death experiences (Rivas et al.) I.87–8
self-effort III.199, III.255
Self-enquiry I.xxxviii
self enquiry III.263
self-evident truths III.140
Self-expression III.369
self-expression III.10, III.166, III.173, III.375
self-glorification III.334
self-harming III.274
Selfhood I.308
selfhood I.77, II.20
Self-image III.263
self-interest III.194
selfish attachment II.82
selfish gene III.244–5
The Selfish Gene (Dawkins) I.350, II.176
selfish instincts III.193
selfish molecules II.117
selfishness II.25, III.244–5
self-knowledge III.263
Self of matter III.333
SELF of Spirit III.333
Self-possessession III.204
self-questioning III.263
self-realization I.283
Self-realized master III.104
self-reflective approach III.331, III.332
self-reliance I.298
self-sacrifice III.199
self-serving lives II.82
self-serving thoughts II.107
semi-consciousness II.79
Semmelweis, Ignaz III.318
Senancou, Etienne de III.302
senary (human constitution *q.v.*) III.67
sensate experience III.137–9
sensation I.34–5, II.229, III.134, III.135, III.136, III.137, III.154–5
and divine forces III.172
and external world III.150
and Newton III.179
and Prāṇa III.174
sensed presence II.54, II.56
see also Māyāvi-rūpa
sense observations III.51
sense of being stared at III.201
The Sense of Being Stared At (Sheldrake) III.377
sense of self III.197, III.339
sense organs II.28, II.120, III.41, III.127, III.174
functions III.161
instrumentality of III.154
and Lower Mind III.166
and mind III.137
and pineal gland III.182
and third current III.149–50
sense perception III.92, III.118, III.148
senses I.13, I.46, I.153, I.195, I.230, I.235, II.xvii, II.75, II.120–1, II.204, III.93, III.145, III.199
astral counterpart III.127
and Cosmic Elements III.148, III.154
in dream-life III.87

external, quantifiable input to III.131
five III.112, III.113
and five objects III.115
and five streams III.10
and five Tattvas III.158
Indriyas III.160
instruments of mind III.172
and knowledge III.377
and the mind III.137
and mind–sensation problem III.135, III.136
normal III.187
physical II.xvii
and Plato I.33
and principles III.101
refraction in water/five dirty windows III.254
and Śrī Yukteswar III.105
and subjective experience III.134
and Tattvas III.158
twelve II.184
sensibilities, blinded by science *q.v.* II.99
sensible world III.26
sensing, a presence/the deceased II.95
sensitive persons II.29
sensitive vehicles III.246
sensitivity III.xviii, III.xix–xx, III.149, III.163
sensorium III.113, III.185
sensory deprivation II.55, II.56
sensory impulses III.14
sensory, Indriyas III.160
sensory input II.120, III.267
sensual energies II.81
see also Kāma-rūpa; shell
sensual gratification III.186
sensuous images III.154, III.167
sentience II.184
sentient computer II.138, II.139
separate existence III.111, III.161
separate mortal kind of Soul II.175
Sepher ha Zohar I.193–4
Sephīrāh III.60, III.61, III.64
Sephīrōth III.59, III.60, III.63
Sephirothic Tree III.55, III.60–4, *III.62*, III.71
the septenary III.67
septenary composition, kosmos *q.v.* III.92
septenary constitution of man II.16, II.18, *II.21*, II.22–30, II.149, II.196, III.55
functions *II.13*
and Greek teachings II.175
make-up II.13
rationale II.18–20
and Saptaparṇa III.57–8
and seven states of matter, colours and sounds III.77–9
septenary law III.99
septenary nature II.39–43
Septenary Principles of Man III.95–8
see also Principles of Man
septiform nature III.93
sepulchre I.263, I.266, III.13
Serapis I.180
Sergi, Giuseppe III.232–3
serial killers II.89
series (mathematical simile for methodology of occult science *q.v.*) III.73–4, III.77
serpent (symbol of) III.199
see also Goethe; *Knowledge of the Higher Worlds* (Steiner)
Seth, Anil I.357, III.115, III.315
seven (number) III.67
seven circuits III.7–8
see also labyrinth; Knossos; Ptolemaic cosmology
seven colours III.77–9
seven concentric circles (Kosmos *q.v.*, depiction of) III.87
Seven Creations III.74
Seven Experiments that Could Change the World (Sheldrake) I.335
Seven Governors I.265, I.266
Seven Harmonies III.40
seven-layer model of the energy field II.165
seven-leafed man-plant III.56–8
seven main developmental stages III.375
seven major cākras III.192
seven planes III.86, III.87–8, *III.88*, *III.89*, III.95–8
seven principles of constitution of man II.64–5
see also septenary constitution of man
The Seven Principles of Man (Besant) II.153
seven principles of man's nature *II.49*
see also septenary nature
seven sounds III.77–9
seven states of consciousness III.95–8
seven states of matter III.77–9
seventh kosmic physical plane III.97–8, *III.97*
Seventh limb III.191
sexes, divine nature of relationship between III.257
sexuality (spirituality *q.v.*, polarity of) III.184–5
Shackleton, Sir Ernest II.54–5
shades of meaning (terminology in) III.70

shadows I.194, I.248, I.264, I.265, II.89, II.97, III.286
Avītchi and Devachan II.84
of death II.74
and evil I.268
and matter III.333
physical bodies III.342
subject to change III.142
Shadows of the Mind: A search for the missing science of consciousness (Penrose) III.164, III.352–3
al-Shahrazuri I.228
Shakespeare, William III.5, III.144
sham spirituality III.296
Shankland, Robert II.208
shape (biological dilemma in) III.246
Shapiro, Robert I.351
Shattering the Myths of Darwinism (Milton) I.137
sheaths II.19, II.35, II.42, II.43, II.52, II.196–7, III.181
see also kośas
Shekhīnah III.64
Sheldrake, Rupert I.46, I.50, I.174, I.346, II.131–2, II.223, III.177, III.265, III.289
and Dawkins I.320–1
and establishment biology I.220
and memory I.71, I.76
and modified materialism I.40
and morphic resonance I.78
and morphogenesis I.69, I.72, I.74
A New Science of Life I.49, I.351–2, I.356
The Presence of the Past I.138
The Sense of Being Stared At III.201, III.377
Seven Experiments that Could Change the World I.335
shell II.81, II.88, III.85
see also Kāma-rūpa; post-mortem states
Shelley, Percy Bysshe I.160, I.170, III.101, III.116, III.165, III.327–8
Shermer, Michael I.12, I.13, I.15, I.30, I.86
Sherrington, Sir Charles I.42, I.76–7, II.197, III.172
Shimon, Abner I.111
shining garment II.73
see also Zohar
shoe buckles III.60
see also Rosicrucian Rose
shoe print (evolution *q.v.*) III.231–2, *III.231*
Shrapnell-Smith, E. S. III.201, III.376
Shu, Degan III.324, III.325
sickness of spirit III.273
sickness of the soul III.196–7
siddhis I.98, I.235, I.341, III.191
see also psychic powers
sidereal anima mundi III.36
Sidgwick, Henry III.244
Siegfried (Wagner) I.214
Siena Cathedral I.247
sight II.142, III.186, III.189, III.249
significance (pointlessness of universe) III.276
signs II.86
of the zodiac III.23, III.24
Silberstein, Richard I.101
silent door of eternity II.101
Silent Pool (symbol of) III.10–11
silhouettes III.286
silver 'thread' III.125
simian primates III.236
similes II.64, III.2, III.55
similitude III.106
see also Newton; 'General Scholium'
simple folk (intuition *q.v.* of) III.325
single III.202
see also eyes of spirit; light experiences
single entity II.18, II.196
single human entity II.14
Sinnett, Alfred Percy II.107, II.149, III.130
Sinnett, A. P. II.227
Sīta I.280, III.9, III.16
Sitter, Willem de I.333
Śiva I.45, III.144, III.243
Śiva–Śakti III.145
Śiva Tattva III.244
six
fundamental numbers III.238–9
number III.67
Sixth limb (yoga *q.v.*) III.191
Sixth Root-Race III.187
skandhas III.247
see also karma
skeletons (evolution *q.v.*) III.232–3
Skeptical About Skeptics I.50
skin, physical texture of (implications) III.110
skull (Fourth Way teaching *q.v.*) II.181
Sky Man I.265
see also Corpus Hermeticum
slander (Blavatsky, H. P. *q.v.*) I.219
slave trade III.270
see also religion and Weinberg
sleep II.70, II.95, II.102, II.165, III.234, III.256
cycles II.76

deprivation II.55
dreamless II.68
sleeping consciousness II.164–5
sleep walking II.178
Slipher, Vesto I.333
slug I.135, I.136
see also brain and fungi
small mentalities III.17
Smaragdine I.248, I.249
see also Emerald Tablet
smears, discrediting by I.120
smelling II.95
Smith, E. Lester I.90, I.308, II.223, II.224
Smith, Huston I.121
smoke III.366, III.367, III.368
A Smooth Exit from Eternal Inflation? (Hawking and Hertog) I.343
snares III.109
social media III.197, III.274
social problems III.127
society III.14
see also chess
Society for Psychical Research I.85
Socrates I.204, I.218, I.262–3, II.175, III.xvii
Socratic Method I.47
sodium chloride (human body *q.v.*) I.2
soft problem of consciousness *q.v.* I.28, I.146–7
software II.115, II.118, II.128, II.129, II.130
android II.141
of the brain II.113
tear- and emotion-producing II.122
Sohravardi, al-Maqtul I.218, III.35, III.226
soil, for enlightenment III.199
Solar Astral body II.165
Solar Brotherhood I.277, I.280
Solar Causal Body II.165
solar consciousness III.223
Solar Disc I.276–7
Solar Logoi III.152, III.174
Solar Mental Body II.165
solar plexus (Fourth Way teaching *q.v.*) II.181
solar Races I.270
Solar systems III.84
solar systems II.222, III.47, III.84, III.151
soldiers, killed in World War II II.82
the solid (gross material body *q.v.*, aspect of) III.115
Solovine, Maurice I.133, II.213
solutions, cut-and-dried III.140
Some Papers on the Bearing of Occult Philosophy on Life (E. S. T. Instructions) III.121
Some Problems of Philosophy (James, William) I.317
Sons of God III.35, III.111, III.115, III.155
Sons of Light III.333
Sor-Apis I.267
The Sorcerer's Apprentice (Goethe) I.208, I.209
sorcery I.199, I.200, I.275
Soria, Albert I.276, I.280
Soul I.175, II.19, II.165
irrational Spiritual III.129
and Jinarâjadâsa System II.160
and mind I.154
as permanent principle in man I.296
and Plato II.175
and Pythagoras II.176
and Rāma III.9
and reincarnation I.297
and Saint Paul II.178
separate mortal kind of I.324
and Spirit III.341
and Theseus III.6
threefold II.164
and triple constitution II.17
twofold III.12
Universal I.239
see also Human Soul; Spiritual Soul
soul I.3, I.55, I.324, II.xviii, II.24, II.34, III.210, III.338
anchored in III.56
in the Aristotelian sense of an organizing field I.82
and body III.362
and the Butterfly III.304
and cākras III.192
cleanse from all stains of impurity III.252
as conveyor II.37–8
and Darwinism I.57
duad II.25
dwelling place of man's divine nature III.252
eyes windows to III.201
feminine II.73
and Fourth Principle I.239
group II.110
and hidden chamber III.50
as immaterial II.127
immortal II.102, II.197, III.67, III.338
individual III.303
and lotus plant III.219
memory of I.152
and physical chrysalis III.357–8
and Plutarch II.177
purified III.186

soul (continued)
and reminiscence I.154
returning to Earth III.361
role and function in man I.326–7
and *The Self Does Not Die: Verified paranormal phenomena from near-death experiences* I.88
and selfhood I.77
sepulchre of I.263
and spirit II.106–7
spiritual III.316
and Steiner II.183
and Strömberg I.80, I.81
suffering and poverty of III.273
three II.45, II.195
transmigration of II.80
vehicle of spirit I.182
see also human soul; Animal soul
soul-eclipse II.215
soul experience (of composers into their music) II.100
soulless appearance II.201
soulless beings II.89–90
soul nature III.201, III.321
The Soul of the Universe (Strömberg) I.80, I.81–2, I.335
soul poverty I.5
soul-sickness II.9
soul-yearnings II.73
sounding board (human body *q.v.*) II.60
sounds III.77–9, *III.79*, III.107, III.108, III.159
Source III.6, III.95, III.117, III.152, III.237, III.248
and devolution III.254
and Divine Consciousness III.80
and evolution III.255
originating III.59
and salmon (symbol) III.10
and Universals III.74
of the Universe III.155
source II.188, III.4, III.83, III.150, III.285–6
South America
conquest of I.273
Mysteries I.276–80, I.281
South Pole of the spine III.185
South: The Endurance Expedition The Third Man Factor: Surviving the Impossible (Shackleton) II.55
SPACE III.65
Space I.80, III.107, III.141, III.167
space II.5, II.154, III.42, III.142–4, III.353
Space Odyssey II.138
Spanish Inquisition I.273, I.276
sparks II.73, II.215, III.58–9, III.89, III.173
specialization II.124, III.285
special status (sun and stars of) III.268
see also Weinberg
Special Theory of Relativity *see* relativity theory
specific instruction (victims in mortal danger) II.56
see also Māyāvi-rūpa
spectators (science, Schrödinger *q.v.* on) II.127
spectral being III.198
spectral energies II.83
spectrum III.98
of consciousness I.145–51, *I.146*, I.154–5
of teachings II.220
speed of light II.207, II.209
Spence, Lewis I.274
Spento-Mainyush I.267–8, II.172, II.174
Sperry, Roger I.54, I.83, I.353–4
sphere III.35, III.83
spine II.59, II.181, III.80, III.182, III.185
SPIRIT II.73, III.218
Spirit I.266, I.280, II.2, II.19, II.53, II.69, III.179
definition III.217, III.218
Divine I.266, II.99, II.164
in garments II.196
and Matter III.145
and New Thought I.289
nucleus III.224
and *Paper 1* III.122
of the planets I.265
and Plato II.175
and Saint Paul II.178
and science and religion I.295
threefold II.164
and triple constitution II.17
and Truth I.300
Universal I.301, II.170, III.173
spirit I.3, I.324, II.xviii, III.199, III.316–17
active and positive principle II.11
ask questions of III.xix
and bottom-up approach I.55
centre (significance of) III.4
complete separation with matter II.125
definition I.182, III.217–18
evolution of III.225
eyes of I.194
and force III.350
of man III.36
masculine II.73–4

and matter III.225
and number three III.77
origin in III.65
positive pole III.333
quenchless II.120
role and function in man I.326–7
of Science III.281
and soul II.37–8, II.107
and Steiner II.183
temple of III.37
third III.36
and universe III.86
spirit attachment III.41
Spirit body II.185
Spirit Fire III.190
Spirit of Evil I.267
Spirit of Good I.267
spirit of science III.316, III.317–19
spirit possessions III.198
Spirit Self-potent II.2
spirit-side of emanational descent (evolution *q.v.*) III.155, III.159, III.225
Spirits of the Earth III.130
the Spiritual II.39, III.80
spiritual, definition I.182
spiritual affinity III.266
spiritual agencies III.245
spiritual aggregates II.168
spiritual aroma II.68
spiritual aspects of man II.172
spiritual aspirants III.194
spiritual atom III.156
spiritual authority II.220
spiritual awakening II.101
Spiritual being II.17
spiritual beings I.lxii, II.196
spiritual body I.264, II.32, II.96, II.178, III.316
spiritual centres I.284, III.50, III.181
spiritual consciousness II.22
spiritual conservation, matter and energy III.29
spiritual content (life review *q.v.*) II.67
spiritual core II.141, III.112
spiritual crisis III.273–7
The Spiritual Crisis of Man (Brunton) III.275
spiritual culture III.14
spiritual currents II.202
spiritual deed II.215
spiritual derelicts III.195
spiritual dimensions
on evolution III.228
of life III.188
Spiritual Ego II.46, II.47, II.52, II.73, III.293
spiritual ego (Troward *q.v.*) I.301
spiritual energy II.165
spiritual enlightenment III.16, III.199
spiritual enquiry II.190
spiritual entity, enduring I.297
spiritual evolution III.122, III.224, III.327
spiritual existence II.124–5
spiritual experiences II.183, III.200
spiritual eye III.186
spiritual faculties III.183, III.189, III.194
spiritual for evil III.294
spiritual function III.184
spiritual guidance II.97
spiritual healing II.164
spiritual hero III.6
spiritual hunger II.xv
spiritual illumination I.262, I.308
spiritual impulses II.75
spiritual insight III.184
spiritual intimations III.325
spiritual intuition III.186
spiritualism I.15, I.58, I.102–3, I.106, II.91
Spiritualist I.68
spiritualistic phenomena II.107
spiritualists *II.108*
spirituality I.53, I.204, II.153, III.187, III.271, III.275
dark Janus face of III.293–4
and immortality III.340
meaning III.196
and psychiatry III.34
and science III.229
and sexuality III.184–5
spiritualized Atom III.112, III.113
spiritual level III.219
spiritual life III.47
Spiritual Light III.109
of the World III.36
spiritual light III.16, III.333
spiritual mask III.294
Spiritual-Mental II.41
Spiritual Monad II.201
spiritual mysteries, of Old and the New Testaments III.60
spiritual nature II.38, II.88, II.174, III.35–6, III.44, III.316
attached to the material form II.59
and the Devil II.174
distinguishing from physical I.3
and divine Beings III.130

spiritual nature (continued)
and genius III.129
and heart III.39
and incarnation III.127
and The Judgement (Tarot cards) III.13
Spiritual particles III.83
spiritual path II.203
spiritual perspective II.205
spiritual plasm III.248
spiritual poverty II.xv
spiritual powers I.201
spiritual practices III.265
spiritual principles II.23, III.19
spiritual prototypes *III.27*, III.57
spiritual qualities II.177
spiritual quest II.218
spiritual realization III.15
spiritual realm II.38–9
spiritual rebirth II.69
spiritual revival III.265
spiritual science II.182
spiritual scientist III.196–7
spiritual sleep-walkers II.58–9
spiritual societies II.90
Spiritual Soul II.17, II.19, II.45, *II.108*, II.175, III.205
and Ariadne III.6
and Buddhi II.22, II.52, II.170
and Esoteric Buddhism II.168
and Human Soul II.110, III.16
and Plutarch II.177, II.178
and Puruṣa III.155
and Sīta III.9
and transformer II.38, II.202
and Trojan Horse (allegory) III.48
and upādhi II.47
spiritual sources II.221, II.228, III.4
spiritual spark II.9
spiritual status II.71, II.86
spiritual teachers III.194, III.243
the spiritual to the physical III.123
spiritual trance III.204, III.206
spiritual unfoldment III.60
spiritual vehicle III.166
spiritual visions I.236, III.185, III.186
Spiritus Mundi III.179
Spiritus Vitæ III.179
spirit world/spiritual world II.2, II.5
spleen (role in occult physiology *q.v.*) II.60
splendour of man III.257
sponge (evolution *q.v.*) III.325
spontaneous understanding III.184
spooks II.81–2, II.150
spooky action at a distance I.110, I.111
sportsman III.295
see also destiny
square I.278, III.66, III.67, *III.67*
Śrī Aurobindo I.99, I.217, I.346, I.348
Śrī Dalada Maligawa III.18
Śrī Śankarācārya I.271
Śrī Yukteswar *see* Swami Śrī Yukteswar Giri, Jnanavatar
stable principle (spirit *q.v.*) II.74
stages III.61, III.263, III.304
analogous to Earth life II.78–9, II.92
ascending III.223
of being and becoming III.221
of descent III.168, III.254
four basic III.92
intermediary III.340
intermediate III.199
life III.263
seven III.375
three III.126
stagnation II.85
see also Avītchi
Stahl, George I.345
Standard Model of Big Bang III.310
Stanzas III.74
Stanzas of Dzyan III.89
Stapp, Henry I.337, I.338
Star of Bethlehem III.17
star pool III.241
see also Carr; multiverse
stars III.22, III.172–3, III.268–9
star stuff III.75
state of humanity III.235
states of being II.129, III.26
States of Consciousness II.44, II.204
states of consciousness II.6, II.10, II.17, II.85, II.162, III.xix, III.254
altered III.196
and the brain III.39
and Christ II.69
definition II.60
higher III.171
and Inferno and Purgatorio II.66, II.86
and seven planes III.91
and Sūtra 5 III.110
statistical population (multiverse *q.v.*) III.241
statistics (perils of) III.282
statues (idolization of) III.16, III.37

status, ancient cultures III.18
status quo III.230
Stefano, Giovanni di I.247
Steiner, Rudolf I.lxxx, I.122, II.148, II.182–5, II.219, II.220
 and Goethe I.42, I.43
 on *The Green Snake and the Beautiful Lily* III.199
 Knowledge of the Higher Worlds III.198
Steiner's doctrine III.197–8
Steinhardt, Paul I.341
Stenmark, Mikael I.121
'step down,' graded (human soul *q.v.*) II.38
Stephen, Henrie III.17
sterility, underlying (functionalism of) II.119
 see also computationalist master analogy
Stevenson, Ian I.14, I.100–1, I.102, I.152, II.75, II.91, III.275
Stevenson, Robert Louis II.89
Stewart, Peter I.92
St.-Germain, Comte de I.218, II.58
Sthūla-śarīra II.29–30, II.35, III.13, III.58, III.59, III.97, III.114
 and Sūtras III.115
Sthūlopadhi II.170
stifling (human spiritual nature *q.v.*) II.48
stimulators (human senses *q.v.*) III.148, III.154
stimuli, responding to III.163
St. John I.188
stock exchange I.262
stones III.233, *III.233*, III.268
storehouse II.52, III.306
Strange Case of Dr Jekyll and Mr Hyde (Stevenson) II.89
strategy, computationalists II.117–20
The Strategy of the Genes (Waddington) I.349
Strawson, Galen I.9
stream of consciousness II.73, II.76, III.149
streams III.10–11, III.154
string theory II.154, III.353
stroke survivors I.162, II.122, II.128
Strömberg, Gustaf I.57, I.79–82, I.335, II.6
strong anthropic principle III.241
strong closure I.27
structural stages II.186
structure II.7, II.16, II.123, III.87, III.246
 of the Body of Experience III.357–8
 for experience III.355–7
 inner III.121
structured environments III.334
students II.224, III.121
study II.4, III.5, III.19, III.277, III.282
A Study in Consciousness (Besant) II.162, III.163
stuff of dreams II.74
stupidity
 distinguished from ignorance I.221
 evoking compensating centre of spirituality I.284
Subba Row, Tallapragada II.3, II.168
Subba Row Medal II.161, II.224
the subconscious III.363
subconscious mind III.357, III.362
Subject III.145
subject-dependent reality II.132
subject–expectancy effect I.84
the subjective I.138, II.4
subjective activity III.149, III.167
subjective aspects
 emanational descent III.155, III.156
 mind III.161
 unitary consciousness III.168
subjective experiences I.31, I.38, I.39, III.131, III.134, III.167
subjective feelings II.129
subjective function III.154
subjective influences III.24
subjective level, inter-species transitions III.245
subjective mental states III.136
subjective opinion II.117
subjective perception III.161
subjective phenomena III.145
subjective planes III.86
subjective quality II.136
subjective states II.74
subjectivity II.117, II.118, II.186, III.44
subject–object duality III.140
Subject–Object relationship III.145–6, III.148, III.154, III.155–61, III.167
Subject of Cognizance I.48
sublimation of man III.192
sublime doctrines, grotesque distortion of III.246
sublime music III.165
sublime precepts II.36
subordinate creative principle III.238
sub-planes III.86
sub-principles III.98
Substance III.82, III.95, III.105, III.113, III.145, III.156
substance II.73, II.210, III.105, III.147, III.218, III.263

the substantial III.117
substitute II.36
see also upādhi(s)
subsumed (human characteristics) II.12
subsurface III.222, III.223
subterfuge III.47–8
subterranean Galapagos III.223
subterranean vaults (consciousness *q.v.*) II.85
subterranean world (North America, Mysteries *q.v.*) I.273, I.278
subtle bodies I.48, I.58, I.69, I.82, I.87, I.90, I.139, II.xviii, II.2, II.34, III.47
and Besant System II.154
and Blavatsky II.150
collectively form man's entire composition III.224
and Fourth Way teaching *II.180*, II.181
and hearing II.121
and Heindel II.164
Kāma-rūpa II.24, II.25
layers II.166
like onion skins II.10
Lower Quaternary I.148
and man's principles II.5
and non-physical planes III.94
and physical instruments I.261
and post-classical Theosophy II.153
and Reincarnating Ego II.79
and Sūtras III.113
and three nails I.206
Subtle Bodies (Tansley) II.166
subtle energies II.165
subtle forces III.126
subtle material III.237
subtle matter III.97
subtler dimensions of existence III.245
subtle realms II.4
subtler realms/worlds III.87, III.250, III.353
subtler senses III.87
subtle spirit II.210, III.179, III.180
subtlety, infinite (Kosmos *q.v.*) III.86
succession of mental images III.141
sudden death II.81–2
suffering II.78, III.187, III.296
Sūfī masters III.35, III.227
Sufi saint II.48
suicide II.83–4
Sukhavati II.70
Sūkṣmopadhi II.170
sulphur I.241
Summer of Love III.196
Sun I.276, I.280, II.178, III.202, III.254–5, III.289
Central Spiritual III.253
and level of consciousness III.256
and signs of the Zodiac III.31
store-house of life-force III.179
sun II.177, III.56, III.268
sacred correspondence with the heart III.44
and Solar Logos III.174
symbolising vital principle I.266
three III.39
visible III.253
Sun Force III.180
sunlight III.253, III.256
supercausality I.44, I.335
supercomputer II.114
super-egocentric thinking III.321
superhuman artificial intelligence II.116
superhuman powers II.58, III.335
superhuman state III.99
Superior Intelligences III.342
superior part, twofold constitution of God *q.v.* and man *q.v.* III.38
superior principle II.34
superior worlds II.6
Supermind II.188
supernatural beings I.23, I.276
supernatural creation III.313
the superphysical III.250
super-physical powers III.171
super-physical realms II.53
super-physical universes III.61
super-science II.141
super-sensible contact III.198
super-sensible region III.199
superstition I.120, I.181–2, III.30, III.261, III.267, III.312, III.319
superstring theory I.98, I.99, II.7, III.250
supervenience I.29, I.30, I.48
supporting evidence III.30
see also pseudoscience; scientific evidence
suppression (new discoveries of) I.322, II.209
see also knowledge suppression mechanisms
Supramentalisation (Aurobindo *q.v.*, teaching on) II.188
supraphysical realms, subtlest grades of III.163
The Supreme Adventure: Analyses of Psychic Communications (Crookall) II.92–4
Supreme Consciousness III.362, III.363, III.365, III.370
supreme Consciousness III.176

Supreme Deity I.238, II.175, II.177, II.178, III.48
Supreme Divinity III.26, *III.27*
Supreme Genie I.81
  see also Strömberg
Supreme Mind I.264, I.265
Supreme Mystery II.51
Supreme Power I.301
supreme power III.26
Supreme Soul III.211
supremum (mathematics *q.v.*) III.358
survivability purpose II.118
survival I.14–15, II.92
survival machines (consciousness *q.v.*) II.176
  see also Dawkins, Richard on lumbering robots
susceptible individuals II.82
Sūtras from *The Holy Science* III.104–20
Sūtrātman III.125
Svabhavat III.94
Svapna II.170
Swami Śrī Yukteswar Giri, Jnanavatar III.102, III.104
  on Sūtras III.105, III.106, III.107, III.109, III.111, III.113–14, III.115–16
Swann, Ingo I.92
Swanson, John III.352
Swastika I.200
Swedenborg, Emanuel I.167–8, I.248, I.287
Swine (symbol of) III.303
symbiosis III.222
symbolically illiterate culture III.310
symbolic nature I.189
symbolic pattern III.7
symbolic proofs III.9
symbolic representations III.172
symbolic teaching III.303–4
symbolism I.266–7, I.273, II.205, III.33, III.44–9, III.67
  of Altar of Burnt Incense III.252
  and Cube unfolded III.66
  of lotus and rose III.60
  and Maheśa III.168
  universal III.55, III.253
  universal key to to wisdom III.5–19
symbols I.190–1, I.193, I.282, II.3, III.1, III.2, III.47–50
  and diagrams III.5
  fish and pool III.10–11
  human body III.34, III.37, III.52
  labyrinth and the forest III.7–9
  of light and darkness III.44–5
  lotus flower III.72
  uroborus III.3–4
symmetry II.123
sympathetic resonance I.213
synaptic clefts III.351
synaptic transmission II.xvi
synchronicity I.45, I.286
syncretism II.222
synthesis III.104
syntropy I.44–5, I.335, II.124
Syria I.284
System (universe *q.v.*) III.90
  see also Newton; *Opticks*
Systematics and Origin of Species (Mayr) I.348–9
systemic thinker II.125
systems approach I.43

Tabernacle III.250–5
Tabernacle of Moses III.250–2, *III.251*, III.253
tablets II.60, III.24–5
Tagore, Rabindranath I.1
Tahuantinsuyo (South America, Mysteries *q.v.*) I.276
T'ai Chi Ch'uan III.181
Taimni, Iqbal Kishen I.lxxxi, I.lxxxiii, II.153, II.160–2, II.219, II.222, III.225
Taimni System II.160–2, *II.163*
tala II.6
Tamas III.113
the tangible II.4
taṇhā II.79, III.8
Tanmātras III.113, III.114, III.157, III.158, III.159
Tansley, David V. II.166
Taoist Masters III.116
The Tao of Physics (Capra) II.125, III.143
Taormina, Robert I.341
Tao-te-King II.172
Tāraka Rāja-Yoga II.43, II.52, II.167, II.168, *II.169*, II.170, II.171
Tarot cards III.11–13
Tart, Charles I.145, II.221
task of man III.216
Tat Tvam Asi II.9
Tattvas III.59, III.157, III.158, III.159
tautology III.241
  see also multiverse; anthropic principle
taxi drivers I.161–2
taxonomy II.35, II.161, II.196
Taylor, Jill Bolte I.83, I.162, II.91, II.122

Taylor, John I.119
Taylor, Matthew I.4
Taylor, Thomas III.39
teachings II.141, II.218, II.221, II.223, III.63
on the antiquity of the human race III.235
close interrelation of III.246–7
fossilized II.219
major II.146
oral III.4
spectrum of II.220
of the Vedas III.247
by word-of-mouth III.17
see also Mystery Teachings
tears II.118, II.121, II.122
technology II.xv, III.118, III.268, III.274, III.307, III.309–10, III.322
advanced III.266
attitudes towards III.334
excessive III.xix, III.261
and science I.39
and transhumanism III.336
Teilhard de Chardin, Pierre I.45
Tejobindu Upaniṣad III.119
teleology I.40, I.45, I.52, I.58, I.70, I.102, I.345
telepathic phenomena II.36
telepathy I.14, I.74, I.79, I.86, I.341, II.128
and Hardy I.53, I.350
and Josephson II.132–3
telescope (limitations of) II.100
televangelists I.290–1, III.323
Templars I.209, I.287
temple II.195, II.200, *II.201*, III.37, III.50
of the Divine II.30
of the Spirit II.53
Temple of Apollo, Delphi *I.xxxvii*, I.xxxviii, I.1
Temple of the Pagan Idols (Ṣadrā) III.226
Temple of the Sacred Tooth Relic III.18
Templeton World Charity Foundation (TWCF) III.313–14
the temporal (state) III.80
temporary phase state (consciousness *q.v.*) III.326
see also enlightenment
Ten Commandments of the physical law III.46
Ten Commandments of the spiritual law III.46
'On the Tendency of Species to form Varieties; and on the Perpetuation of Varieties and Species by Natural Means of Selection' (Darwin and Wallace) I.346
Tennyson, Alfred III.68
terminal lucidity III.165
terminology II.4–5, II.34, II.35–6, II.153, II.155
confusing III.247
esoteric and occult systems III.5
for Sanskrit terms II.227
terms of consciousness III.71, III.72
terra incognita to exact science III.77
terrestrial atmosphere II.81–2
terrestrial body III.36
terrestrial composition of man *q.v.* II.197
terrestrial existence II.105, II.106, II.200–3
terrestrial life III.7, III.234
terrestrial personality II.201–2, III.256
terrestrial plane II.41, II.42
terrestrial soul II.107, III.6
see also Kāma-rūpa; shell
terrestrial sphere II.81
see also Kāma-loka
terrestrial vehicle II.106
'territory' and the 'map' II.196, III.3, III.150, III.230, III.232
Tertius Interveniens (Kepler) III.264
Tesla, Nikola I.123, I.307
testimony of sages *q.v.* III.xx
testing, of aspirant III.129
Tetractys III.65, III.371
A Textbook of Theosophy (Leadbeater) II.156
textbooks, popular III.78
Thales of Miletus I.xxxvii
thaumaturgy III.159
theatre drama III.5
theologians I.164
theology I.164, I.191, I.193–4, II.125, III.37, III.47, III.90
Newton's I.231
prosperity I.290
theoretical existence III.240
theories of mind II.91
theory II.126, III.108, III.265, III.288
limitations of II.122, II.128
over experience I.46, II.124
Theory of a Nervous Ether (Richardson) I.347
Theory of Relativity *see* relativity theory
theosophia I.xxxix, I.183, *I.185*, I.204
Theosophical doctrine II.160, III.121
Theosophical Esoteric Society II.183
Theosophical imagination II.147
Theosophical literature II.2, II.4, II.148–51
Theosophical movement I.283–4, II.222, III.51
Theosophical Research Centre II.223–4

Theosophical Society I.lxxix, I.lxxxii–lxxxiii, I.lxxxiv, I.204, I.209, I.215, I.286, II.166, II.186, II.218, III.102
and Algeo I.283
and comparative study II.218–19
and Crookes III.172
division in II.155
Esoteric Section III.121, III.181
Fourth International President II.158
and freedom II.224–5
and Guénon I.208
in India II.3
and inner poverty I.5
see also Wordsworth; Jung and 'homesickness' of the soul
and James, William I.167
no spiritual authority II.220
and Ouspensky II.181
outstanding scientists have been drawn to II.222–3
primary aims I.88
seal III.3
Second International President II.153
Second Object II.7–8
and Steiner II.183
and Taimni II.160, II.161
Theosophical teachings II.162–7, II.204
Theosophical tradition *II.147*
Theosophists I.209, I.283, II.4, II.44
Theosophy I.lxxx–lxxxi, I.167, I.184, *I.185*, I.245, II.219
classical II.146
concepts and beliefs II.7–8
good and bad II.221
and Indian Mystery Schools I.271
later expositions of II.189
modern II.175
and mysticism II.149–50
and *philosophia perennis* II.162, II.164
and Transcendentalism I.298
Universal Teaching I.300
theosophy I.182, I.183–4, II.182
Theosophy Explained in Questions and Answers (Pavri) II.160
Theresa of Avila, Saint III.202
Theresienstadt II.55
thermal artefacts II.208
see also relativity theory and ether
Thermodynamics, Second Law of III.239
Theseus III.5–6, III.16
Theurgy I.239
the thinker II.22, II.137
thinking II.19, III.135
categorical II.123–4
independent II.224
metaphorical II.129–30
Thinking principle II.160
third mental current III.149–50
Third Eye III.79, III.182–5, III.194–5
Third Fundamental Proposition III.108
Third Logos III.61, III.84, *III.175*
The Third Man Factor: Surviving the impossible (Geiger) II.55
third part, Divine Nature III.127
third person perspective I.146–7
Third Reich I.200
Third Root Race III.236
third spirit III.36
Third stage (post-mortem states *q.v.*) II.97, *II.98*
see also reincarnation
thirst, for things and familiar scenes II.79
Thom, René I.72
Thompson, Francis I.252
Thompson, Richard I.352, III.230
Thompson, Sir D'Arcy Wentworth I.74, I.348
Thomson, J. J. I.95
Thomson, Sir John Arthur I.332–3, I.348, III.278
Thomson, Sir William, Lord Kelvin I.104
Thoreau, Henry David I.287
Thoth I.247
Thoth Hermes Trismegistus I.247, I.264
Thought I.289, I.317, I.327, III.35, III.226, III.236, III.263, III.362
Higher I.288, I.291
thought II.107, II.137, II.229, III.105, III.163, III.262, III.342
and the Absolute III.119
abstract III.1
can affect our physical body III.192
closed system of III.118
distinguished from mind I.301
distorting II.124
divided nature of II.123
freedom of II.189, II.224–5
God's III.110
great *III.27*
internal III.72
and mathematics III.349
and neural correlate III.135
primacy of I.303, I.307–8
produced I.2

thought (continued)
sterility of III.311
ungoverned III.9
and the Universe III.60
thought body II.56, II.57
thought experiment III.162, III.305
Thought of God II.71
Thought Producer I.166, I.323, III.112
thought producer I.2, I.10
thread (symbol of) III.5–6
thread doctrine I.236, I.302, I.303, III.284
thread of union II.215
the Three III.66
three (number) III.77
three attributes III.113
three centres III.38–9
three currents III.149–53
three degrees, Mystery Schools III.304
three dimensions III.249
threefold division II.149
see also triple constitution
threefold world III.26
three Forces III.175–6
three higher states III.95
three levels II.8–9
three nails (human constitution *q.v.*) I.206
three-piece mortal vesture (human constitution *q.v.*) II.99
three-piece suit (human constitution *q.v.* simile) II.99
three pillars (Qabbalah *q.v.*) III.64
three primaries III.77
three primary colours III.86
three primary divine forces III.171, III.210
three primary entities (human constitution *q.v.*, simile) II.18
three primary principles of human constitution *q.v.* II.18
Three Selves II.51
three-staged emanational descent III.123, III.126, *III.128*, III.130
three-storey temple (human constitution *q.v.*, simile) II.200, *II.201*
three suns III.39
three upādhis II.200
three worlds III.22, III.56
Through the Looking-Glass (Carroll) III.117
Thumos II.176, II.177
Thunburg, Greta I.150, II.134
The Tibetan Book of the Dead I.89, II.97
Tibetan language I.205, II.3
Time III.107, III.141, III.145, III.167
time II.70, II.75–6, II.99, III.110, III.142–4, III.234, III.353
certain moment in III.122
higher dimensions II.154
relative nature of II.92
sense of I.153
time cycles III.229
timelessness III.256
timeless wisdom III.183
In Times of War – Messages of Wisdom from Soldiers in the Afterlife (Beecher) II.82
Tiphereth III.63
Tipler, Frank I.339, III.241
titans III.183
see also Third Eye
Todd, Dennis I.353
toes (anatomical symbolism of) III.46
Toffler, Alvin I.229
tombs I.263, I.266, III.13, III.37
tongues, different II.188
tooth relic III.18
top-down approach I.31, I.54, I.105, I.230, I.345, III.146, III.196–7
top-down causal role III.351
totalitarian dictators II.89
touch II.121, III.66
Towards a Theory of Consciousness (Chalmers) I.352
toys III.118
see also Māyā; māyā
traditionalism II.223
traditionalists II.218–25
traditional societies III.197
traditions III.10, III.183, III.332
traffic accident, road (post-mortem energy field of) II.83
training II.222, III.281–2, III.296
traits II.85, II.88–90, II.119
transcendence I.52, I.139, I.327, II.88–9
Transcendentalism I.260, I.286, I.287, I.288, I.291, I.298
transcendental metaphysics III.30
transcendent and subjective level II.8, III.16
transcendent origins I.244
transcendent power I.54, I.56
transcendent state III.75
transducers I.78, III.136, III.137, III.166, III.172
Transference, Law of II.79
transformational, personal III.200
transformational learning III.xix
the transformed man I.xlii

transformers I.78, II.38, II.165, II.200, II.202, III.27
transformer stations (simile) II.38
transformer substations (simile) II.202, II.203
transformer-vehicle II.45
see also Soul: threefold; and triple constitution
transhumanism II.116, III.272, III.335, III.336–40
transitional species (evolution *q.v.*) I.138
transitional state (Root Races *q.v.*) III.187
transitions II.63, II.64, II.97, II.101, II.133, III.117, III.187
to enlightenment III.326–7
evolutionary III.304
and Janus III.264
from one phase state to another III.78
state between life and afterlife II.91–2
unnecessary difficulties during II.82
transitory body II.30
transitory experiences II.46
transitory nature of existence III.116
transitory period III.142
transitory pursuits III.xxi
translation of will into action III.164
transmigration II.30, II.79, II.80
transmission I.246, III.4, III.165, III.247
transmissive function of brain *q.v.* I.169, I.170, I.172, I.174, III.166
see also James, William
transmutation I.245, III.161–5, III.168
transmuting substance III.162
Transpersonal category II.188
transpersonal nature III.10
transpersonal psychology II.185–8
Trapezium Rule (mathematics *q.v.*) III.360
travails of life *q.v.* III.110
see also secrets, eternal youth
Tree of Life II.165, III.60–4
Tressoldi, Patrizio I.142
triad (human constitution *q.v.*) II.196
see also individuality
triangle III.66, *III.67*, III.123
trick III.47–8
see also Trojan Horse
trigonometry III.23
Trimūrti *III.27*, III.173
Trine, Ralph Waldo I.239, I.286, I.302–5
Tri-netram III.168
triple constitution of man *q.v.* II.16, II.17–19
triple functioning II.38
triple lower part II.178
triple make-up *II.13*
triple nature II.38–9
triplicity II.18, II.196
triune constitution III.14
triune nature III.36
Trojan Horse III.47–8, III.49
Troward, Thomas I.239, I.300–2, II.47
tṛṣṇā II.79, III.8
see also taṇhā
the true III.211
true and inner nature III.49
true knowledge II.171
trunk (symbol of) III.55
Truth I.1, I.309, II.204, III.14, III.111, III.271, III.317
ambassadors of I.218–20
and authority I.lxxxiv
cannot be fossilised II.224
and the establishment I.220
ever living; its expressions must be contemporary I.lxxxiii
and humility II.224
and Krishnamurti I.lxxxii
and lies I.300, I.301
litmus tests of I.233
no picture will ever represent I.165
Real III.119
and science I.254
and symbolism III.17
Universal III.332
truth III.202–3, III.267, III.332
and accuracy II.117
and Brunton II.146
can only be learned within III.257
and dialectics I.47
direct cognition of III.189
and doubt and scepticism III.280
dove of III.261
from education III.1
and esotericism and exotericism I.193
and Feynman III.205
mangled by small mentalities III.17
and materialism II.133
mathematical III.352
mental science of III.357
obfuscated by III.211
opposition to II.131
outside our experience I.68
of the *philosophia perennis* III.342
and poets I.3

truth (continued)
  and precision II.124
  questing for II.221
  realm of II.99, II.100
  relation between man and God III.35
  relative and ultimate III.106, III.119
  self-evident III.140
  universal I.236
  unlocking III.19
  and Wallace I.114
Truth-bearer III.303
see also Boar; Boar Avatar; Boar's Head
Truzzi, Marcello I.142
Tryon, Edward I.337
In Tune with the Infinite (Trine) I.302, I.305
tunnel vision (Plato, allegory of the cave *q.v.*) III.378
  see also intellectual myopia
Turing, Alan I.73, I.349, II.114, II.140
Turing test II.140
turning point II.24
Turok, Neil I.341
tutor (shadow of death, as) II.74
Twain, Mark I.115, I.288
twelve senses II.184
Twelve Tribes of Israel III.251
two aspects III.168
two births II.64
two classes III.334
two deaths II.64
two dimensional consciousness III.249
twofold constitution III.35, III.38
twofold Soul III.12
two opposite forces III.225
two paths III.332–5, III.340
two poles III.114
two streams III.154
two-way closure, and causal closure I.27
tyranny III.16
tyrants (exclamatory utterances by) III.35

ubercausalität I.44, I.335
UFO aliens III.239
ultimate benchmark (*The Secret Doctrine q.v.*) II.221
ultimate contact with original Self *q.v.* / spiritual Sources *q.v.* III.248
  see also raising consciousness
Ultimate Reality III.142, III.148, III.173, III.303
Ultimate Space III.141
ultimate truth III.106
ultra-materialistic science II.154
umbilical connection II.86, II.88, II.90
umbilical cord II.88
  see also Antaḥakaraṇa
unaccountable phenomena II.91
unbottled waves I.37
  see also Jeans
uncalled-for conclusions (evolution, scientific preconceptions and prejudics on) III.244
uncertainties (living with) II.135
  see also negative capability; Keats
uncertainty principle I.96, I.109, I.333, III.351
the uncompounded II.105
  see also Individuality
unconsciousness II.68, II.77
underground streams (symbol of) III.10–11
Underhill, Evelyn I.186
underlying consciousness III.295
underlying sterility (computationalist ideology of) II.119
underlying unity II.218
understanding II.84, II.86, III.184
  of consciousness II.100, II.135–6
underworld I.273, I.278
underwriting whole, self-consistent, versions of the world II.123
  see also divided nature of thought; McGilchrist
undeserved extraordinary powers III.194
undesirable behaviour III.193
  see also cākras
undifferentiated Consciousness III.254
  The undiscover'd country (*Hamlet q.v.*) II.64, *II.66*
undogmatized theological speculation III.38
unearned extraordinary powers III.194
unexhausted spiritual impulses II.75
unfolding of innate faculties *q.v.* III.57, III.224
unfolding consciousness III.175, III.246, III.286
unfoldment
  emanational II.30
  threefold constitution II.16
  of the Word III.107
unfulfilled spiritual yearnings II.70, II.71
unhappiness, suicide victims, dependent on motive II.84
uni-cursal labyrinth III.7
unified being II.12
Unified Reality Theory: The evolution of existence into experience (Kaufman) I.355
uniformity III.334
union I.233, I.234, II.53, III.35, III.43, III.77

Unit II.176, II.216
unitary system II.107
unitary whole II.10
unit of life III.223
Unity I.237
 see also Propositions/Axioms; Three Fundamental
unity I.xxxix–xli, II.2, II.18, II.106, II.146, II.162, III.264, III.334
 in all religions III.102
 and diversity I.294, III.86
 of Eternal and Ageless Wisdom III.253
 of existence III.78
 of life III.223
 organic II.34
 and perennial philosophy II.188
 and secret doctrine III.6
 of teachings I.lxxv, III.63
 underlying II.218
Unity of kosmos *q.v.* III.99
universal agent III.95
universal and divine Consciousness III.221
Universal Being III.83
Universal Brotherhood II.225
universal brotherhood II.153
Universal Consciousness III.86–7, III.172, III.217
universal Consciousness II.73, III.221
Universal Divine Principle II.227
Universal Egg III.38
universal esoteric wisdom III.284
Universal Idea III.26, *III.27*
Universal Intelligence and Consciousness III.112
universality I.233, II.153, II.204, III.10, III.52
of outlook III.200
of symbolism III.253
and truth I.236
universal keys III.5
Universal Law III.72
universal law II.68
Universal Love III.111, III.113
universal love III.245
universal mantra, of science I.322
Universal Memory III.82, III.209
universal memory III.234
Universal Mind I.252, I.317, II.199, III.96, III.97, III.148, III.264
 Ideas in III.368
 mirroring of III.148
universal Mind III.263
universal myths III.183
Universal Nature I.195, I.197, I.198
Universal Observer I.xlvii, III.119
The Universal One (Russell, Walter Bowman) I.268, I.305, I.306, I.307
universal outlook II.190
Universal Over-Soul III.108
Universal Power III.37
Universals III.72, III.74
Universal Self III.112
universal selfhood II.20
Universal Soul I.239
Universal Spirit I.301, II.170, III.173
universal symbolism III.34, III.55
Universal Teaching I.300
Universal Truth III.332
universal truths I.236
Universal Wisdom I.211, I.237
universal wisdom II.189, II.204, III.284
Universe I.184, II.176–7, III.72, III.86, III.104
universe I.139, II.162, II.204, II.205, III.108, III.289
 all other possible III.85
 chance event I.54–5
 conditioned III.172
 constitution III.28
 definition III.86
 fabric of III.145
 holographic III.358
 an idea, or a great thought, in the mind of God I.36
 and Ideas III.109
 and man III.47, III.52, III.319
 miniature II.29, III.xviii, III.34, III.82
 objective III.36, III.156, III.161
 orchestrated III.239
 origins III.262
 physical III.61, III.110
 pointlessness of III.22, III.268, III.269, III.311
 unlimited number of III.240
 visible III.92
A Universe of Consciousness (Edelman and Tononi) I.9
Universe or Multiverse? (Carr) I.342, III.241
Unknown God III.84
unknowns III.178
unknown sources II.71
Unmanifest III.80, III.141, III.146, *III.146*
Unmanifested Logos III.147
Unmanifest inner planes III.87

Unmanifest Reality III.173
Unmanifest Worlds III.61, III.63, III.86, III.91, III.92
unprepared heart III.199
unprepared mind III.199
the Unreal III.117
unreality, of the body II.29–30
unregenerate man III.304
unscientific assumptions III.288
the unseen I.303, I.304
unseen powers III.51
unseen world I.36, I.102, I.212
unsupportable presuppositions and assumptions III.162, III.306, III.307, III.308
unwarranted inference II.119
upādhi(s) II.36–7, II.41, II.43–5, II.46, II.170–1, II.200
  and numbers III.371
  and Spiritual Soul II.47
Upaniṣads I.287, II.198, III.17, III.102, III.120, III.169, III.290
  definition I.270–1
  and Prāṇas II.27
Up from Eden (Wilber) I.351
Upper being II.17
upper centre III.38
Upper Duad II.41, II.68
upper intellectual centre II.178
upper pole II.185, III.123
Upper Triad II.18, II.19, II.20, *II.21*, II.22–3, II.73, II.105
  and *The Chemical Marriage* III.14
  and genius II.100
  and The Judgement (Tarot cards) III.13
  and Pavri System II.160
  and Plato II.175
  and Saptaparṇa III.59
  and Upper Triangle III.127
Upper Triangle III.127
upper triangle III.123
Upper Triplicity I.148
upside down image III.123
upward arc II.79
  see also reincarnation
urgency to act, and Kāma II.109
uroboros III.3–4
uterus III.184
Utts, Jessica I.92, I.122
U-turns, in science I.108

vaccines III.320
vāhana II.37, II.38, II.41
Valhalla II.70, II.71
Valhallic condition II.71
validation, inter-subjective III.11
values III.239, III.241, III.313
Vāmana I.272
vampire II.81
  see also kāma-rūpa
Vānara III.236
  see also Rāmāyaṇa
van der Post, Sir Laurens II.130
Varāha I.271
Varāha Upaniṣad III.303
Varela, Francisco I.58, I.351
variables I.14
  see also Ganzfeld studies
'Varieties of Causal Closure' (Montero) I.27
variety III.86, III.115, III.156
Vaughan, Thomas II.57, III.60
Vedānta philosophy I.270, I.271, III.293
Vedantic classification II.43, II.52, II.153, II.167, II.168, *II.169*, II.170–1
and Besant System II.154, *II.157*
comparison with Fourth Way II.181, *II.182*
Vedantins II.35, II.168
Vedas I.175, I.270, I.271, I.287, III.17, III.102, III.229
  and archæological evidence III.234–7
  and Puruṣa III.155
  on reincarnation III.247
Vedic ape III.236
Vedic concept of time III.234
Vedic cosmological calendar III.234
Vedic maxim III.256–7
Vedic seers I.217
Veena III.70, III.80, *III.80*
Vegetable Diet: As sanctioned by medical men, and by experience in all ages (Alcott) III.208
vehicles II.7, II.34, II.37–8, II.197, III.93, III.236, III.375
  complex III.221, III.291
  of consciousness II.46, II.47–8, II.86, II.105, II.150–1, II.161, III.137, III.166, III.263
  and conscious self III.235
  of expression II.37, III.146–7, III.218, III.248, III.296–7, III.317, III.368, III.371
  and involution III.182–3
  lunar II.165
  mental II.110
  physical III.337
  and prāṇa III.162

primary II.52
and principles III.140–1
of projection II.54, II.56
purified III.256
sensitive III.246
terrestrial II.106
Vehicular-side, Element–Principles III.158
veiled information II.4
veils II.106, III.118, III.181, III.277
venerated absurdities III.17–18
Venus (possible signs of life on) I.107, III.8
veridical experience I.49, I.70–1
veridical nature II.56
verifiable source references III.210
verification III.308–9
Versluis, Arthur I.287, II.164
vertical arm (secondary differentiation) III.145
see also Subject–Object relationship
vertical differentiation III.144
Vespro della Beata Vergine (Monteverdi) III.327
vestures II.xviii, II.97, II.196, III.10, III.11–12, III.75
see also garments
via negativa I.292–3, III.280
via positiva I.293
vibrations II.120, II.230, III.78, III.95, III.107, III.135, III.250
vibratory scales III.95
vice III.12
Victoria, Queen I.302
Victorian spiritualism movement I.lxxx
Vienna School, legacy III.308–10
viewpoint III.288
Vijnāna II.170, II.171
Vijnānamaya-kośa II.52, II.168, II.170
Vikarana bhava III.164–5
Viṣṇu (Vishnu) I.271, II.27, III.173, III.174, III.176, III.303
violent animals (humans) III.243
violent death II.81–2
violinists I.162
Virgin Mary II.53
virtual machine II.115, II.127
virtual reality III.197
virtue III.12
viruses III.131
visible body III.36
visible cosmos III.91
visible object III.1
visible sun III.253
visible symbols III.16
visible universe III.92
vision II.123, III.196, III.250, III.311
prospective II.79
sight III.136, III.377
The Vision I.264, I.265
see also Egyptian Mysteries
Vital Body II.164
vital force III.163, III.179, III.246
vitalism I.53, I.70–1, I.72, I.348, III.174, III.176–9, III.309
vitality III.13, III.152, III.246
Vital principle II.19
vital principle I.266
in vitro fertilization (IVF) I.350
vituperation (scientific backlash) III.230
see also The Hidden History of the Human Race
vivisection III.272
vociferous attacks by scientific establishment II.133, II.134
Vogt, Karl I.9, I.32, I.38
voice II.95, II.120, II.188, II.230
Voice of the Silence III.xxi
The Voice of the Silence (Blavatsky) I.222, I.236, I.322–3, *I.323*, II.99–100
Vyâsa I.217, I.270

Waddington, Conrad I.71, I.72, I.349
Wagner, Richard I.214, II.71, III.5, III.325
Waite, Arthur Edward I.206, II.57
wake-up call II.58–9, III.188
waking III.117, III.234
waking consciousness II.57, III.254
waking cycle II.76
waking reality II.53
waking sleep II.178
Walach, Harald I.142, III.329
Walder, Dr Ray III.355
Waldorf education II.182
Walker, Evan Harris I.336
Wallace, Alfred Russel I.58, I.114, I.297, II.131, III.316–17, III.326
on consciousness I.346
on limitations of natural selection I.52, I.347, III.228, III.237–8
and spiritualism I.102, I.106
walls (simile) III.253
Walshe, Sir Francis I.18, II.127, III.140–1, III.306
wandering stars (astronomy) III.23
war I.267, I.296, II.116, II.130, III.13
Warcup, Adam III.287

Ward, Sir Benjamin
warning I.281–2, II.89
'The Waste Land' (Eliot) II.54
water III.56, III.76, III.253
water divining III.282
water droplets III.237
Water Element I.276
water-tight compartments (composition of man) II.204
Watson, James I.8, I.349
Watson, John I.29
waveless state II.84, II.85
 see also Avītchi; Eighth Sphere
wave nature of matter III.163
The Wave Nature of the Electron (de Broglie) I.333
wave–particle duality I.96–7
waves III.201, III.262, III.376–7
wave-structures, immaterial I.80–1, I.82
wave theory of light II.207
Way of the Heart III.227
Ways to Go Beyond (Sheldrake) III.265
weak anthropic principle III.241
weak closure I.27
Weber, Renée I.186–7, I.339, III.308
The Web of Life: A new scientific understanding of living systems (Capra) I.353
Weinberg, Steven I.120, I.317, I.318–19, III.22, III.268, III.269, III.270, III.271
The First Three Minutes: A modern view of the origin of the universe I.337
Weinberg's syndrome I.120, I.318
Weisberg, Josh I.39
Weismann, August I.347, III.228, III.247–8
Weiss, Paul I.71
welfare of others III.245
wellspring
 of consciousness III.42
 of genius II.90
Wesson, Robert I.352
the West II.146
 and ageless wisdom III.91
 and 'Book of the Apocalypse' III.303
 meeting East III.102–20
Westcott, William Wynn III.25
Western *Chaldean Kabala* III.89
Western doctrines II.174–88
Western esoteric tradition III.122
Western mind III.204
Western Mystery tradition I.187, I.188, I.214, I.280
Western rationalism III.73
Western science III.255
Western teachings III.155
Western traditions II.57, *II.147*, II.149, II.164, II.183, II.221
Western world II.220
wet computer I.18, I.45, II.53, II.112, II.196
 see also brain and computationalists
the 'what'
 of brain hemispheres II.123
 in space III.141
'What is the Soul?' (Joad) II.198–9
wheel of life *q.v.* and death *q.v.* III.129
 see also reincarnation
Wheeler, John I.xlvi, I.43, I.337, III.291, III.351
'when' in time III.141
Where is Science Going? (Planck) I.334
Whewell, William I.198
Whirling Dervishes III.194–5
White, Paula I.290
White, Robert III.339
Whitehead, Alfred North I.xviii–xix, I.l, I.36, I.243, I.244, I.333, I.334, III.269
white king (chess *q.v.*) III.13, III.14
white light II.189, III.202
White Light Refracted Through a Prism into Seven Colours *I.171*
white magic I.199, I.200–1, I.202
 see also Right-Hand Path
White Radiance of Eternity Stained by 'Refraction' Through the Brain into Countless Streams of Consciousness *I.171*
Whitman, Walt I.291
Whittington, Miles I.170
the whole II.135, III.83, III.93, III.95, III.189, III.237, III.238
wholeness II.19, III.28, III.80, III.256
Wholeness and the Implicate Order (Bohm) I.339
Why I believe in God: Science and religion, as a scientist sees it (Eddington) I.333
Why Religion Matters (Smith) I.121
Wickland, Carl II.82
Wickland scripts II.82
Wickramasinghe, Chandra I.107
Wigner, Eugene I.xlv, I.94
Wikipedia (censorship practices) I.49–50
Wilber, Ken I.xxxix, I.346, I.351, II.185–6, III.11
Wilkins, Maurice I.8
Wilkinson, David Todd I.336
will II.34, II.123
Williams, Ted III.339

Williamson, George Hunt I.277
will power II.168
Wilson, Edward Osborne I.xl, I.319, II.110
Wilson, President Woodrow I.272
Wilson, Robert I.336
Wiltse, Dr II.91–2, III.129
windows (human constitution *q.v.*, simile) III.253, *III.254*
wings III.84, III.304
Wisdom II.225, III.15, III.176
  Ancient (Ageless) I.xxxix, III.11, III.64, III.253
  Divine I.xxxix, I.xlix, I.184, I.327, II.225
  and the Light III.111
  One universal fount of III.59
  Universal I.211, I.237
  see also Eternal Wisdom
wisdom II.222, III.xviii, III.165
  accumulated II.146
  ageless/timeless III.91, III.183
  from antiquity to modern times II.2
  becoming suffocated II.99
  of both the West and East I.300
  divine II.7–8
  and guided end I.72
    see also teleology; chreodes; morphogenetic/morphic fields; organizing fields
  and The Hermit (Tarot cards) III.11
  and ignorance I.221
  keys to II.205, III.xx, III.19
  love of I.xxxix
  of the past III.264
  promote in academia III.273
  and symbols III.49
  and the Tarot III.13
  and transformational learning III.xix
  universal II.189, II.204
  and Venus III.8
    see also labyrinth; Ptolemaic cosmology
Wisdom Religion II.167, II.170, II.191
wisdom–seeker II.189
wisdom-Source III.101
wisdom tradition III.248
the wise II.167
wishful thinking III.270
witchcraft III.316
Witelson, Dr Sandra I.134, I.135
Wolfe-Simon, Felisa I.240, I.356
wolves parable II.26
women, and rocks (symbol of) III.9
wonderchild (Newton *q.v.*) III.205
Wood, Ernest II.160
wooden horse of Troy III.47–8
Wood Wide Web III.223
the Word III.46, III.107
word-of-mouth transmission III.17
words
  choice of II.35
  limitations of II.36
Wordsworth, William I.152–3, III.xix
work, on Earth II.29
workshop, and Devachan II.70
world
  of appearances III.119
  definition III.86
  of energy II.229
  external III.334
  higher III.199
  of illusion III.56
  inner III.245
  manifest III.226
  meaning of loka II.6
  non-visible III.92
  outer living III.178
  outside III.319
  physical and objective III.148
  of sense III.64
  of spirit III.64
  subterranean Galapagos III.223
  subtler III.353
  three III.22, III.56
  underwriting whole, self-consistent, versions of II.123
world image III.149, III.150, III.167
worldly weariness III.xviii
World of Ghosts I.274
World of No Form I.165, I.166
A World of Wonders (Stephen) III.17
world periods II.77
world religions I.lxxv
  see also religion
Worlds
  Chaldean Kabala III.89, III.92
  Higher II.164
worlds, higher III.199
World Soul I.80, I.81
world's top experts (neuroscientists *q.v.*) III.162
world-views III.43, III.60, III.263, III.269, III.275, III.287, III.291
World War II II.82
worldwide teachings II.147

worship I.192, I.289
Wyller, Arne I.355

Xbalanque I.275, I.279
Xibalbian Mysteries (Central America *q.v.*) I.275, I.278–9
X-rays (physical body *q.v.*, investigation of) I.261
see also microscope; MRI scans

yang II.74, III.225
Yasna II.172
Yavancharya (Pythagoras *q.v.*) I.216
Yesōd III.63, III.64
yin II.74, III.225
yoga I.165, I.283, II.202, III.102, III.142, III.180, III.199, III.204
philosophy III.155
Yogananda, Paramahansa II.82, II.102, II.202, III.102, III.203–4
Yoga Sūtras III.181, III.190–1
yogic science III.104
yogis II.202, III.201
young man, died in road traffic accident (post-mortem energy field of) II.83
Young Musician of the Year competition I.9
young people/youth I.4, III.12, III.274
'Your brain hallucinates your conscious reality' (Seth) III.115
'Your Deceptive Mind: A Scientific Guide to Critical Thinking Skills' (Novella) I.11–12

Zaehner, R. C. I.xxxix–xl
Zanoni (Bulwer-Lytton) III.198
Zarathuśtra I.217, I.218, I.267, I.268, I.326
Zarathuśtrian classification II.172, *II.173*, II.174
Zarathuśtrianism I.267–9, I.293
Zarathuśtrian religion II.174
Der Zauberlehrling (Goethe) I.208, I.209
Zend-Avesta II.172
Zend tradition II.172
Zimmermann, Robert von II.183
zodiac III.22–4, III.28–9
zodiacal light III.23
zodion III.24
Zohar II.73, III.60
zombieism II.117–18
see also functionalism; brain states
zoöphites II.231, III.56
Zoroaster I.217
Zuckerberg, Mark II.141
Zweig, George I.99